W9-BOT-668

THE AMERICAN REPUBLIC

★ ★ ★ ★ ★ ★ ★ ★ THIRD EDITION ★ ★ ★ ★ ★ ★ ★ ★

RACHEL C. LARSON, PhD

bju press®

Greenville, South Carolina

NOTE: The fact that materials produced by other publishers may be referred to in this volume does not constitute an endorsement of the content or theological position of materials produced by such publishers. Any references and ancillary materials are listed as an aid to the student or the teacher and in an attempt to maintain the accepted academic standards of the publishing industry.

STUDENT ACTIVITIES FOR AMERICAN REPUBLIC
Third Edition

Contributing Authors
Lauren Kowalk
Michael Matthews
Dennis Peterson

Editor
Manda Kalagayan

Cover & Book Design
John Cunningham
Drew Fields
Elly Kalagayan

Cover Illustration
Dave Shuppert

Page Layout
Drew Fields
Melissa Horne
Jennifer Lowry
Ealia Padreganda

Project Managers
Dan Berger
Kevin Neat

Photo Acquisition
Joyce Landis
Holly Nelson

Photograph credits and text acknowledgments are listed on pages 343–44

Produced in cooperation with the Bob Jones University Departments of History and Social Studies of the College of Arts and Science, the School of Education, and Bob Jones Academy.

Our Commitment.
Your Confidence.

Creative
Updated look. Colorful, interesting pages.

Credible
Thorough research. Solid content.

Christian
Nothing to conflict with Truth. Everything to support it.

Table of Contents

Unit I: Settling a Wilderness

Chapter 1 Discovery of a New World
Activity 1: American Indian Cultures........................ 1
Activity 2: Explorers of a New World 2
Activity 3: Captain John Smith's Account of the Founding of
Jamestown 3
Activity 4: Chapter Review........................... 4

Chapter 2 Settling the Thirteen Colonies
Activity 1: Founding Your Own Colony 5
Activity 2: Selection from William Bradford's *Of Plymouth
Plantation* 7
Activity 3: Map Study: The Original Colonies................. 9
Activity 4: Thirteen Different Colonies...................... 10

Chapter 3 Expansion and Establishment
Activity 1: The Population of the Colonies................... 11
Activity 2: Early Colonial Differences...................... 12
Activity 3: Life Among the Indians 13
Activity 4: The Colonies Become Established 15

Chapter 4 Daily Life in the Colonies
Activity 1: All in a Day's Work............................ 17
Activity 2: Family Life in New England 19
Activity 3: Life on a Southern Plantation 21
Activity 4: Scripture in Colonial Society.................... 24
Activity 5: Chapter Review............................... 25

Chapter 5 American Colonies in the British Empire
Activity 1: The French and Indian War..................... 27
Activity 2: George Washington's Report on the Defeat of
Braddock 29
Activity 3: The Boston Tea Party 31
Activity 4: Causes and Effects............................ 33
Activity 5: The Shot Heard 'Round the World 34
Activity 6: Writing Your Own Glossary 35

Unit II: Establishing a Nation

Chapter 6 Independence for the Colonies
Activity 1: Map Study: The War for Independence............. 37
Activity 2: Major Battles 38
Activity 3: Taking Sides.................................. 39
Activity 4: The Bad Winter............................... 41
Activity 5: A Young Recruit on the Frontlines in South Carolina . . 43
Activity 6: Chapter Review............................... 46

Chapter 7 Confederation and Constitution
Activity 1: Write Your Own Encyclopedia Entry............... 47
Activity 2: The Need for a Constitution 48
Activity 3: What God Says About Government................ 49
Activity 4: The Federalist Papers 50
Activity 5: Powers of Government.......................... 51
Activity 6: Chapter Review............................... 52

Chapter 8 Establishment of the New Government
Activity 1: Eyewitness Accounts of Washington's Inauguration . . 53
Activity 2: Government Then and Now 55
Activity 3: What God Says About Honor 56
Activity 4: Abigail Adams's Letter About Washington, D.C. 57
Activity 5: Words You Need to Know: Precedents 58
Activity 6: Chapter Review: Timeline of the Early Republic 59

Unit III: Spanning a Continent

Chapter 9 Growth of a Nation
Activity 1: Map Study 61
Activity 2: The Journals of Lewis and Clark.................. 63
Activity 3: Steps to War.................................. 67
Activity 4: The Sinking of the *Guerrière* 68
Activity 5: Chapter Review............................... 69

Chapter 10 The Era of Good Feelings
Activity 1: Comparing Presidential Campaigns 71
Activity 2: The Year that Changed America................... 72
Activity 3: Map Study 73
Activity 4: Chapter Review............................... 75

Chapter 11 Jacksonian America
Activity 1: The Inauguration of President Andrew Jackson, 1829. . 77
Activity 2: Nullification Crisis 79
Activity 3: Political Cartoons 80
Activity 4: Jackson on the Bank Veto 81
Activity 5: Presidents of the Jacksonian Era................. 83
Activity 6: Modified True/False 84

Chapter 12 Changing American Life
Activity 1: Map Study: Growth of Transportation.............. 85
Activity 2: The Canal Boat 87
Activity 3: Improvements in Transportation and Communication. . 91
Activity 4: Rev. Henry A. Miles on Lowell, *As It Was and As It Is* . . 93
Activity 5: American Inventions 95
Activity 6: Reforming America 96
Activity 7: Chapter Review............................... 97

Chapter 13 Westward Expansion
Activity 1: Map Study: Manifest Destiny 99
Activity 2: Trails to the West.............................. 101
Activity 3: Oregon Trail Diary 103
Activity 4: Map Study: Mexican War and Western Expansion ... 109
Activity 5: Chapter Review............................... 111

Unit IV: Facing a Crisis

Chapter 14 Storm Clouds Over the Nation
Activity 1: Differences Between the North and the South 113
Activity 2: Who Has the Greater Authority? 114
Activity 3: Frederick Douglass's Escape from Slavery.......... 115
Activity 4: Differing Viewpoints: The Sumner-Brooks Episode . . 118
Activity 5: Map Work: The Divided Nation 122
Activity 6: Account of the Firing on Fort Sumter 123
Activity 7: Chapter Review............................... 124

Chapter 15 The States at War
Activity 1: Comparing Lincoln and Davis 125
Activity 2: Major Battles of the War Between the States........ 126
Activity 3: Political Cartoons of the Civil War................ 127
Activity 4: Soldiers' Accounts of the War 129
Activity 5: Lincoln's Gettysburg Address 131
Activity 6: Lincoln's Second Inaugural Address............... 132
Activity 7: Lee's Farewell to His Troops 134
Activity 8: Chapter Review............................... 136

Chapter 16 Reconstruction
Activity 1: Lee and Johnson: Their Postwar Attitudes 139
Activity 2: Major Events of Reconstruction 141
Activity 3: Saved by One Vote: An Eyewitness Account of the Trial
of Andrew Johnson........................... 143

Activity 4: Interpreting a Reconstruction-Era Political Cartoon . . 145
Activity 5: Writing a History Essay 146
Activity 6: Sandhog: Building the Brooklyn Bridge, 1871 147
Activity 7: Eyewitness to Ku Klux Klan Violence, 1868 149
Activity 8: Chapter Review 151

Unit V: Growing to Meet Challenges

Chapter 17 Industrialism
Activity 1: Emma Lazarus's Most Famous Poem 153
Activity 2: Eyewitness Tells of "Last Spike" Driving 155
Activity 3: Ways of Doing Business 158
Activity 4: Andrew Carnegie: The Gospel of Wealth, 1889 159
Activity 5: Chapter Review 161

Chapter 18 The Last Frontier
Activity 1: Mining Methods in the Old West 163
Activity 2: A Cowboy in Dodge City, 1882 165
Activity 3: Ranchers and Farmers Collide in Nebraska, 1884 167
Activity 4: The Death of Billy the Kid, 1881 169
Activity 5: Massacre at Wounded Knee, 1890 171
Activity 6: Chapter Review 173

Chapter 19 America and the World
Activity 1: "The White Man's Burden" 175
Activity 2: American Imperialism 177
Activity 3: Sensationalism, Jingoism, and Impartiality 178
Activity 4: The United States Declares War on Spain, 1898 179
Activity 5: The Panama Canal 181
Activity 6: Chapter Review 183

Chapter 20 Progressivism
Activity 1: Changing American Life at the Turn of the Century . . 185
Activity 2: Booker T. Washington 187
Activity 3: Billy Sunday Blasts Liquor 193
Activity 4: Progressivism 196
Activity 5: Roosevelt's Speech Following Assassination Attempt . . 197
Activity 6: The Progressive Presidents 200
Activity 7: Find the Message 201

Unit VI: Taking the Lead

Chapter 21 World War I
Activity 1: Experiences of World War I 203
Activity 2: The Sinking of the *Lusitania*, 1915 205
Activity 3: Objectivity and Propaganda 208
Activity 4: America Declares War on Germany, 1917 209
Activity 5: U.S. Preparedness: The Run-Up to War 211
Activity 6: The Heroism of Sgt. Alvin C. York 213
Activity 7: What God Says About War and Peace 216
Activity 8: Wilson's Fourteen Points 217

Chapter 22 The 1920s: A Decade of Change
Activity 1: The Washington Naval Treaty 219
Activity 2: The Immigration Act of 1924 221
Activity 3: The Impact of Technology in the Twenties 223
Activity 4: From Progressivism to Normalcy 224
Activity 5: Darrow versus Bryan in the Scopes Trial 225
Activity 6: Sports in the Roaring Twenties 228
Activity 7: Herbert Hoover on the Role of Government 229
Activity 8: Decade of Change 231

Chapter 23 Crash and Depression
Activity 1: "Crash!" 233
Activity 2: Hoover versus FDR 236

Activity 3: Roosevelt's First Inaugural Address, March 4, 1933 . . . 237
Activity 4: FDR's Fireside Chat, March 12, 1933 241
Activity 5: Huey Long's Plan to "Share the Wealth" 245
Activity 6: Graphing Negative Numbers: Between the Wars
(1920–1940) 249
Activity 7: Interpreting Political Cartoons of the New Deal Era . . 251
Activity 8: Chapter Review 253

Chapter 24 World War II
Activity 1: Prelude to World War II 255
Activity 2: The War Begins: Chronological Order 256
Activity 3: FDR's Request for a Declaration of War Against
Japan 257
Activity 4: Life for a Japanese-American Internee 259
Activity 5: V-Mail from a Soldier 262
Activity 6: Mapping World War II: European Theater 263
Activity 7: Mapping World War II: Pacific Theater 264
Activity 8: A Marine's Journal from Guadalcanal 265
Activity 9: Chapter Review 267

Unit VII: Preparing for the Future

Chapter 25 Recovery, Cold War, and Coexistence
Activity 1: Jackie Robinson Breaks Baseball's Color Barrier, 1945 . . 269
Activity 2: Understanding the United Nations 271
Activity 3: The Berlin Candy Bomber 273
Activity 4: Two Views of the Firing of General MacArthur 275
Activity 5: Chapter Review 279

Chapter 26 The 1960s—The Nation in Crisis
Activity 1: Kennedy's Inaugural Address, 1961 281
Activity 2: Gulf of Tonkin Resolution, 1964 284
Activity 3: Summary of the Vietnam War 285
Activity 4: One Soldier's Experience in Vietnam 287
Activity 5: The Resignation of Richard Nixon 293
Activity 6: Chapter Review 297

Chapter 27 Conservative Surge
Activity 1: Ford's Dilemma: The Nixon Pardon 301
Activity 2: The Story Behind the Camp David Accords 304
Activity 3: Interpreting Editorial Cartoons 310
Activity 4: The Attempted Assassination of Reagan—In His Own
Words 311
Activity 5: Federal Spending Under Recent Presidents 315
Activity 6: Chapter Review: The Presidents after Nixon 317

Chapter 28 Bridge to the 21st Century
Activity 1: Hillary Clinton and the Health-Care Debate 319
Activity 2: Contract with America 321
Activity 3: What the Bible Says About Modern Issues 323
Activity 4: Ending the Welfare State Through the Power of Private
Action 325
Activity 5: Impeachment 329
Activity 6: Chapter Review 331

Chapter 29 A New Millennium
Activity 1: "Let's Roll!" The Story of the Passengers of United
Flight 93 333
Activity 2: The Faith of George W. Bush 337
Activity 3: Katrina: A True Story of Grace 339
Activity 4: Chapter Review 341

Name _____

American Indian Cultures

On the following map of North America, outline and color the five regions of American Indians in early America. First, try to outline the regions without the help of your textbook; then refer to the book if necessary. Color the Woodlands Indians green, the Plains Indians yellow, the Southwest Indians red, the Plateau and Great Basin Indians purple, and the West Coast Indians blue.

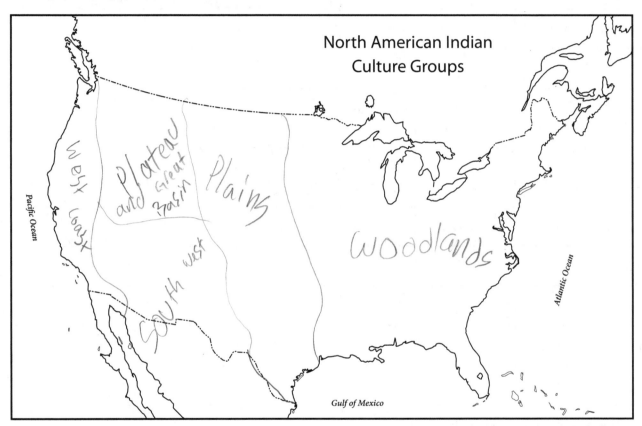

North American Indian Culture Groups

Now fill in the following chart with key words or phrases describing the Indian cultures you read about in the text.

Culture	Nomadic/Settled	Housing	Food	Accomplishments
Woodlands	settled	Wig wam longhouse	Game Fish squash	mounds
Plains	nomadic	teepees	buffalo, seeds, berries, roots	powerful
Southwest	Settled	adobe	small animals, wild plants	advanced pottery and weaving
Great Basin/Plateau	settled	tepees, brush huts, or hogans	buffalo nuts berries	rock drawings
West Coast	Settled	cedar homes	fish oysters	totum poles

Explorers of a New World

Complete the chart. For each explorer, write the country he served, the dates of his explora-tion, and his main accomplishment. Refer to the textbook (including the "Early Explorers" map in Section III) for your answers.

Explorer	Country	Dates	Main Accomplishment
Christopher Columbus	Spain	1492	discovery of the New World
John Cabot	England	1497	laid claim for England
Amerigo Vespucci	Spain/Portugal	1499/1501	"New World"
Juan Ponce de León	Spain	1513	charted florida
Hernando de Soto	spain	1539	discovered Mi. River
Francisco Coronado	Mexico	1540	Discovered Adobe villages
Jacques Cartier	France	1534	Discovered St Lawrence River
Sir Francis Drake	England	1577	Pirate
Samuel de Champlain	France	1603	Built city of Quebec
Robert de La Salle	France	1681–82	Claimed MI. River

Answer these questions based on the chart.

1. Which was the first country to send an explorer to the New World? _Spain_

2. Which was the last country to send an explorer to the New World? _england_

3. Which explorer sailed for two different countries? _Samuel_

4. How many years passed between the first and last explorations? _190 Years_

5. Which country sent the most explorers to the New World? _spain_

Captain John Smith's Account of the Founding of Jamestown

John Smith wrote eight books about his adventures in the New World. After you read about the founding of Jamestown in Smith's own words, answer the questions that follow.

While the ships stayed, our allowance was somewhat bettered by a daily proportion of biscuit, which the sailors would pilfer to sell, give, or exchange with us, for money, sassafras, or charity. But when they left, there remained neither tavern, beer house, nor place of relief, but the common kettle. Had we been as free from all sins as gluttony and drunkenness, we might have been canonized for saints. But our president would never have been admitted, for he ingrossed for his private use oatmeal, white wine, oil, aqua vitae [brandy], beef, eggs or what not. But the kettle that he allowed to be distributed was half a pint of wheat and as much barley boiled with water for a man a day; and this having fried some six weeks in the ship's hold, contained as many worms as grains. Our drink was water, our lodgings castles in the air.

With this lodging and diet, our extreme toil in bearing and planting palisades [fort posts] so strained and bruised us, and our continual labor in the extremity of the heat had so weakened us, and were sufficient cause to have made us as miserable in our native country or any other place in the world.

From May to September those that escaped lived upon sturgeon and sea-crabs. Fifty in this time we buried; the rest seeing that the president (who all this time had neither felt want nor sickness) planned to escape these miseries in our pinnance [small ship] deposed [him]. . . .

But now was all our provision spent, the sturgeon gone, all helps abandoned, each hour expecting the fury of the savages, when God the patron of all good endeavors in that desperate extremity so changed the hearts of the savages that they brought so much of their fruits and provision that no man wanted for anything.

The new president and Martin, being little beloved, weak judgment in dangers, and less industrious in peace, committed the managing of all things abroad to Captain Smith who by his own example, good words, and fair promises, set some to mow, others to bind thatch, some to build houses, others to thatch them. He himself always bore the greatest task for his own share, so that in short time, he provided most of them with lodging, neglecting any for himself.

1. What was wrong with the colony's first president? _selfish_

2. What is meant by "castles in the air"? _Dreams that wont come true_

3. How many men died during the first few months? _50_

4. What did Smith call the Indians? _Savages_

5. How did God save the starving colonists? _the indians brought them food_

6. What was wrong with the second president? _little beloved, not smart, poor judgment, lazy_

7. What was Smith's opinion of himself? _smart, kind, good delegate, selfless_

8. List four hardships the colonists faced. _hunger, no lodging, poor leadership, extreme heat._

Chapter Review

Read each phrase and write in the blank the person, place, or thing it describes.

Who Am I?

_____ 1. discovered the strange land of Vinland

_____ 2. suggested that Columbus had discovered a New World

_____ 3. explored up into present-day Kansas and discovered the Grand Canyon

_____ 4. strongest champion of Roman Catholicism in Europe

_____ 5. Frenchman who claimed the Mississippi River

_____ 6. the Father of New France

_____ 7. Englishman who tried to colonize Roanoke Island

_____ 8. chief of the Woodland Indian tribes near Jamestown

_____ 9. secretly encouraged pirating raids on the Spanish

Where Am I?

__Plateau_____ 10. Indians here lived in tepees and hunted buffalo.

__Florida_____ 11. future state first explored by Juan Ponce de León

____Jamestown_____ 12. oldest city in the present United States

_____ 13. region explored by Samuel de Champlain

_____ 14. English settlement named for the king

_____ 15. English settlement that mysteriously disappeared

_____ 16. land around the Great Lakes and St. Lawrence River that was rich in furs

What Am I?

_____ 17. made of earth and filled with weapons, pottery, and jewelry

__Totum Pole_____ 18. carved from wood and depicted legends and events

__Animism_____ 19. the belief that spirits live in objects in nature as well as in natural events

__A_____ 20. invasion fleet sent to destroy England

__Adobe_____ 21. clay and straw mixture used to build houses

_____ 22. winter of 1609–10 when Jamestown was devastated by famine

_____ 23. gained passage to the colonies in return for work

____Martin?_____ 24. first representative government in America

_____ 25. a French Protestant

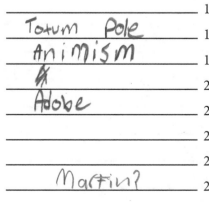

4

Founding Your Own Colony

The year is 1605. You are a young English nobleman who has just inherited a great deal of money. The king has asked you to found a colony anywhere on the coast of North America. You need to answer these questions as you make preparations to settle your colony. Can you avoid the costly mistakes that other colonists made?

1. How do you plan to attract people to your colony? Check at least one attraction.
   - ☐ profit
   - ☐ land ownership
   - ☐ employment
   - ☐ religious freedom
   - ☐ political freedom
   - ☐ adventure

2. What kind of colony will you have?
   - ☐ charter colony
   - ☐ proprietary colony
   - ☐ royal colony

3. Which features will determine where your colony will be? Check at least two features.
   - ☐ good harbor
   - ☐ furs
   - ☐ safety
   - ☐ gold
   - ☐ climate
   - ☐ nearby Indians
   - ☐ navigable river
   - ☐ soil
   - ☐ woods

4. Which region will be the best site for your colony?
   - ☐ northern region
   - ☐ middle region
   - ☐ southern region

5. What difficulties is your colony likely to face?
   - ☐ famine
   - ☐ disease
   - ☐ lazy settlers
   - ☐ bad weather
   - ☐ poor leadership
   - ☐ Indian attack
   - ☐ bankruptcy

6. How will the colony pay for itself?
   - ☐ mining
   - ☐ fur trade
   - ☐ sale of lands
   - ☐ shipbuilding
   - ☐ gifts from the king
   - ☐ fishing
   - ☐ tobacco
   - ☐ indigo
   - ☐ rice

7. What basic supplies will you need? Place an *x* in the boxes beside items you will need to bring only once, and fill in boxes beside items you will need to resupply from England.
   - ☐ seeds
   - ☐ flour
   - ☐ salt
   - ☐ meat
   - ☐ fresh water
   - ☐ guns
   - ☐ boats
   - ☐ money
   - ☐ paper/ink
   - ☐ clothes/linen
   - ☐ tools/instruments
   - ☐ candles/lanterns
   - ☐ _____
   - ☐ _____
   - ☐ _____

8. Whom must you bring along on your first trip? Check the ten most important occupations. You may need to use a dictionary.

- ☐ smith
- ☐ shipwright
- ☐ cooper
- ☐ baker
- ☐ sawyer
- ☐ miner
- ☐ husbandman
- ☐ carpenter
- ☐ divine

- ☐ mason
- ☐ soldier
- ☐ fowler
- ☐ weaver
- ☐ salt maker
- ☐ sturgeon dresser
- ☐ fisherman
- ☐ physician
- ☐ tailor

9. Write a brief summary of the first three years of your colony. Try to avoid a very short account if all colonists disappear, die, or decide to return to England. Mention the major accomplishments and setbacks during each time period (for example: completing the fort, finishing the houses, harvesting the first crop, arrival of a supply ship, etc.).

First Month _____

_____

_____

_____

First Six Months _____

_____

_____

_____

First Year _____

_____

_____

_____

Second Year _____

_____

_____

_____

Third Year _____

_____

_____

_____

Selection from William Bradford's *Of Plymouth Plantation*

William Bradford wrote an entire book, called *Of Plymouth Plantation*, about the first few years in the Plymouth Colony. After you read the following selection from the book, answer the questions that follow.

On the Mayflower

Being thus arrived in a good harbor, and brought safe to land, they fell upon their knees and blessed the God of Heaven who had brought them over the fast and furious ocean, and delivered them from all the perils and miseries thereof, again to set their feet on the firm and stable earth, their proper element. . . .

But here I cannot but stay and make a pause, and stand half amazed at this poor people's present condition; and so I think will the reader, too, when he well considers the same. Being thus passed the vast ocean, and a sea of troubles before in their preparation (as may be remembered by that which went before), they had now no friends to welcome them nor inns to entertain or refresh their weatherbeaten bodies; no houses or much less towns to repair to, to seek for succor. It is recorded in Scripture as a mercy to the Apostle and his shipwrecked company, that the barbarians showed them no small kindness in refreshing them, but these savage barbarians, when they met with them (as after will appear) were readier to fill their sides full of arrows than otherwise. And for the season it was winter, and they that know the winters of that country know them to be sharp and violent, and subject to cruel and fierce storms, dangerous to travel to known places, much more to search an unknown coast. Besides, what could they see but a hideous and desolate wilderness, full of wild beasts and wild men—and what multitudes there might be of them they knew not. Neither could they, as it were, go up to the top of Pisgah to view from this wilderness a more goodly country to feed their hopes; for which way soever they turned their eyes (save upward to the heavens) they could have little solace or content in respect of any outward objects. For summer being done, all things stand upon them with a weatherbeaten face, and the whole country, full of woods and thickets, represented a wild and savage hue. If they looked behind them, there was the mighty ocean which they had passed and was now as a main bar and gulf to separate them from all the civil parts of the world. If it be said they had a ship to succor them, it is true; but what heard they daily from the master and company? But that with speed they should look out a place (with their shallop) where they would be, at some near distance; for the season was such that he would not stir from thence till a safe harbor was discovered by them, where they would be, and he might go without danger; and that victuals consumed space but he must and would keep sufficient for themselves and their return. Yea, it was muttered by some that if they got not a place in time, they would turn them and their goods ashore and leave them. Let it also be considered what weak hopes of supply and succor they left behind them, that might bear up their minds in this sad condition and trials they were under; and they could not but be very small. It is true, indeed, the affections and love of their brethren at Leyden was cordial and entire towards them, but they had little power to help them or themselves; and how the case stood between them and the merchants at their coming away hath already been declared.

What could now sustain them but the Spirit of God and His grace? May not and ought not the children of these fathers rightly say: "Our fathers were Englishmen which came over this great ocean, and were ready to perish in this wilderness; but they cried unto the Lord, and He heard their voice and looked on their adversity," etc. "Let them therefore praise the Lord, because He is good: and his mercies endure forever. Yea, let them which have been redeemed of the Lord, show how He hath delivered them from the hand of the oppressor. When they wandered in the desert wilderness out of the way, and found no city to dwell in, both hungry and thirsty, their soul was overwhelmed in them." "Let them confess before the Lord His lovingkindness and His wonderful works before the sons of men."

1. What was the first thing the Pilgrims did once they reached land?

   Fell on their knees and worshipped the
   Lord

2. During what season did the Pilgrims land? Why was this a problem?

   Winter. Too cold, not lots of food

3. Bradford claims the Pilgrims "could have little solace or content in respect of any outward objects." Describe their physical surroundings, according to Bradford, and why this would have been frightening.

   _?_

4. What did the ship's captain urge the Pilgrims to do as soon as possible? Why was he in such a hurry?

   build houses. because they
   would've died

5. At the end of this selection, Bradford mentions two groups that the Pilgrims knew of but could expect little help from. What two groups did he mention?

6. Critical Thinking: Bradford speaks of an "apostle." To whom is he referring? What was the difference between the "barbarians" that greeted the apostle and those that met the Pilgrims?

Map Study: The Original Colonies

Refer to the maps in the textbook to complete the map below.

1. Label each of the thirteen colonies.

2. Using three colored pencils, color the key and the corresponding regions on the map.

3. Label these settlements: Jamestown, Plymouth, Albany, Salem, Boston, St. Mary's, Providence, Charleston, Philadelphia, Williamsburg, and Savannah.

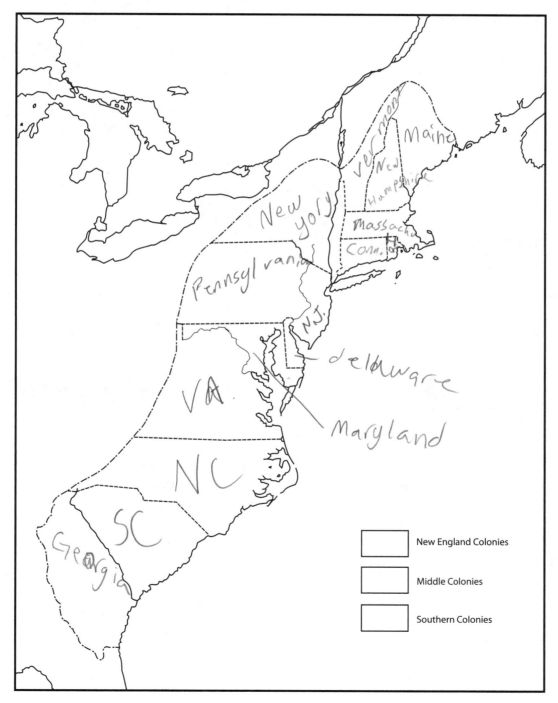

Thirteen Different Colonies

Complete the chart (except for the shaded areas). Refer to the textbook (including "The American Colonies" chart). The important leaders, first settlements, and facts of interest are listed below the chart.

Colony	Important Leaders	First Settlement	Date	Facts of Interest
Massachusetts	John Carver William Bradford John Winthrop	Plymouth	1620	Puritans, Separatists Mayflower Compact Great Migration
New Hampshire				
Connecticut				
Rhode Island				
New York	1. 2.			1. 2.
New Jersey	1. 2.			
Delaware				
Pennsylvania				
Virginia				
Maryland	1. 2.			1. 2.
North Carolina				
South Carolina				
Georgia				

Leaders

John Berkeley
Cecilius Calvert
George Calvert
George Carteret
Duke of York
Thomas Hooker
Peter Minuit
James Oglethorpe
William Penn
John Rolfe
Roger Williams

Settlements

Albany
Albemarle Sound
Charleston
Jamestown
Odiorne's Point
Philadelphia
Providence
Savannah
St. Mary's
Wilmington
Windsor

Facts

Act of Toleration
colony for Roman Catholics
debtors' colony
Fundamental Orders
indigo and rice
once a portion of New York
originally New Netherland
originally New Sweden
patroons
Quaker "Holy Experiment"
tobacco

The Population of the Colonies

Historians can learn many important things by studying population statistics. Since 1790, the U.S. government has recorded population. Before that time, the population was estimated. Use the following chart, your textbook, and, if necessary, a calculator to answer the questions below.

Estimated Population of the American Colonies						
	1640	1660	1680	1700	1720	1740
Virginia	10,400	27,000	43,600	58,600	87,800	180,400
Massachusetts (includes Plymouth Colony before 1700)	9,900	22,100	46,200	55,900	91,000	151,600
Rhode Island	300	1,500	3,000	5,900	11,700	25,300
Connecticut	1,500	8,000	17,200	26,000	58,800	89,600
New Hampshire	1,100	1,600	2,000	5,000	9,400	23,300
New York	1,900	4,900	9,800	19,100	36,900	63,700
New Jersey	--	--	3,400	14,000	29,800	51,400
Maryland	500	8,400	17,900	29,600	66,100	116,100
Pennsylvania	--	--	700	18,000	31,000	85,600
Delaware	--	500	1,000	2,500	5,400	19,900
North Carolina	--	1,000	5,400	10,700	21,300	51,800
South Carolina	--	--	1,200	5,700	17,000	45,000
Georgia	--	--	--	--	--	2,000
Total	25,700	75,100	151,500	250,900	466,200	905,600

1. Which colony almost always had the largest population? _____

2. Which colony almost always had the second-largest population? _____

3. Can you think of why these two colonies were the largest? _____

4. Which colony had the smallest population in 1740? Why? _____

5. Which colony ended up as the largest of the middle colonies? _____

6. Give the five largest colonies in 1700. Then list the five largest colonies in 1740. How are the two lists different? _____

7. During which twenty-year period did the total population multiply the fastest? (e.g. 1660–1680, 1680–1700, etc.) _____

8. How much did the total population grow between 1720 and 1740? Did it double? triple? quadruple? _____

9. What two factors contributed to population growth? _____

Early Colonial Differences

Complete the chart (except for the shaded areas) using your textbook. The answers are listed below the chart. Some spaces have more than one answer.

	New England	Middle Colonies	Southern Colonies	Frontier
Occupations	1. 2.	1. 2.	plantations	subsistence farming
Physical Features	1. 2.	1. 2.		Appalachian Mountains
Main Ports	1. 2. 3.	Philadelphia	1. 2. 3.	███████
Settlers				variety
Indian Relations	1. 2. 3.	███████		frequent skirmishes over land
Local Government		variety		███████
Facts of Interest		███████		the Wilderness Road

Occupations
bread colonies
fishing/whaling
fur trade
shipbuilding

Physical Features
hilly
navigable rivers
rich, thick soil
thin, rocky soil
tidewater (wide coastal plain)

Main Ports
Boston
Charleston
Jamestown
Nantucket
New Bedford
Savannah

Settlers
melting pot
mostly English
mostly English

Indian Relations
Bacon's Rebellion
John Eliot
King Philip's War
Pequot War

Local Government
county/parish
township

Facts of Interest
coldest climate
first blacks

Life Among the Indians

Excerpts from A True History of the Captivity and Restoration of Mrs. Mary Rowlandson

Mary Rowlandson was a minister's wife living in Lancaster, Massachusetts, during King Philip's War in 1676. While her husband was away from home, her town was attacked by Indians, and she and her children were taken captive. Mrs. Rowlandson was held captive for over eleven weeks. During that time, one of her children died, and the others were taken from her. Read the following excerpts and answer the questions at the end.

On the tenth of February, 1675, came the *Indians* with great number upon Lancaster. Their first coming was about Sun-rising. Hearing the noise of some guns, we looked out; several Houses were burning, and the smoke ascending to Heaven. . . . At length they came and beset our own House, and quickly it was the doleful-lest day that ever mine eyes saw. The House stood upon the edge of a Hill; some of the *Indians* got behind the Hill, others into the Barn, and others behind any thing that would shelter them; from all which Places they shot against the House, so that the Bullets seemed to fly like Hail; and quickly they wounded one Man among us, then another, and then a third. About two Hours . . . they had been about the House before they could prevail to fire it. . . . Some in our House were fighting for their Lives, others wallowing in their Blood; the House on fire over our Heads, and the bloody Heathen ready to knock us on the Head if we stirred out. . . . Then I took my Children . . . to go forth and leave the House; but as soon as we came to the Door and appeared, the *Indians* shot so thick that the Bullets rattled against the House. . . . But out we must go, the Fire increasing and coming along behind us roaring, and the *Indians* gaping before us with their Guns, Spears, and Hatchets to devour us. No sooner were we out of the House but my Brother-in-Law . . . fell down dead, whereat the *Indians* scornfully shouted and hallowed, and were presently upon him, stripping off his Clothes. The Bullets flying thick, one went thorow my side, and the same . . . thorow the Bowels and Hand of my dear Child in my Arms. . . . Yet the Lord, by his Almighty power, preserved a number of us from death, for there were twenty-four of us taken alive; and carried Captive. . . .

But now . . . I must turn my back upon the Town, and travel with them into the vast and desolate Wilderness, I know not whither. It is not my tongue or pen can express the sorrows of my heart and bitterness of my spirit that I had at this departure: but God was with me in a wonderful manner. . . . One of the *Indians* carried my poor wounded Babe upon a horse: it went moaning all along, I shall die, I shall die! I went on foot after it, with sorrow that cannot be exprest. . . . My sweet Babe, like a Lamb, departed this life, on Feb. 18, 1675 [1676] it being about six years and five months old. It was nine dayes (from the first wounding) in this miserable condition, without any refreshing of one nature or other, except a little cold water. I cannot but take notice how, at another time, I could not bear to be in the room where any dead person was; but now the case is changed; I must and could lye down by my dead Babe, side by side, all the night after. . . .

The first week of my being among them I hardly ate any thing; the second week I found my stomach grow very faint for want of something; and yet 'twas very hard to get down their filthy trash; but the third week (though I could think how formerly my stomach would turn against this or that, and I could starve and die before I could eat such things, yet) they were pleasant and savory to my taste. I was at this time knitting a pair of white Cotton Stockings for my Mistress; and I had not yet wrought upon the Sabbath-day: when the Sabbath came, they bade me go to work; I told them it was Sabbath-day, and desired them to let me rest, and told them I would do as much more to-morrow; to which they answer me, they would break my face. . . .

During my abode in this place Philip spake to me to make a shirt for his Boy, which I did; for which he gave me a shilling; I offered the money to my Master, but he bade me keep it; and with it I bought a piece of Horse flesh. Afterwards I made a Cap for his Boy, for which he invited me to Dinner; I went, and he gave me a Pancake about as big as two fingers; it was made of parched Wheat, beaten and fryed in Bears grease, but I thought I never tasted pleasanter meat in my life. There was a Squaw who spake to me to make a shirt for her Sannup; for which she gave me a piece of Bear. Another asked me to knit a pair of Stockings, for which she gave me a quart of Pease. I boyled my Pease and Bear together, and invited my Master and Mistress to Dinner; but the proud Gossip, because I served them both in one Dish, would eat nothing, except one bit that he gave her upon the point of his Knife. . . .

We came that day to a great Swamp; by the side of which we took up our lodging that night. When I came to the brow of the hill that looked toward the Swamp, I thought we had been come to a great *Indian Town*, (though there were none but our own Company,) the *Indians* were as thick as the Trees; it seemed as if there had been a thousand Hatchets going at once: if one looked before one there was nothing but *Indians*, and behind one nothing but *Indians*; and so on either hand; I myself in the midst, and no Christian Soul near me, and yet how hath the Lord preserved me in safety! . . . After a restless and hungry night there, we had a wearisome time of it the next day. The Swamp by which we lay was, as it were, a deep Dungeon, and an exceeding high and steep hill before it. Before I got to the top of the hill, I thought my heart and legs and all would have broken and failed me; what through faintness and soreness of Body, it was a grievous day of Travel to me. . . .

Being got out of her [my Mistress] sight, I had time and liberty again to look into my Bible, which was my guide by day, and my Pillow by night. Now that comfortable Scripture presented itself to me, *Isaiah liv. 7, For a small moment have I forsaken thee; but with great mercies will I gather thee.* Thus the Lord carried me along from one time to another; and made good to me this precious promise, and many others.

1. How did the Indians try to drive the settlers out of the house after they had been shooting at it for so long?

    _____

2. Even though twenty-four settlers made it out alive into captivity, who was killed on the way out of the house? _____

3. How long had they been wandering through the wilderness before Mary's daughter died? Why did she die?

    _____

4. How did Mary feel about Indian food at the beginning of her captivity?

    _____

5. For what did Mary's mistress say she would break Mary's face?

    _____

6. What did Mary find to do to occupy her time? _____

7. How was she rewarded for her occupation? _____

8. How do you think Mary gained strength to endure her captivity?

    _____

The Colonies Become Established

Underline the word or phrase that best completes each sentence.

1. The most important type of growth in the colonies was (immigration, natural increase).

2. After the English, the (Germans, Scots-Irish) made up the largest group of immigrants.

3. The majority of slaves were sent to (North America, the Caribbean and South America).

4. A colony influenced by diverse peoples is called a (melting pot, salad bowl).

5. A popular term for the colonial frontier was the (trenches, back country).

6. Settlers usually followed (rivers, dirt roads) inland.

7. The main north-south colonial highway was the (Great Wagon, Wilderness) Road.

8. Most early colonists were (merchants, farmers).

9. A farmer who raises just enough crops and livestock to feed his family is called a (subsistence, tidewater) farmer.

10. New England's climate was (warmer, colder) than the climates of other colonial regions.

11. Almost all the settlers in Massachusetts were (British, French).

12. The middle colonies grew an abundance of (cereal grains, indigo).

13. A major advantage of the middle colonies was their (tidewater areas, navigable rivers).

14. An early center for fur trade was (New Bedford, Albany).

15. Coopers used lumber to make barrels, and wainwrights used it to make (boats, wagons).

16. Britain's large estates became the pattern for the (plantations, townships) in the southern colonies.

17. The foothills of the (Appalachian, Blue Ridge) Mountains are called the Piedmont.

18. The first important money crop in the southern colonies was (tobacco, indigo).

19. The largest and most important crop in all the colonies was (corn, rice).

20. The trade routes of the Atlantic were (circular, triangular).

21. The most important reason for sending missionaries to the Indians was to (convert them, explore the land).

22. John Eliot printed the first (Bay Psalm Book, Bible) in the colonies.

23. Indians who converted to Christianity lived in (praying towns, praying huts).

24. The Puritans began allowing slavery after (King Philip's War, the Pequot War).

25. King Philip was the son of (Massasoit, Powhatan).

26. The governor of Virginia during the time of Indian unrest was (Nathaniel Bacon, William Berkeley).

27. In (charter, proprietary) colonies, the people elected their own governor and legislature.

28. One method that colonial legislatures used to limit the royal governor's power was the (power of the purse, justice of the peace).

29. The main source of income for the colonial governments was (property, income) taxes.

30. The basic unit of government in New England was the (parish, township).

31. The town meeting was America's purest form of (direct, representative) government.

32. "Putting out" was a common form of (poor relief, punishment) in New England.

All in a Day's Work

Imagine that you are a female house slave in a southern household. The head of the house is the town merchant. Your work day begins before dawn, when your mistress assigns you a list of errands and chores to do for her. Using your textbook, answer the following questions about your lifestyle and daily chores.

1. Because you are a servant in an upper-class household, your owners are called _____ .

2. In addition to several slaves, the master also employs a(n) _____ servant, who is required to assist him in his business as a merchant.

3. Your first job of the day is to pick up some medicine for your mistress's son, who is sick. Which shop do you visit? _____

4. On the street outside the shop, you see the local clergyman, who is a member of the _____ and _____ classes.

5. Your mistress also asks you to stop at the _____'s shop on the way home to pick up the candles she ordered.

6. When you arrive home, your mistress tells you to polish the dining room furniture, which was imported from _____ .

7. As the time for the mid-day meal quickly approaches, your mistress realizes that she forgot to have the cook make pastries for dessert. You have to run immediately to the _____'s shop.

8. While the family eats together in the house, you and your fellow slaves eat in the outside kitchen. During the conversation you learn that one of the slaves next door ran away. His master had immediately spoken with the _____ about putting a runaway ad in the newspaper.

9. After the meal, there are more chores to be done. The vegetable garden behind the house needs to be tended. When you finish this task, your mistress allows you a few minutes of free time. But you know that not all slaves are given this freedom. Why not? _____
_____
_____
_____

10. Your mistress decides to walk into town and be fitted for some new clothes. You accompany her. You head to the _____, who fits the mistress for a new dress and cloak.

11. While you are walking in town, you notice a commotion on the other side of the street. A free black man is being forced to show his _____ in order to prove that he is free.

12. When you return home, the master's children are hard at work at their studies. You have always wanted to learn how to read. Would you be allowed to join them? Why or why not? _____

_____

_____

13. After the evening meal has been prepared and cleaned up, you still have several chores to do. Because this is summertime, you usually work _____ hours a day.

14. When you finally head to bed, you realize that, even though tomorrow is Saturday, you still must work the full day. How many days off do you receive per week? _____

Family Life in New England
Excerpts from *The Journal of Esther Edwards Burr, 1754–1757*

One of the most important ways that historians learn about the past is through the journals and letters of the people that lived in the past. These journals and letters show how the surroundings and current events affected the people that wrote them. Esther Edwards Burr was the daughter of Jonathan Edwards, the most famous minister in colonial New England, and the wife of Aaron Burr Sr., the president of the College of New Jersey (later Princeton). As the daughter of such a prominent minister, Esther received more education than most women of her time. When she married and moved away from home, she began writing letters to her closest friend, Sarah Prince. Esther wrote her letters to Sarah like a journal, writing daily and then sending many of them at the same time. Read the following entries from her journal and see what you can learn about life for a woman in colonial New England.

{October 5, 1754} Saturday Morn.

I write just when I can get time. My dear you must needs think I cant get much, for I hav my Sally to tend, and domesteck affairs to see to, and company to wait of besides my sewing, [so] that I am realy hurried. [50]

{October 6, 1754} Sabbath-day.

In the Morning I went to Meeting, heard Mr Joans Preach from 1. Corinthians. 12 Chap. 3 vers. . . . O I am ashamed, and that justly, that I spend my Sabbaths no better! I wonder God does not deprive me of these blessed oppertunitys! I am sure I deserve it!

Eve. If you knew my dear friend how gloomy our house was you would pety me. Mr Burr has been gon one long week and if every week seems as long as this, it will be *an Age* before Mr Burr comes home. I am so concernd about his helth (as he was poorly when he left) that at times I cant rest—I wish I could leve him in the hands of a kind and gracious God who has preserved him, and me, so many journeys. . . .

{October 7, 1754} Monday Eve.

This day I rode out to see some sick people, and to do country business, such as speak for Winter Tirneps, Apples, and syder, and butter. . . . [51]

{October 9, 1754} Wednsday Eve.

My time for writing is after I have got Sally a sleep. This day I rode out to see some sick people and Mrs Serjent amongst the rest tho' I hope she is not daingerous. This afternoon Mrs Belcher and Mrs Woodruff came to drink Tea with me. I have been very poorly all day with a pain in my brest and am now so ill I can but just set up. . . . [52]

{October 26, 1754} Saturday. Octbr 26.

These several days I could not get one minutes [rest] to say one word to you, for I had a quilt on the fra[me] and my Ironing to do, and could get no help. . . . [57]

{November 8, 1754} Fryday

Am a little better. A gentleman from Albany has been here to day and brings the sertain news that all the Indians in Stockbridge have left the place except two or three famalys. He say they are much disgusted, and say the white people are jelous of em and they will not live among em any longer. He said farther that they had a mind to send for a neighboring Tribe to assist em to kill all the people in Stockbridge. O my dear what a dismal aspect things have! I am almost out of my witts! What will become of my Dear father and his afflicted family! O help me to commit em to God who orders all things in mercy, and don't willingly afflict nor grieve any of his Children! . . . [60–61]

{NOVEMBER 21, 1754} **THURSDAY NOVBR. 21.**

You may remember that this day week I told you I was very poorly, and so have been ever since, some of the time very bad. The Doct was affraid I was taken with the long fever, and is still affraid it may prove that or some other bad fever. I have not been able to walk alone for almost a week past, but today as our people were all at meeting . . . I crawld as far as the case of drawers and got my paper and thought I would try to write a little but can no more. . . . [65]

{DECEMBER 11, 1754} **WEDNSDAY EVE.**

Mr Tennent looks at me and says, "Poor creature, she is to have no comfort in life I see! but always to be hurried to Death." But Mr Tennent is mistaken for even in my being hurried I take pleasure, for it has always been recond by me amongst my greatest pleasures to wait on my friends. Tis true sometimes I have those to attend on that are not the most agreable, but how many I am rejoiced to see enter my doors—Went down to Elizabethtown with Mr and Mrs Tennent, dined at Mr Woodruffs, drank Tea at the Governors. . . . [71–72]

{JANUARY 16, 1755} **THURSDAY EVE.**

I am realy my dear, *very* uneasy, and *much* concernd that I hear *nothing* from you for so long a time—Are you alive? You are *sick*, and have kept your Chamber this *six weeks*, and perhaps will *die* before I can hear one word from you. . . . [81]

{MARCH 1, 1755} **SATURDAY MARCH 1. day**

A woman here Ironing for me, and I am very busy mending stockings and one thing and another, so would beg your pardon for this day. [95]

{APRIL 27, 1755} **SABBATH EVE**

Tis several days since I have said one word to you, but my heart has been at Boston with you very often.

My dear Little Sally has been very sick and as we feard near to death . . . but Gods goodness is continued and repeated in spareing her as yet, perhaps only to give us time to prepare us for the sore tryal we have apprehended so nigh.

She is still quite low and as I apprehend not out of dainger. The Doct think she has had somthing of a Pleursy, to be sure she has had a very violent feaver. She has been extreamly tendsome, would go to no stranger, so Sukey and I have been obliged to watch every Night ever since her sickness [so] that I am almost got to be as bad as the Child.

1. What duties does Esther have around the house? Does she have much leisure time? _____

_____

2. Does Esther do all of her housework alone? What does this say about her social class?

_____

_____

3. What activities draw Esther from the house? _____

_____

4. Describe Esther's social life. _____

_____

5. What often worries Esther? Do modern women have these same concerns? Why or why not?

_____

_____

_____

_____

_____

_____

Life on a Southern Plantation
Excerpts from the *Journal and Letters of Philip Vickers Fithian*

As you learned in the text, wealthy Southerners hired private tutors to teach their children so that they could remain at home. In 1773, Philip Fithian, a young ministerial student from New Jersey, traveled to Virginia to "Nomini Hall" to be a tutor on the plantation of Robert Carter, one of the wealthiest men in Virginia. In his journal, Fithian records not only the daily activities of the schoolroom but also the other people and scenery around the plantation. Read the following passages, and answer the questions at the end.

[Carter] has two sons, and one Nephew; the oldest is turned of seventeen, and is reading Salust and the greek grammer; the others are about fourteen, and in English grammer, and Arithmetic. He has besides five daughters which I am to teach English, the eldest is turned of fifteen, and is reading the spectator; she is employed two days in every week in learning to play the Forte-Piana, and Harpsicord—The others are smaller, and learning to read and spell. Mr Carter is one of the Councellors in the general court at Williamsburg, and possest of as great, perhaps the clearest fortune according to the estimation of people here, of any man in Virginia: He seems to be a good scholar, even in classical learning, and is remarkable one in English grammar; and notwithstanding his rank, which in general seems to countenance indulgence to children, both himself and Mrs Carter have a manner of instructing and dealing with children far superior, I may say it with confidence, to any I have ever seen, in any place, or in any family. They keep them in perfect subjection to themselves, and never pass over an occasion of reproof. . . . [26]

The manner here is different from our way of living in Cohansie—In the morning so soon as it is light a Boy knocks at my Door to make a fire; after the Fire is kindled, I rise which now in the winter is commonly by Seven, or a little after, By the time I am drest the Children commonly enter the School-Room, which is under the Room I sleep in; I hear them round one lesson, when the Bell rings for eight o-clock . . . the Children then go out; and at half after eight the Bell rings for Breakfast, we then repair to the Dining-Room; after Breakfast, which is generally about half after nine, we go into School, and sit til twelve, when the Bell rings, & they go out for noon; the dinner-Bell rings commonly about half after two, often at three, but never before two.—After dinner is over, which in common, when we have no Company, is about half after three we go into School, & sit til the Bell rings at five, when they separate til the next morning; I have to myself in the Evening, a neat Chamber, a large Fire, Books, & Candle & my Liberty, either to continue in the school room, in my own Room or to sit over at the great House with Mr & Mrs Carter—We go into Supper commonly about half after eight or at nine & I usually go to Bed between ten and Eleven. . . . [31]

After Breakfast, we all retired into the Dancing-Room, & after the Scholars had their Lesson singly round Mr Christian [the dance master], very politely, requested me to step a *Minuet*; I excused myself however, but signified my peculiar pleasure in the Accuracy of their performance—There were several Minuets danced with great ease and propriety; after which the whole company Joined in country-dances, and it was indeed beautiful to admiration, to see such a number of young persons, set off by dress to the best Advantage, moving easily, to the sound of well performed Music, and with perfect regularity, tho' apparently in the utmost Disorder. . . . [33] [Fithian later reveals that he does not know how to dance and has to sit out during the balls given while he is in Virginia.]

Miss *Priscilla*, and Miss *Nancy* rode this morning in the Chariot over to Mr *Turburvills* [to dance]—Bob, every day at twelve o-clock, is down by the River Side with his Gun after Ducks, Gulls &c.—Ben is on his Horse a Riding, Harry, is either in the Kitchen, or at the Blacksmiths, or Carpenters Shop. They all find places of Rendesvous so soon as the Beell rings, and all seem to choose different Sports! . . . [37]

Mr *Carter* now possesses 60000 Acres of Land; & about 600 Negroes—But his Estate is much divided, & lies in almost every county in this Colony; He has Lands in the neighbourhood of Williamsburg, & an elegant & Spacious House in that City—He owns a great part of the well known Iron-Works near Baltimore in Maryland—And he has one or more considerable Farms not far from Anopolis. He has some large tracts of Land far to the West. . . . This House is built with Brick, but the bricks have been covered with strong lime Mortar; so that the building is now perfectly white; It is seventy-six Feet long from East to west; & forty-four wide from North to South, two Stories high. . . . It has five Stacks of Chimneys, tho two of these serve only for ornament. . . . The North side I think is most beautiful of all; In the upper Story is a Row of seven Windows with eighteen Lights a piece; and below six windows, with the like number of lights; besides a large Portico in the middle, at the sides of which are two Windows each with eighteen Lights. . . . There are four Rooms on a Floor, disposed of in the following manner. Below is a dining Room where we usually sit; the second is a dining-Room for the Children; the third is Mr Carters study; & the fourth is a Ball-Room thirty Feet long—Above stairs, one Room is for Mr & Mrs Carter; the second for the young Ladies; & the other two for occasional Company—As this House is large, & stands on a high piece of Land it may be seen a considerable distance. . . . At equal Distances from each corner of this Building stand four other considerable Houses, which I shall next a little describe. First, at the North East corner, & at 100 yards Distance stands the School-House; At the North-West Corner, & at the same Distance stands the stable; At the South-West Corner, & at the same Distance, stands the Coach-House; And lastly, at the South-East corner, & at an equal distance stands the Work-House. . . . In each Room [of the School-House] is a fire; In the large Room below-Stairs we keep our School; the other two Rooms below which are smaller are allowed to Mr Randolph the Clerk; The Room above the School-Room Ben and I live in; & the other Room above Stairs belongs to *Harry* & *Bob*. . . . From the front yard of the Great-House, to the Wash-House is a curious *Terrace*, covered finely with Green turf, & about five foot high with a slope of eight feet, which appears exceeding well to persons coming to the front of the House. . . . Due East of the Great House are two Rows of tall, flourishing, beautiful, Poplars, beginning on a Line drawn from the School to the Wash-House. . . . These Rows of Poplars form an extremely pleasant avenue, & at the Road, through them, the House appears most romantic, at the same time that it does truly elegant. [79–81]

About ten an old Negro Man came with a complaint to Mr Carter of the Overseer that he does not allow him his Peck of corn a Week—The humble posture in which the old Fellow placed himself before he began moved me. . . . He seem'd healthy, but very old, he was well dress'd but complained bitterly—I cannot like this thing of allowing them no meat, & only a Peck of Corn & a Pint of Salt a Week, & yet requiring of them hard & constant Service. [129]

1. How many students does Fithian have to teach? _____

2. What are the girls learning? _____

_____

3. Why is Fithian so impressed with Mr. and Mrs. Carter? _____

_____

_____

_____

4. Briefly describe the schedule for the school day. _____

_____

_____

5. What skill does Mr. Christian teach the children? _____

6. What do the children do during their free time between noon and the afternoon meal? _____

_____

_____

7. Describe the property that Mr. Carter owns. _____

_____

_____

8. Briefly describe the main house. _____

_____

_____

_____

9. Where does Fithian live? _____

10. What bothered him when an old slave visited the house? _____

_____

_____

Scripture in Colonial Society

Scripture had a major impact on the colonies. Almost everyone could quote it, and most people accepted its morals. But knowledge of the Bible does not save people or keep them from error. During the Great Awakening, the Holy Spirit awakened many Americans from their spiritual sleep, while others remained in their sins. Use your Bible to answer these questions.

1. One influence of Christianity in America was "the Protestant work ethic." Believing that labor had spiritual value, the Puritans emphasized honest hard work. Americans have been industrious ever since.

   ★ What type of labor is profitable (Prov. 14:23)? _____

   ★ How hard does God expect us to work (Eccles. 9:10)? _____

   ★ What is one purpose of our work (Eph. 4:28)? _____

2. Benjamin Franklin was a leader in the Enlightenment. He believed in hard work and accepted Jesus's "system of morals," but he rejected the Savior. He believed that our "most acceptable service of God was the doing of good to man."

   ★ Whose help do we need to accomplish good (John 15:4–5)? _____

   ★ What does Jesus call the work of those He never knew (Matt. 7:22–23)? _____

   ★ What is the most important commandment (Mark 12:30)? _____

3. Franklin trusted his own reasoning above Scripture. Raised a Presbyterian, he rejected the church's teachings because they were "unintelligible" or "doubtful." He even said of George Whitefield, "He used, indeed, sometimes to pray for my conversion, but never had the satisfaction of believing that his prayers were heard."

   ★ How well can an unbeliever understand spiritual truths (1 Cor. 2:14)? _____

   ★ How does God's intelligence compare to ours (Isa. 55:8–9)? _____

   ★ How trustworthy is our own heart (Jer. 17:9)? _____

   ★ Whom should people trust above their own understanding (Prov. 3:5–6)? _____

   ★ Where does knowledge start (Prov. 1:7)? _____

4. Many churchgoers attacked the Great Awakening because of its emotional displays, so Jonathan Edwards wrote a book to defend the revival as a great work of God.

   ★ Why do some churchgoers despise good preaching (2 Tim. 4:2–3)? _____

   ★ What does God call the worship by unbelievers (Isa. 1:13–16)? _____

   ★ What is one biblical response to warnings of judgment (Hab. 3:16)? _____

   ★ What is the main evidence of true conversion (2 Cor. 5:17)? _____

   ★ What is a key ingredient of true revival (2 Chron. 7:14)? _____

Chapter Review
Modified True/False

If the statement is true, write the word *true* in the blank. If it is false, write words to replace the underlined words to make the statement true.

_____ 1. The colonists were much <u>less</u> concerned about social class than we are today.

_____ 2. The <u>aristocrats</u> in the colonies were the only people who could afford servants and household luxuries.

_____ 3. <u>Indentured servants</u> came from continental Europe with their families and possessions in hopes that a friend or relative would pay their passage when they arrived in America.

_____ 4. The indentured servant received land and his <u>redemption money</u> when he completed his service.

_____ 5. The Puritans believed that the family was meant to be a reflection of <u>civil government</u>.

_____ 6. The colonial family had to act as a hospital, school, church, and <u>business place</u>.

_____ 7. By the end of the colonial period, the family had become more affectionate and open because life was <u>so uncertain</u>.

_____ 8. Instead of being self-sufficient, slaves had to depend on their <u>owners</u> for everything.

_____ 9. Schools established in the homes of widows or single ladies were called <u>grammar schools</u>.

_____ 10. Because there was no consistent model for spelling, schoolmasters sometimes used the <u>King James Bible</u> as their guide.

_____ 11. Colonial children learned to read from a <u>prayer book</u>.

_____ 12. The first institution of higher learning in the colonies was <u>the College of New Jersey</u>.

_____ 13. Yale was founded when the Puritans saw that Harvard had been affected by the ideas of the <u>Great Awakening</u>.

_____ 14. Boys learned trades under the <u>apprenticeship</u> system.

_____ 15. The Puritans came to be called <u>Congregationalists</u> because they believed the congregation should have a say in running the church.

_____ 16. The <u>Congregational</u> Church was the established church in the southern colonies.

_____ 17. Catholics enjoyed more freedom in <u>Delaware</u> than in any other American colony.

_____ 18. Most of the members of the Anglican Church were from the <u>middle class</u>.

_____ 19. The <u>Moravians</u> wanted to be missionaries to the Indians, slaves, and German settlers.

_____ 20. Because the <u>Quakers</u> did not believe in Christ, the colonists treated them like pagans.

_____ 21. <u>Gilbert Tennent</u> founded the "log college" to train young Presbyterians.

_____ 22. <u>Samuel Blair</u> was the greatest figure in the southern Great Awakening.

_____ 23. "Sinners in the Hands of an Angry God" was preached by <u>George Whitefield</u>.

_____ 24. George Whitefield is known for building <u>a hospital</u> in Savannah, Georgia.

_____ 25. <u>David Brainerd</u> is the best-known missionary to the Indians following the Great Awakening.

_____ 26. The Great Awakening <u>unified</u> the churches in New England.

_____ 27. The Great Awakening <u>increased</u> the gap between church and state in the colonies.

_____ 28. Men who believed in the power of reason were part of the <u>Enlightenment</u>.

_____ 29. <u>Unitarianism</u> teaches that God designed the universe and then left it alone.

_____ 30. Unitarians deny the doctrine of the <u>Trinity</u>.

The French and Indian War

Refer to your textbook to complete the map below.

Taken from France

Taken from Spain

1. Label these rivers: St. Lawrence, Mississippi, Allegheny, Monongahela
2. Label these cities and forts: Quebec, Montreal, Albany, Fort Duquesne, Boston, Philadelphia, New Orleans
3. Using a colored pencil, color the region that France lost to Britain in the Peace of Paris (1763).
4. Using another colored pencil, color the region that Spain lost to Britain in the Peace of Paris.

Complete the chart by describing the advantages and disadvantages of each side at the start of the French and Indian War.

	French	British
Unity of Government		
Defenses/Forts		predominance of coastal cities
Army Training		inexperienced regular army and colonists
Support of Indians		
Population		
Size of Region to Defend		compact on the Atlantic coast
Navy	moderate size	

George Washington's Report on the Defeat of Braddock

Edward Braddock's defeat near Fort Duquesne had a major influence on colonial opinion of British troops. Read Washington's letter to his mother, dated July 18, 1755. Then answer the questions.

Honored Madam: As I doubt not but you have heard of our defeat, and, perhaps, had it represented in a worse light, if possible, than it deserves, I have taken this earliest opportunity to give you some account of the engagement as it happened, within ten miles of the French fort, on Wednesday, the 9th instant.

We marched to that place, without any considerable loss, having only now and then a straggler picked up by the French and scouting Indians. When we came there, we were attacked by a party of French and Indians, whose number, I am persuaded, did not exceed three hundred men; while ours consisted of about one thousand three hundred well-armed troops, chiefly regular soldiers, who were struck with such panic that they behaved with more cowardice than it is possible to conceive. The officers behaved gallantly, in order to encourage their men, for which they suffered greatly, there being near sixty killed and wounded; a large proportion of the number we had.

The Virginia troops showed a good deal of bravery, and were nearly all killed; for I believe, out of three companies that were there, scarcely thirty men were left alive. . . . The dastardly behavior of those they call regulars exposed all others, that were inclined to do their duty, to almost certain death; and, at last, in despite of all the efforts of the officers to the contrary, they ran, as sheep pursued by dogs, and it was impossible to rally them.

The General was wounded, of which he died three days after. Sir Peter Halket was killed in the field, where died many other brave officers. I luckily escaped without a wound, though I had four bullets through my coat, and two horses shot under me. Captains Orme and Morris, two of the aides-de-camp, were wounded early in the engagement, which rendered the duty harder upon me, as I was the only person then left to distribute the General's orders, which I was scarcely able to do, as I was not half recovered from a violent illness, that had confined me to my bed and a wagon for above ten days. I am still in a weak and feeble condition, which induces me to halt here two or three days in the hope of recovering a little strength, to enable me to proceed homewards; from whence, I fear, I shall not be able to stir till toward September; so that I shall not have the pleasure of seeing you till then, unless it be in Fairfax.

I am, honored Madam, your most dutiful son.

1. Why did Washington think he should write his own account of the battle for his mother?

   _____

   _____

2. Whom did Washington blame for the defeat? _____

3. Which troops performed well? _____

4. What evidence do you see of Washington's bravery? _____

5. What factors limited Washington's performance as an aide? _____

6. The French had about nine hundred men at the battle. Why do you think Washington underestimated their numbers? How does his mistake affect our opinion of the British? _____

_____

_____

7. Why doesn't Washington give an opinion of Braddock? _____

_____

8. What made it difficult for Washington to carry out General Braddock's orders and that caused him to be delayed for several days? _____

_____

_____

The Boston Tea Party
From the "Recollections of George Hewes"

George Hewes was one of the "Indians" who destroyed the tea in Boston Harbor on December 16, 1773. Read his account of the Tea Party and answer the questions that follow.

The tea destroyed was contained in three ships, lying near each other at what was called at that time Griffin's wharf, and were surrounded by armed ships of war, the commanders of which had publicly declared that if the rebels, as they were pleased to style the Bostonians, should not withdraw their opposition to the landing of the tea before a certain day, the 17th day of December, 1773, they should on that day force it on shore, under the cover of their cannon's mouth. On the day preceding the seventeenth, there was a meeting of the citizens of the county of Suffolk, convened at one of the churches in Boston, for the purpose of consulting on what measures might be considered expedient to prevent the landing of the tea, or secure the people from the collection of the duty. At that meeting a committee was appointed to wait on Governor Hutchinson, and request him to inform them whether he would take any measures to satisfy the people on the object of the meeting. To the first application of this committee, the Governor told them he would give them a definite answer by five o'clock in the afternoon. At the hour appointed, the committee again repaired to the Governor's house, and on inquiry found he had gone to his country seat at Milton, a distance of about six miles. When the committee returned and informed the meeting of the absence of the Governor, there was a confused murmur among the members, and the meeting was immediately dissolved, many of them crying out, "Let every man do his duty, and be true to his country"; and there was a general huzza for Griffin's wharf.

It was now evening, and I immediately dressed myself in the costume of an Indian, equipped with a small hatchet, which I and my associates denominated the tomahawk, with which, and a club, after having painted my face and hands with coal dust in the shop of a blacksmith, I repaired to Griffin's wharf, where the ships lay that contained the tea. When I first appeared in the street after being thus disguised, I fell in with many who were dressed, equipped and painted as I was, and who fell in with me and marched in order to the place of our destination.

When we arrived at the wharf, there were three of our number who assumed an authority to direct our operations, to which we readily submitted. They divided us into three parties, for the purpose of boarding the three ships which contained the tea at the same time. The name of him who commanded the division to which I was assigned was Leonard Pitt. The names of the other commanders I never knew. We were immediately ordered by the respective commanders to board all the ships at the same time, which we promptly obeyed. The commander of the division to which I belonged, as soon as we were on board the ship, appointed me boatswain, and ordered me to go to the captain and demand of him the keys to the hatches and a dozen candles. I made the demand accordingly, and the captain promptly replied, and delivered the articles; but requested me at the same time to do no damage to the ship or rigging. We then were ordered by our commander to open the hatches and take out all the chests of tea and throw them overboard, and we immediately proceeded to execute his orders, first cutting and splitting the chests with our tomahawks, so as to thoroughly expose them to the effects of the water.

In about three hours from the time we went on board, we had thus broken and thrown overboard every tea chest to be found in the ship, while those in the other ships were disposing of the tea in the same way, at the same time. We were surrounded by British armed ships, but no attempt was made to resist us.

We then quietly retired to our several places of residence, without having any conversation with each other, or taking any measures to discover who were our associates; nor do I recollect of our having had the knowledge of the name of a single individual concerned in that affair, except that of Leonard Pitt, the commander of my division, whom I have mentioned. There appeared to be an understanding that each individual should volunteer his services, keep his own secret, and risk the consequence for himself. No disorder took place during that transaction, and it was observed at that time that the stillest night ensued that Boston had enjoyed for many months. . . .

The next morning, after we had cleared the ships of the tea, it was discovered that very considerable quantities of it were floating upon the surface of the water; and to prevent the possibility of any of its being saved for use, a number of small boats were manned by sailors and citizens, who rowed them into those parts of the harbor wherever the tea was visible, and by beating it with oars and paddles so thoroughly drenched it as to render its entire destruction inevitable.

1. What threat did the British make if the colonists did not stop their opposition to the tea?

_____

2. What was the first action of the group that met at the Boston church? _____

_____

3. What was the governor's response to the people? _____

_____

4. What did the group decide to do when they realized the governor had left? _____

_____

5. Describe the costumes that the men wore to the wharf. _____

_____

6. Why were the men at the wharf divided into three groups? _____

_____

7. What task was assigned to the narrator? Was he successful? _____

_____

8. Why did the men break open the cases of tea instead of just throwing them overboard?

_____

9. Why do you think the British did nothing to stop the destruction of the tea? _____

_____

_____

10. Why do you think the men dressed as Indians did not tell each other their names? _____

_____

_____

Causes and Effects

Although the American Revolution surprised many people, in hindsight it seems the natural outgrowth of a long series of events. One group's actions led to another group's reactions. Historians want to know the causes (*why* these actions took place) and the effects (*what* the results were). Complete the chart by filling in the causes of the British actions and the effects, or colonial reactions. The answers are listed at the bottom.

Cause	British Action	Colonial Reaction
lack of colonial unity	failure in the French and Indian War (1754)	*Albany Plan of Union*
William Pitt's system	Peace of Paris (1763)	desire for no more British troops
	Proclamation of 1763	
	Quartering Act of 1765	
	Stamp Act of 1765	
strong leadership in Parliament after the repeal of the Stamp Act	Townshend Acts (1767)	
	Boston Massacre (1770)	
	Tea Act of 1773	
British anger at the refusal of Massachusetts to obey the Tea Act	Intolerable Acts (1774)	
	George III now says: "Submit or Triumph."	
	Battles of Lexington and Concord (1775)	

Causes

British attempt to capture colonial arms
British need for more money
British troops stationed in Boston
costly British troops in America
Declaration of Rights and Grievances
difficulties of the British East India Company
Pontiac's revolt

Colonial Reactions

anger over closed lands
anger over troops in homes
Boston Tea Party
First Continental Congress
new boycotts and smuggling
radical accounts of "martyrs"
Stamp Act Congress
start of the War for Independence
stockpiling of colonial arms

The Shot Heard 'Round the World

Identify each of the following people, places, or events by placing the answers in the spaces provided. Then identify (in the vertical box) the theme of this section and write it in the spaces labeled "theme."

1. city placed under siege after the first skirmishes of the War for Independence
2. commander of British troops in the colonies
3. name given to members of the colonial militia
4. series of parliamentary measures that led colonists to violent resistance
5. site of the *second* skirmish on April 18, 1775
6. one of two colonial leaders British troops were sent to arrest on April 18, 1775
7. the other of the two colonial leaders British troops were to arrest that day
8. site of the *first* skirmish on April 18, 1775
9. meeting of colonial delegates in Philadelphia in September 1774 to organize in opposition to Parliament's measures
10. one of the little-known riders who warned the colonists, "The British are coming!"
11. the most famous of the riders who warned the colonists that British troops were on the move
12. another of the little-known riders who warned the colonists of British troop movement

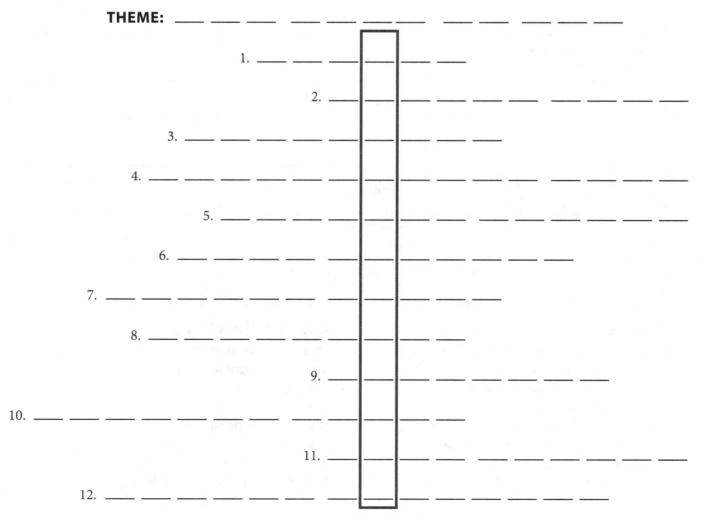

THEME: ___ ___ ___ ___ ___ ___ ___ ___ ___ ___ ___

AMERICAN REPUBLIC

Name _____

CHAPTER 5 ACTIVITY 6

Writing Your Own Glossary

A glossary is a list of important terms with their definitions. Write a short description of each term below. Your description should include the words in the right column.

Example		
France	*Britain's* greatest *rival* during the eighteenth century	rival, Britain
People		
1. Iroquois		confederation, British ally
2. George Washington		Virginia, lost, aide
3. Edward Braddock		British general, lost, died
4. William Pitt		British leader, new system
5. James Wolfe		British general, won
6. Pontiac		Ottawa chief, frontier
7. Samuel Adams		Massachusetts, opposition
8. Patrick Henry		Virginia, speech, liberty
Terms		
9. mercantilism		economic system, gold
10. writs of assistance		search warrants, British
11. duties		taxes, imported goods
12. Committees of Correspondence		opposition, alerted

Places		
13. Ohio Valley		struggle, war
14. Fort Duquesne		Fort Pitt, Ohio
15. Quebec		New France, defeat
16. Lexington and Concord		skirmishes, beginning
Events		
17. French and Indian War		Seven Years' War, America
18. Albany Plan		unite, colonies
19. Proclamation of 1763		forbade, west, Appalachian
20. Navigation and Trade Acts		regulated, colonial trade
21. Sugar Act		British, money, duties
22. Stamp Act		British, revenue, stamps
23. Townshend Acts		renewed duties, resentment
24. Boston Massacre		death, five, "martyrs"
25. Boston Tea Party		protest, tea ships
26. Intolerable Acts		punish, Massachusetts
27. Quebec Act		favored, French, Catholicism

AMERICAN REPUBLIC

Name _____

Map Study: The War for Independence

Refer to the maps in the textbook to complete the map below.

1. Label these bodies of water: Lake Champlain, Hudson River, Delaware River

2. Label these locations (black dots): Valley Forge, Albany, Boston

3. Label these battle sites (red dots for British victories and blue for colonial victories): Bunker Hill, Montreal, Quebec, Saratoga, Harlem Heights, Monmouth, Trenton, Brandywine, Yorktown, Guilford Courthouse, Kings Mountain, Cowpens, Camden, Charleston, Savannah

4. Using a colored pencil, draw a line to connect the battle sites of the northern campaigns (1775–76) in the order the events occurred. (Hint: Begin with Bunker Hill and end with the evacuation of Boston.) Using another color, connect the sites in the middle campaigns (1776–78). Using a third color, connect the sites in the southern campaigns (1779–81). Draw an arrow at the end of each line.

Major Battles

Complete the chart. For each battle, include the commanders of each side if they are mentioned in the text. Place a "B" next to the battle name if the British won or an "A" if the Americans won.

	Battle	Year	Leaders	Significance
Northern Campaigns	Fort Ticonderoga	1775		
	Bunker Hill			
	Quebec			
Middle Campaigns	Long Island			
	Trenton			
	Saratoga			
	Vincennes	1779		
Southern Campaigns	Kings Mountain			
	Cowpens			
	Yorktown			

Answer these questions based on the chart.

1. What was the colonists' first defeat? _____

2. What was the last major battle of the middle campaigns? _____

3. Which year includes the most battles? _____

4. Which colonial commander won the most battles? _____

5. In which region did the colonists win the most battles? _____

6. Which battle did *not* take place in the three major regions? _____

7. Which battle do you think was the *least* important? Why? _____

_____

8. What battle caused the greatest changes in the war? Why? _____

_____

AMERICAN REPUBLIC

Name _____

CHAPTER 6 ACTIVITY 3

Taking Sides

Read the following two newspaper articles from 1775 and 1776. The first article, written by the inhabitants of Fairfield, Connecticut, opposed any move by the colonies to declare independence. The second article, written by Thomas Paine under the pseudonym of "The Forester," strongly calls for independence. Answer the questions following the articles.

RIVINGTON'S NEW-YORK GAZETTEER; OR CONNECTICUT, NEW-JERSEY, HUDSON'S-RIVER, AND QUEBEC WEEKLY Advertiser, 23 February 1775

Mr. Rivington,

Sir,

IN the present critical situation of public affairs, we, the subscribers, freeholders and inhabitants of the town of Reading, and the adjoining parts, in the county of Fairfield, and colony of Connecticut, think it necessary . . . to assure the public, that we are open enemies to any change in the present happy constitution, and highly disapprove of all measures, in any degree calculated to promote confusion and disorder . . . adopted for the purpose of opposing British government. . . .

Resolved, that whilst we enjoy the privileges and immunities of the English constitution, we will render all due obedience to his most gracious Majesty King George the third; and, that a firm dependance [*sic*] on the mother country is essential in our political safety and happiness. . . .

Resolved, that the privileges and immunities of this constitution are yet . . . continued to all his Majesty's American subjects, except those, who . . . have justly forfeited their title therein. . . .

Resolved, that notwithstanding, we will, in all circumstances, conduct with prudence and moderation, we consider it as an indispensable duty we owe to our King, our constitution, our country, and posterity, to defend, maintain, and preserve, at the risk of our lives and properties, the prerogative of the crown, and the privileges of the subject from all attacks, by any rebellious body of men, and any committees of inspection, correspondence, &c.

Signed by 141 inhabitants.

✪✪✪

PENNSYLVANIA JOURNAL; AND THE WEEKLY ADVERTISER (PHILADELPHIA), 24 APRIL 1776

. . . TO THE PEOPLE.

IT is not a time to triffle. Men, who know they deserve nothing from their country, and whose hope is on the arm that hath sought to enslave ye, may hold out to you, as Cato [a Loyalist writer] hath done, the false light of reconciliation—There is no such thing. 'Tis gone! 'Tis past!—The grave hath parted us—and death, in the persons of the slain, hath cut the thread of life between Britain and America.

Conquest, and not reconciliation is the plan of Britain. . . . *[W]e will make peace with you as with enemies, but we will never re-unite with you as friends.* . . .

Can this continent be happy under the government of Great-Britain or not? . . . [C]an she be happy under a government of our own? To live beneath the authority of those whom we cannot love, is misery, slavery, or what name you please. In that case, there will never be peace. Security will be a thing unknown, because, a treacherous friend in power, is the most dangerous of enemies. The answer to the . . . question, can America be happy under a government of her own, is short and simple, viz. as happy as she please; she hath a blank sheet to write upon. Put it not off too long. . . .

The FORESTER.

© BJU Press. Reproduction prohibited.

1. What do the inhabitants of Fairfield think will be the results of moves to oppose Britain?

   _____

2. Why do the inhabitants of Fairfield decide to remain obedient to the king? _____

   _____

   _____

   _____

3. What do the Fairfield residents resolve to "defend, maintain, and preserve"? _____

   _____

   _____

4. What do they risk by doing this? _____

5. What does "The Forester" call a "false light"? _____

6. Why can the colonies never be reconciled with Britain, according to "The Forester"? _____

   _____

7. What does "The Forester" believe is Britain's plan? How is this different from what the Fairfield residents

   believe about the crown and constitution? _____

   _____

   _____

8. What does "The Forester" believe is the result of remaining under England's government? Compare this to
   what the Fairfield residents believe will happen if the colonies *don't* remain under England's government.

   _____

Name _____

The Bad Winter

Read the following account of winter at Valley Forge by Surgeon Albigence Waldo of Connecticut. Then answer the questions.

December 13.—The army marched three miles from the west side the river and encamped near a place called the Gulph and not an improper name neither, for this Gulph seems well adapted by its situation to keep us from the pleasures and enjoyments of this world, or being conversant with any body in it. It is an excellent place to raise the ideas of a philosopher beyond the glutted thoughts and reflexions of an Epicurian. . . .

. . . [I]t is, upon consideration, for many good purposes since we are to winter here: 1st, there is plenty of wood and water. 2ndly, there are but few families for the soldiery to steal from—tho' far be it from a soldier to steal. 4ly [*sic*], there are warm sides of hills to erect huts on. 5ly, they will be heavenly minded like Jonah when in the belly of a great fish. 6ly, they will not become home sick as is sometimes the case when men live in the open world—since reflections which will naturally arise from their present habitation will lead them to the more noble thoughts of employing their leisure hours in filling their knapsacks with such materials as may be necessary on the Journey to another Home.

December 14.—Prisoners and deserters are continually coming in. The army, which has been surprisingly healthy hitherto, now begins to grow sickly from the continued fatigues they have suffered this campaign. Yet they still show a spirit of alacrity and contentment not to be expected from so young troops. I am sick—discontented—and out of humor. Poor food—hard lodging—cold weather—fatigue—nasty cloathes—nasty cookery—vomit half my time—smoked out of my senses—the Devil's in't—I can't endure it—Why are we sent here to starve and freeze?—What sweet felicities have I left at home: A charming wife—pretty children—good beds—good food—good cookery—all agreeable—all harmonious! Here all confusion—smoke and cold—hunger and filthyness—a pox on my bad luck! There comes a bowl of beef soup, full of burnt leaves and dirt, sickish enough to make a Hector spue—away with it, boys!—I'll live like the chameleon upon air.

Poh! Poh! crys Patience within me, you talk like a fool. Your being sick covers your mind with a melancholic gloom, which makes everything about you appear gloomy. See the poor soldier when in health—with what cheerfulness he meets his foes and encounters every hardship. If barefoot, he labours thro' the mud and cold with a song in his mouth extolling War and Washington. If his food be bad, he eats it notwithstanding with seeming content—blesses God for a good stomach and whistles it into digestion.

But harkee, Patience, a moment. There comes a soldier; his bare feet are seen thro' his worn out shoes, his legs nearly naked from the tattered remains of an only pair of stockings, his breeches not sufficient to cover his nakedness, his shirt hanging in strings, his hair dishevelled, his face meagre; his whole appearance pictures a person forsaken and discouraged. He comes, and crys with an air of wretchedness and despair, I am sick, my feet lame, my legs are sore, my body covered with this tormenting itch. My cloaths are worn out, my constitution is broken, my former activity is exhausted by fatigue, hunger and cold. I fail fast, I shall soon be no more! and all the reward I shall get will be: "Poor Will is dead."

People who live at home in luxury and ease, quietly possessing their habitations, enjoying their wives and families in peace, have but a very faint idea of the unpleasing sensations and continual anxiety the man endures who is in a camp, and is the husband and parent of an agreeable family. These same people are willing we should suffer every thing for their benefit and advantage, and yet are the first to condemn us for not doing more!!

December 15.—Quiet. Eat pessimmens, found myself better for their lenient opperation. Went to a house, poor and small, but good food within—eat too much from being so long abstemious, thro' want of palatables. Mankind are never truly thankfull for the benefits of life until they have experienced the want of them. The man who has seen misery knows best how to enjoy good. He who is always at ease and has enough of the blessings of common life is an impotent judge of the feelings of the unfortunate. . . .

December 16.—Cold rainy day. Baggage ordered over the Gulph of our division, which were to march at ten, but the baggage was ordered back and for the first time since we have been here the tents were pitched, to keep the men more comfortable

"Good morning, Brother Soldier," says one to another, "how are you?"

"All wet I thank'e, hope you are so," says the other.

The enemy have been at Chestnut Hill opposite to us near our last encampment the other side Schuylkill, made some ravages, killed two of our horsemen, taken some prisoners. We have done the like by them. . . .

December 21.—[Valley Forge.] Preparations made for hutts. Provisions scarce. Mr. Ellis went homeward—sent a latter to my wife. Heartily wish myself at home. My skin and eyes are almost spoiled with continual smoke. A general cry thro' the camp this evening among the soldiers, "No meat! No meat!" The distant vales echoed back the melancholly sound—"No meat! No meat!" Immitating the noise of crows and owls, also, made a part of the confused musick.

What have you for your dinners, boys? "Nothing but fire cake and water, Sir." At night: "Gentlemen, the supper is ready." What is your supper, lads? "Fire cake and water, Sir."

Very poor beef has been drawn in our camp the greater part of this season. A butcher bringing a quarter of this kind of beef into camp one day who had white buttons on the knees of his breeches, a soldier cries out: "There, there, Tom, is some more of your fat beef. By my soul I can see the butcher's breeches buttons through it."

December 22.—Lay excessive cold and uncomfortable last night. My eyes are started out from their orbits like a rabbit's eyes, occasioned by a great cold and smoke.

What have you got for breakfast, lads? "Fire cake and water, Sir." The Lord send that our Commissary of Purchases may live [on] fire cake and water till their glutted gutts are turned to pasteboard.

Our division are under marching orders this morning. I am ashamed to say it, but I am tempted to steal fowls if I could find them, or even a whole hog, for I feel as if I could eat one. But the impoverished country about us affords but little matter to employ a thief, or keep a clever fellow in good humour. But why do I talk of hunger and hard usage, when so many in the world have not even fire cake and water to eat?

1. Use a dictionary to define the word "Epicurean." Why did Surgeon Waldo use this term here?

_____

_____

2. List the "good purposes" that Waldo finds in their winter quarters. Do you think he is being entirely

   serious? _____

   _____

   _____

   _____

3. What are the reasons Waldo gives for being sick and out of humor? _____

   _____

4. Describe the appearance of the soldier that Waldo writes of. _____

   _____

5. What is Waldo's complaint about men living at home? _____

6. What did the men eat for breakfast? dinner? supper? _____

7. Describe Waldo's attitude throughout his journal. Is he contented, angry, or discouraged? How do you

   think you would fare under similar conditions? _____

   _____

   _____

A Young Recruit on the Frontlines in South Carolina

James P. Collins was a young man of about seventeen when he was involved in the battles of Kings Mountain and Cowpens. Read his accounts of the battles and answer the questions that follow.

Kings Mountain

The enemy was posted on a high, steep and rugged ridge—very difficult of access. . . . The plan was to surround the mountain and attack them on all sides, if possible. In order to do this, the left had to march under the fire of the enemy to gain the position assigned to them on the stream on the right of the enemy, while the right was to take possession of the other stream. In doing this they were not exposed, the cliff being so steep as to cover them completely.

Each leader made a short speech in this own way to his men, desiring every coward to be off immediately. Here I confess I would willingly have been excused, for my feelings were not the most pleasant. This may be attributed to my youth, not being quite seventeen years of age—but I could not well swallow the appellation of coward. I looked around. Every man's countenance seemed to change. Well, thought I, fate is fate; every man's fate is before him and he has to run it out. . . .

We were soon in motion, every man throwing four or five balls in his mouth to prevent thirst, also to be in readiness to reload quick. The shot of the enemy soon began to pass over us like hail. The first shock was quickly over, and for my own part, I was soon in profuse sweat. My lot happened to be in the center, where the severest part of the battle was fought. We soon attempted to climb the hill, but were fiercely charged upon and forced to fall back to our first position. We tried a second time, but met the same fate; the fight then seemed to become more furious. Their leader, Ferguson, came in full view, within rifle shot as if to encourage his men, who by this time were falling very fast. He soon disappeared. We took to the hill a third time; the enemy gave way.

When we had gotten near the top, some of our leaders roared out, "Hurrah, my brave fellows! Advance! They are crying for quarter."

By this time, the right and left had gained the top of the cliff; the enemy was completely hemmed in on all sides, and no chance of escaping—besides, their leader had fallen. They soon threw down their arms and surrendered. After the fight was over, the situation of the poor Tories appeared to be really pitiable; the dead lay in heaps on all sides, while the groans of the wounded were heard in every direction. I could not help turning away from the scene before me with horror and, though exulting in victory, could not refrain from shedding tears. . . .

On examining the body of their great chief, it appeared that almost fifty rifles must have been leveled at him at the same time; seven rifle balls had passed through his body, both of his arms were broken, and his hat and clothing were literally shot to pieces. Their great elevation above us had proved their ruin. They overshot us altogether, scarce touching a man, except those on horseback, while every rifle from below seemed to have the desired effect. . . .

Next morning, which was Sunday, the scene became really distressing; the wives and children of the poor Tories came in, in great numbers. Their husbands, fathers and brothers lay dead in heaps, while others lay wounded or dying—a melancholy sight indeed! while numbers of the survivors were doomed to abide the sentence of a court martial, and several were actually hanged. . . .

We proceeded to bury the dead, but it was badly done. They were thrown into convenient piles and covered with old logs, the bark of old trees, and rocks; yet not so as to secure them from becoming a prey to the beasts of the forest or the vultures of the air; and the wolves became so plenty that it was dangerous for any one to be out at night, for several miles around. . . . I saw, myself, in passing the place a few weeks after, all parts of the human frame lying scattered in every direction. . . .

Cowpens

. . . About sunrise on the 17th of January, 1781, the enemy came in full view. The sight, to me at least, seemed somewhat imposing. They halted for a short time, and then advanced rapidly as if certain of victory. The militia under Pickins and Moffitt was posted on the right of the regulars some distance in advance, while Washington's cavalry was stationed in the rear. We gave the enemy one fire; when they charged us with their bayonets, we gave way and retreated for our horses. Tarleton's cavalry pursued us. "Now," thought I, "my hide is in the loft."

Just as we got to our horses, they overtook us and began to make a few hacks at some, however without doing much injury. They, in their haste, had pretty much scattered, perhaps thinking they would have another Fishing Creek frolic, but in a few moments Col. Washington's cavalry was among them like a whirlwind, and the poor fellows began to keel from their horses without being able to remount. The shock was so sudden and violent they could not stand it and immediately betook themselves to flight. There was no time to rally, and they appeared to be as hard to stop as a drove of wild Choctaw steers going to a Pennsylvania market. In a few moments the clashing of swords was out of hearing and quickly out of sight.

By this time both lines of the infantry were warmly engaged and we, being relieved from the pursuit of the enemy, began to rally and prepare to redeem our credit, when Morgan rode up in front and, waving his sword, cried out, "Form, form, my brave fellows! Give them one more fire and the day is ours. Old Morgan was never beaten."

We then advanced briskly and gained the right flank of the enemy, and they, being hard pressed in front by Howard and falling very fast, could not stand it long. They began to throw down their arms and surrender themselves prisoners of war. The whole army, except Tarleton and his horsemen, fell into the hands of Morgan, together with all the baggage. . . .

1. At the Battle of Kings Mountain, why did James stay and fight when he was so afraid? _____

_____

2. How many times did they have to climb the hill before they made it all the way to the top? _____

3. Why did the enemy surrender? _____

_____

4. Why did James cry after the battle even though his side had won? _____

_____

5. What reason does James give for the enemy's ruin? _____

_____

_____

6. Do you think it was right for the Patriots to leave the bodies of the dead so exposed? Explain.

_____

_____

7. At the Battle of Cowpens, which group stopped the British advance?

_____

8. Who of the enemy escaped after the battle? What happened to the rest?

_____

9. How was James different at the Battle of Cowpens?

_____

_____

10. How were the battles of Kings Mountain and Cowpens similar? How were they different?

_____

_____

_____

Chapter Review

Fill in the Blank.

Supply the name of the missing man or location in these statements.

1. Ethan Allen and _____ captured Fort Ticonderoga from the British.

2. General Gage and _____ defeated the colonists at Bunker Hill.

3. General Henry Knox brought cannons from _____ to drive the British from Boston.

4. _____ crossed the Delaware River to defeat the Hessians at Trenton.

5. The Americans defeated General Burgoyne at _____.

6. Washington spent a cold, hungry winter with his men at _____.

7. _____ defeated "Hair Buyer" Hamilton in the West.

8. America's most famous Continental naval officer was _____.

9. The Americans trapped the British general _____ at Yorktown.

10. _____ died as a spy for his country.

11. After the victory at Trenton, Washington defeated the British at _____.

12. Daniel Morgan defeated Banastre Tarleton at the Battle of _____ in South Carolina.

13. _____, _____, and _____ were the negotiators of the Treaty of Paris.

14. When the British evacuated Boston, many Loyalists fled to _____.

Matching

Match the following terms to their descriptions.

_____ 15. Hessians

_____ 16. Loyalists

_____ 17. Marquis de Lafayette

_____ 18. privateers

_____ 19. Thomas Paine

_____ 20. Treaty of Paris

_____ 21. Olive Branch Petition

_____ 22. Baron Von Steuben

_____ 23. Nathanael Greene

_____ 24. Thomas Jefferson

_____ 25. Mississippi River

a. author of *Common Sense* pamphlet

b. America's western boundary in 1783

c. conciliatory letter to King George

d. backed the British in the war

e. Frenchman who aided the Americans

f. primary author of the Declaration of Independence

g. Prussian drill master at Valley Forge

h. mercenary troops who fought for the British

i. officially ended the War for Independence

j. trading ships equipped for warfare

k. Patriot quartermaster

Write Your Own Encyclopedia Entry

Complete the following encyclopedia entry titled "Articles of Confederation."

In 1777 the Second Continental Congress drafted the (1) _____, but the states did not (2) _____, or formally approve, the new system of government until the War for Independence was almost over. The last major state to accept the plan was (3) _____. The weak (4) _____, which began in 1781, passed laws but had no (5) _____ branch or judicial branch. Although it had power to raise an (6) _____ to defend the country, it did *not* have power to (7) _____ the states to pay its own expenses. Although Congress received control over all land claims in the (8) _____, each of the thirteen states reserved the right to make separate agreements governing domestic and foreign (9) _____, such as tariffs.

The Congress's most lasting achievement involved the (10) _____ Territory north of the Ohio River. An ordinance issued in 1785 created six-mile-square areas, called (11) _____. These lands were sold in sections, each containing a total of (12) _____ acres, at a minimum price of one dollar per acre. A later ordinance provided for government in the region by dividing the new land into separate (13) _____, each with its own governor appointed by (14) _____.

The confederation's weaknesses were glaring and embarrassing. The country of (15) _____ was angered by the mistreatment of Loyalists, and Spain tried to deny American traders the right of (16) _____. A rebellion of Massachusetts farmers, led by (17) _____ in 1786, was the last straw that brought an outcry for reform. The men who gathered at the (18) _____ Convention in 1787 agreed to create a completely new form of government. These men elected (19) _____ to act as their chairman. (20) _____, who is known as the "Father of the Constitution," kept detailed notes of the proceedings.

The Need for a Constitution

Although Americans feared strong government, they discovered that weakness is just as bad. At the Constitutional Convention, the states accepted some solutions immediately, but others required compromise. For each weakness below, give one harmful result and the solution. If the solution was a compromise, describe the compromise; otherwise, write "none."

Weakness Under Confederation	Harmful Results	Solution Under Constitution	Nature of the Compromise
states' power to coin money	*worthless money; inability of farmers to pay debts; Shays's Rebellion*	*power to coin money reserved to Congress*	*none*
no executive branch			
no judicial branch			
no power to tax			
no power to regulate trade			
equal votes for each state			
tax assessments ignored slaves			

What God Says About Government

The framers of the Constitution were familiar with scriptural principles of government. In fact, the Father of the Constitution, James Madison, spent three years studying under Rev. John Witherspoon, the president of Princeton. Use your Bible to answer these questions about the nature of man, the role of government, and God's role in government.

1. Madison acknowledged man's sinful nature. In *The Federalist* he wrote, "If men were angels, no government would be necessary. . . . In framing a government which is to be administered by men over men, the great difficulty lies in this: you must first enable the government to control the governed; and in the next place oblige it to control itself."

   ✯ How many people have sinful desires (Rom. 3:10–12)? _____

   ✯ Name two sins that people commit (Rom. 1:28–32). _____

   ✯ What is a major temptation for rulers (1 Sam. 8:10–18)? _____

   ✯ How do rulers and their subjects respond to God's rule (Ps. 2:2–3)? _____

2. Although men are sinful, the framers of the Constitution believed that men have a God-given capacity to govern and be governed. Indeed, the Bible says that the ruler is God's "minister" (Rom. 13:4). Governments are His instruments to restrain evil and promote good.

   ✯ What ability has God given mankind (Ps. 8:4–8)? _____

   ✯ What did Israel want from its ruler (1 Sam. 8:19–20)? _____

   ✯ What roles did God fill as Israel's ruler (Isa. 33:22)? _____

   ✯ Whom should rulers punish (1 Pet. 2:13–14)? _____

   ✯ What did Christ say we owe our rulers (Mark 12:13–17)? _____

   ✯ What did Peter say we owe our rulers (1 Pet. 2:17)? _____

3. Madison believed that God is sovereign and the source of all law. He said the success of America depended on obedience to God, not on the government: "We have staked the whole future of American civilization, not upon the power of government, far from it. We have staked the future of all our political institutions . . . upon the capacity of each and all of us to govern ourselves, to sustain ourselves according to the Ten Commandments of God."

   ✯ Who ordains rulers (Rom. 13:1)? _____

   ✯ Who guides rulers' decisions (Prov. 21:1)? _____

   ✯ Who overthrows governments (Dan. 2:20–21)? _____

   ✯ What brings ridicule to any nation (Prov. 14:34)? What brings blessing to any nation? _____

   _____

The Federalist Papers

The following excerpt is taken from *The Federalist* number two, written by John Jay. Read the essay and answer the questions that follow.

To the People of the State of New York:

. . . Nothing is more certain than the indispensable [essential] necessity of government, and it is equally undeniable, that whenever and however it is instituted, the people must cede [give up] to it some of their natural rights in order to vest it with requisite [necessary] powers. It is well worthy of consideration therefore, whether it would conduce more to the interest of the people of America that they should, to all general purposes, be one nation, under one federal government, or that they should divide themselves into separate confederacies, and give to the head of each the same kind of powers which they are advised to place in one national government.

It has until lately been a received and uncontradicted opinion that the prosperity of the people of America depended on their continuing firmly united, and the wishes, prayers, and efforts of our best and wisest citizens have been constantly directed to that object. But politicians now appear, who insist that this opinion is erroneous [wrong], and that instead of looking for safety and happiness in union, we ought to seek it in a division of the States into distinct confederacies or sovereignties. . . .

It has often given me pleasure to observe that independent America was not composed of detached and distant territories, but that one connected, fertile, wide-spreading country was the portion of our western sons of liberty. Providence has in a particular manner blessed it with a variety of soils and productions, and watered it with innumerable streams, for the delight and accommodation of its inhabitants. A succession of navigable waters forms a kind of chain round its borders, . . . while the most noble rivers in the world, . . . present them with highways for the easy communication of friendly aids, and the mutual transportation and exchange of their various commodities [products].

With equal pleasure I have as often taken notice that Providence has been pleased to give this one connected country to one united people—a people descended from the same ancestors, speaking the same language, professing the same religion, attached to the same principles of government, very similar in their manners and customs, and who, by their joint counsels, arms, and efforts, fighting side by side throughout a long and bloody war, have nobly established general liberty and independence. . . .

. . . It is worthy of remark that not only the first, but every succeeding Congress, as well as the late convention, have invariably [constantly] joined with the people in thinking that the prosperity of America depended on its Union. To preserve and perpetuate it was the great object of the people in forming that convention, and it is also the great object of the plan which the convention has advised them to adopt. With what propriety, therefore, or for what good purposes, are attempts at this particular period made by some men to depreciate [lessen] the importance of the Union? Or why is it suggested that three or four confederacies would be better than one? I am persuaded in my own mind that the people have always thought right on this subject, and that their universal and uniform attachment to the cause of the Union rests on great and weighty reasons, which I shall endeavor to develop and explain in some ensuing papers. . . . Whenever the dissolution of the Union arrives, America will have reason to exclaim, in the words of the poet: "FAREWELL! A LONG FAREWELL TO ALL MY GREATNESS."

PUBLIUS.

1. According to Publius, what choice faces the American people regarding their government?

   _____

2. Was the idea of forming a union a new idea or an old one? _____

3. What does Publius believe that Providence has provided in order to create a unified country?

   _____

   _____

4. What was the purpose of forming the Constitutional Convention?

   _____

5. What does Publius believe will happen if there is no Union? _____

Name _____

Powers of Government

Our federal system is described in Article I, Sections 8–10; Article VI; and Amendment X. The national and state governments *share* some powers, some powers are reserved to one or the other, and some powers are *denied* both. Place a check under the place where the power resides, according to the original U.S. Constitution and Bill of Rights. (Hint: Some powers that were denied the national government were *not* denied the states at first.)

Powers	National	State	Neither
power to tax			
power to borrow money			
power to regulate trade with foreign countries			
power to regulate naturalization			
power to coin money			
power to declare war			
power to raise armies and navies			
power to suspend the writ of habeas corpus at any time			
power to pass a bill of attainder			
power to pass an ex post facto law			
power to tax exports for revenue			
power to grant titles of nobility			
power to make treaties			
power to admit new states to the Union			
power to ratify amendments to the Constitution			
power to establish a state-sponsored church			
power to abridge freedom of speech and of the press			
power to enter homes without a search warrant			
power to compel a witness to testify against himself			
power to subpoena witnesses			

Answer these questions about changes that later amendments made in government powers.

1. Name one power that the national government has gained. _____

2. Name one power that the national government has lost. _____

3. Name one power that the state governments have lost. _____

Chapter Review

Who Am I?

Read each phrase and decide who it describes. Write the answer in the blank.

1. treaty maker who negotiated with Spain _____

2. Father of the Constitution _____

3. oldest delegate at the Constitutional Convention _____

4. New York delegate who favored a strong government _____

5. shoemaker who introduced the Great Compromise _____

6. author of the Articles of Confederation _____

7. mob leader in Massachusetts _____

8. creator of the New Jersey Plan _____

Where Am I?

Read each phrase and decide what place it describes. Write the answer in the blank.

9. southern boundary of the Northwest Territory _____

10. territory where slavery was banned in 1787 _____

11. Spanish port that denied Americans the right of deposit _____

12. federal arsenal threatened by Shays's Rebellion _____

13. house where four states discussed trade disputes _____

14. city where five states requested a better union _____

15. building where the Constitution was drafted _____

16. state that proposed the Large State Plan _____

17. state that proposed the Small State Plan _____

18. state that proposed the Great Compromise _____

19. ninth state to ratify the Constitution _____

What Am I?

Read each phrase and decide what thing it describes. Write the answer in the blank.

20. a loose association or league of states _____

21. freedom to stockpile goods at a port until transported _____

22. a count of the population _____

23. series of essays favoring the adoption of the Constitution _____

24. constitutional system to elect the president _____

25. first ten amendments to the Constitution _____

26. system to keep each branch of government from going beyond its powers _____

27. introduction to the Constitution _____

28. two-house legislative system _____

29. return of a bill to the body where it started _____

30. right to vote _____

Name _____

Eyewitness Accounts of Washington's Inauguration

George Washington left Mount Vernon in April of 1789 to travel to New York City, where he would be inaugurated as the United States' first president. The citizens of New York celebrated his arrival and gathered to hear him speak. Read the following two accounts and then answer the questions at the end. The first account details Washington's arrival in the city; the second describes his oath of office.

[The first account was written by Rudolph Von Dorsten, the Secretary of the Dutch Legation in New York City.]

"President George Washington made his entry into New York on Thursday, April 23d. On the previous day a barge left this city. The barge was built expressly by the citizens of New York, and was rowed by thirteen pilots, all dressed in white. A committee of three Senators and five Representatives on behalf of Congress, and three of the first officers on behalf of New York, went to Elizabethtown in New Jersey, to welcome the President, and to await his arrival there. His Excellency was also accompanied by some well-equipped sloops and by a multitude of small craft with citizens of New Jersey and New York on board.

"A Spanish royal packet-boat, happening to be anchored at the entrance of the harbor, at sight of the barge, on board of which was the President, fired a signal-shot, whereupon that vessel was dressed at once with the flags of all nations. When the presidential barge passed, the Spanish vessel saluted his Excellency by firing thirteen guns, which was repeated by the Battery, and again thirteen guns were fired by the fort when the President landed.

"His Excellency was received by Governor George Clinton, the mayor of the city and other officers, and, after a procession had formed, consisting of some companies of uniformed citizens and the merchants and other citizens of the city, the President walked with his escort and, Governor Clinton at his side, to the house prepared by Congress for his use."

[For a week after his arrival, Washington waited for the new Congress to decide how to conduct the inauguration ceremony. The inauguration finally took place on April 30 at Federal Hall. Washington took his oath of office on the balcony before a large crowd. William Maclay, a Pennsylvania senator, described the event.]

"The President advanced between the Senate and Representatives, bowing to each. He was placed in the chair by the Vice-President; the Senate with their president on the right, the Speaker and the Representatives on his left. The Vice-President rose and addressed a short sentence to him. The import of it was that he should now take the oath of office as President. He seemed to have forgot half what he was to say, for he made a dead pause and stood for some time, to appearance, in a vacant mood. He finished with a formal bow, and the President was conducted out of the middle window into the gallery, and the oath was administered by the Chancellor. Notice that the business done was communicated to the crowd by proclamation, etc., who gave three cheers, and repeated it on the President bowing to them.

"As the company returned into the Senate chamber, the President took the chair and the Senators and Representatives their seats. He rose, and all arose also, and addressed them. This great man was agitated and embarrassed more than ever he was by the leveled cannon or pointed musket. He trembled, and several times could scarce make out to read, though it must be supposed he had often read it before.

"He put part of the fingers of his left hand into the side of what I think the tailors call the fall of the breeches (corresponding to the modern side-pocket), changing the paper into his left (right) hand. After some time he then did the same with some of the fingers of his right hand.

"When he came to the words all the world, he made a flourish with his right hand, which left rather an ungainly impression. I sincerely, for my part, wished all set ceremony in the hands of the dancing-masters, and that this first of men had read off his address in the plainest manner, without ever taking his eyes from the paper, for I felt hurt that he was not first in everything.

"He was dressed in deep brown, with metal buttons, with an eagle on them, white stockings, a bag, and sword."

1. Describe the scene that awaited Washington in New York's harbor. How does this compare with what you know about modern presidential inaugurations?

_____

_____

_____

2. Who addressed Washington just before he took his oath? What surprised the writer about this speech?

_____

3. How did the crowd below the balcony hear the speeches?

_____

4. Do you think Washington was comfortable making his inaugural speech? Why is this somewhat

surprising? _____

_____

5. Why is the writer somewhat disappointed in Washington's speech?

_____

_____

Government Then and Now

Our government has changed in many ways. With the help of your text and the *World Almanac* (or other library resource), see how many facts you can find about the salaries of officials and the size and leadership of our government under Washington and now. Also try to answer the questions below.

Salaries		
Individual	**Salary Then**	**Salary Now**
President		
Cabinet Member		
Speaker		
Representative		
Senator		
Justice	$3,500/year	

Size		
Branch	**Size Then**	**Size Now**
Cabinet		
House	65	
Senate	26	
Supreme Court		

Leadership		
Office	**First Office Holder**	**Current Office Holder**
President		
Vice President		
Speaker of the House	*Frederick Muhlenberg*	
Chief Justice		
Secretary of State		
Secretary of the Treasury		
Attorney General		
Secretary of War (Defense)		

1. How long has the U.S. Constitution been in place? _____

2. How many presidents has the United States had? _____

3. What is the current federal employment of civilians (versus 800 at first)? _____

4. How much does the U.S. government spend per year (versus $600,000 at first)? _____

5. List the current cabinet posts. _____

_____

_____

What God Says About Honor

One reason for our country's success is the example the first presidents set. They placed the needs of the nation above personal gain. With the help of your Bible, answer these questions.

1. In his "Farewell Address," Washington quoted his life maxim: "Honesty is always the best policy." He said that the two "great pillars of human happiness" are "religion and morality." He warned against "cunning, ambitious, and unprincipled men" who use party strife to take over government.

   ✬ What are two traits of a good ruler (Exod. 18:21)? _____

   ✬ What is the most important source of honor (John 5:44)? _____

   ✬ What character trait precedes honor (Prov. 18:12)? _____

   ✬ What type of person should not be given a place of honor (Prov. 26:1)? _____

2. In a letter to his wife, President John Adams expressed his dislike of party "jealousies and rivalries." He said, "If the Federalists go to playing pranks, I will resign the office, and let Jefferson lead." The test of Adams's character came when his party and country demanded war with France. His commitment to peace cost him his popularity and his reelection.

   ✬ What could be a good reason for a ruler to avoid war (Luke 14:28–32)? _____

   ✬ Why did Jonathan give up his crown (1 Sam. 16:1; 18:1–4)? _____

   ✬ What should a good ruler *not* do (Deut. 16:19)? _____

   ✬ What is the source of true greatness (Matt. 20:25–28)? _____

3. After the appointment of "the midnight judges," Adams and Jefferson stopped speaking to each other. Later, Abigail Adams broke the silence by sending Jefferson a note of sympathy after the death of his daughter. He replied that honest differences in political convictions should never be permitted to disturb the two men's lifetime friendship and mutual esteem. The two political enemies renewed their friendship until their deaths.

   ✬ What two traits preserve a ruler (Prov. 20:28)? _____

   ✬ What gives stability to government (Prov. 16:12)? _____

   ✬ What attitude prevents strife (Phil. 2:3)? _____

4. Jefferson tried to reassure his Federalist opponents in his inaugural speech: "Let us, then, fellow citizens, unite with one heart and one mind. . . . We have called by different names brethren of the same principle. We are all republicans—we are all federalists."

   ✬ How should we treat our opponents (Rom. 12: 14–21)? _____

   _____

   ✬ What brings a man honor (Prov. 20:3)? _____

   ✬ What destroys a nation (Mark 3:24)? _____

   ✬ What helps a nation survive (Prov. 29:18)? _____

Abigail Adams's Letter About Washington, D.C.

Abigail Adams was the first wife of a president to live in Washington, D.C., which was still under construction. Read Mrs. Adams's letter to her sister, dated November 21, 1800. Then answer the questions.

I arrived here on Sunday last, and without meeting with any accident worth noticing, except losing ourselves when we left Baltimore . . .; woods are all you see, from Baltimore until you reach the city, which is only so in name. Here and there is a small cot, without a glass window, interspersed among the forests, through which you travel miles without seeing any human being. . . .

The [Potomac] river, which runs up to Alexandria, is in full view of my window, and I see the vessels as they pass and repass. The house is upon a grand and superb scale, requiring about thirty servants to attend and keep the apartments in proper order, and perform the ordinary business of the house and stables; an establishment very well proportioned to the President's salary. The lighting of apartments, from the kitchen to parlors and chambers, is a tax [difficulty] indeed; and the fires we are obliged to keep secure us from daily agues [chills] is another very cheering comfort. To assist us in this great castle, and render less attendance necessary, bells are wholly wanting, not one single one being hung through the whole house, and promises are all you can obtain. This is so great an inconvenience that I know not what to do, or how to do. . . . If they will put me up some bells, and let me have wood enough to keep fires, I design [plan] to be pleased.

I could content myself almost anywhere three months; but, surrounded with forests, can you believe that wood is not to be had, because people cannot be found to cut and cart it! . . . We have indeed come into a new country.

You must keep all this to yourself, and when asked how I like it, say that I write you the situation is beautiful, which is true. The house is made habitable, but there is not a single apartment finished, and all withinside, except the plastering, has been done since Briesler came. We have not the least fence, yard, or other convenience, without, and the great unfinished audience room I make a drying room of, to hang up the clothes in. The principal stairs are not up, and will not be this winter. . . .

It is a beautiful spot, capable of every improvement, and, the more I view it the more I am delighted with it. . . . Adieu, my dear. Give my love to your brother, and tell him he is ever present upon my mind.

1. What was the most striking feature of the countryside to Mrs. Adams? _____

2. List five problems she faced. _____

   _____

3. What positive things did she say about the place? _____

   _____

4. Why did she tell her sister not to mention the hardships? _____

   _____

   _____

Words You Need to Know: Precedents

The actions of America's first leaders became precedents (examples for future actions). As you read the chapter, look for the important precedents. Then for each situation below, describe what precedents were set, when they were set, and who set them.

Situation	Precedent(s)	Year	Person(s) Responsible
Washington's inauguration	*left hand on the Bible and right hand raised; end with "so help me God"*	*1789*	*George Washington*
need to organize the executive departments			
need for a source of federal revenue		*1789*	
desire for a national bank			
disputes between political factions		*1792*	
need to stop the Whiskey Rebellion			
demand for long-term alliances in foreign wars		*1793*	
desire to see Washington run for a third term		*1796*	
lack of unity in Supreme Court decisions			
an unconstitutional federal law taken to court			

AMERICAN REPUBLIC

Name _____

Chapter Review: Timeline of the Early Republic

The new government under the U.S. Constitution experienced major challenges, both domestic and foreign. As you read the chapter, list the major events that took place each year at home and abroad. You should find at least twenty major events.

Domestic Events	Year	Foreign Events
	1789	
	1790	
	1791	
	1792	
	1793	
	1794	Jay Treaty with Britain
	1795	
	1796	start of "quasi-war" with France
	1797	

Domestic Events	Year	Foreign Events
	1798	*XYZ Affair revealed*
	1799	
	1800	
	1801	

Map Study

Refer to the maps in your textbook to complete the map on the back of this page and the questions below.

1. Label these bodies of water:

   Rivers—Potomac, Tippecanoe, Mississippi, Missouri, Arkansas, Yellowstone, Columbia

   Lakes—Champlain, Ontario, Erie, Michigan

2. Label these new states: Vermont (1791), Kentucky (1792), Tennessee (1796), Ohio (1803), Louisiana (1812)

3. Label these cities and forts: Washington, D.C.; Detroit; New Orleans; St. Louis; Ft. McHenry

4. Using three colored pencils, color these three things:

   • the boundaries of the Louisiana Purchase

   • the route of the Lewis and Clark Expedition

   • the routes of the Pike Expeditions

5. Draw these figures at the appropriate places:

   △ Pike's Peak   〰 Perry's naval victory
   ✈ Battle of Tippecanoe   ◆ Jackson's greatest victory
   ⚑ brave defense of Baltimore fort

6. What town was the starting point for western expeditions? _____

7. What rivers did Lewis and Clark follow? _____

   _____

8. What rivers did Pike's second expedition follow? _____

9. Based on the scale, about how many miles did Lewis and Clark travel one way? _____

10. Based on the scale, about how many miles did Pike travel one way on his first trip? _____

11. Based on the scale, how many miles did Pike travel to reach Pike's Peak? _____

12. Why might your estimates be about half what they should be? _____

13. If Lewis traveled 8,000 miles and spent $40,000, what was his cost per mile? _____

14. Name the modern states that Lewis and Clark crossed. _____

    _____

    _____

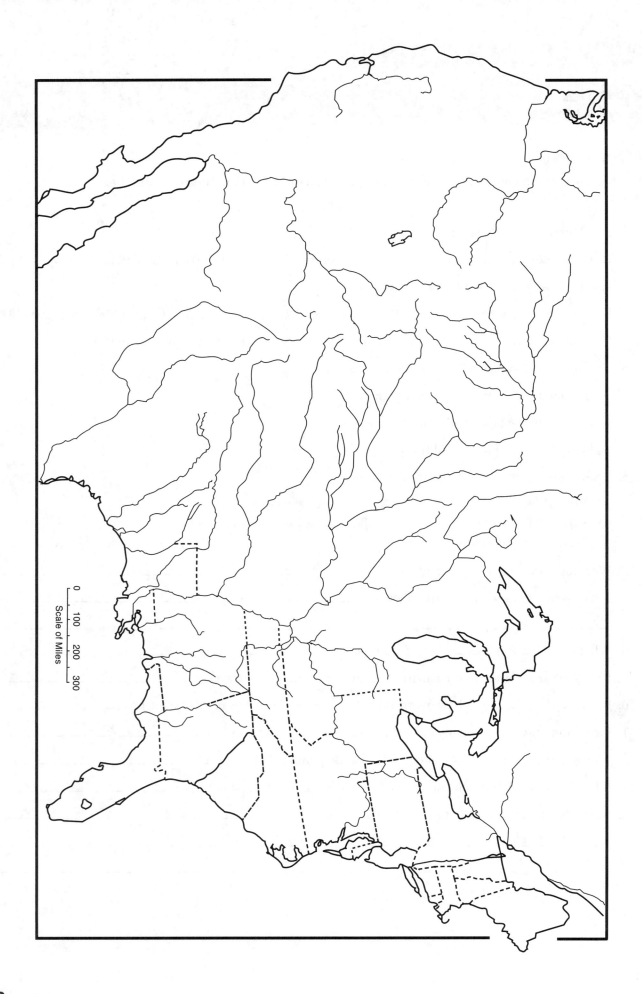

Scale of Miles
0
100
200
300

The Journals of Lewis and Clark
(May 14, 1804–September 24, 1806)

The journals of Lewis and Clark are filled with exciting stories. Both officers kept a daily journal of the trip. Along with their adventures and discoveries, we can see their leadership skills and their endurance through many hardships. As you read these excerpts, list at least three dates that tell about each topic below. Then answer the questions at the end of the activity.

Hardships _____

Leadership skills _____

Bears (grizzly bears) _____

Sacagawea _____

from Clark's Journal

[May 14, 1804] Rained the fore part of the day. I set out at 4 o'clock, P.M., in the presence of many of the neighboring inhabitants and proceeded under a gentle breeze up the Missouri to the upper point of the first island, 4 miles, and camped on the island.

[May 17] A fair day. Compelled to punish [two enlisted men] for misconduct.

[August 19] Sergeant Floyd is taken very bad all at once with a bilious colic [appendicitis?]. We attempt to relieve him without success as yet. He gets worse and we are much alarmed at his situation. All attention to him.

[August 20] Sergeant Floyd as bad as he can be, no pulse, and nothing will stay a moment on his stomach or bowels. . . . Sergeant Floyd died with a great deal of composure. We buried him on the top of the bluff a half mile below a small river to which we gave his name. After paying all the honor to our deceased brother, we camped in the mouth of Floyd's River, about 30 yards wide. A beautiful evening.

[October 9] The day continued cold and windy. Some rain. Sorry. Canoes of skins passed down from the two villages a short distance above, and many [Mandan Indians] came to view us all day, much astonished at my black servant, who did not lose the opportunity of displaying his powers, strength, &c.

[October 13] One man, J. Newman, confined for mutinous expression. Set out early. Passed a camp of Sioux. Those people only viewed us and did not speak one word. We tried the prisoner Newman last night by 9 of his peers. They did "sentence him 75 lashes and disbanded him from the party."

[November 4] A fine morning. We continued to cut down trees and raise our houses [at Fort Mandan]. A Mr. Charbonneau, interpreter for the Gros Ventre nation, came to see us. This man wished to hire as an interpreter. Great numbers of Indians pass, hunting.

from Lewis's Journal

[February 11, 1805] The weather was fair and cold. Wind N.W. About five o'clock this evening, one of the wives of Charbonneau was delivered of a fine boy. It is worthy of remark that this was the first child which this woman had born, and as is common in such cases her labor was tedious and the pain violent.

[April 13] We saw many tracks of the white bear of enormous size, along the river shore. We have not as yet seen one of these animals, though their tracks are so abundant and recent. The men, as well as ourselves, are anxious to meet with some of these bear. The Indians give a very formidable account of the strength and ferocity of this animal, which they never dare to attack but in parties of six, eight, or ten persons; and are even then frequently defeated with the loss of one or more of their party.

[April 29] Set out this morning at the usual hour. About 8 A.M. we fell in with two brown or yellow bear, both of which we wounded. One of them made his escape; the other, after my firing on him, pursued me 70 or 80 yards but fortunately had been so badly wounded that he was unable to pursue so closely as to prevent my charging my gun. We again repeated our fire, and killed him.

. . . It is a much more furious and formidable animal [than the black bear], and will frequently pursue the hunter when wounded. The Indians may well fear this animal, equipped as they generally are with their bows and arrows or indifferent fusees [muskets]; but in the hands of skillful riflemen, they are by no means as formidable or dangerous as they have been presented.

[May 5] Captain Clark and Drouillard killed the largest brown bear this evening which we have yet seen. It was a most tremendous-looking animal, and extremely hard to kill. Notwithstanding he had five balls through his lungs and five others in various parts, he swam more than half the distance across the river, to a sandbar, and it was at least twenty minutes before he died. He did not attempt to attack, but fled, and made the most tremendous roaring from the moment he was shot. We had no means of weighing this monster. Captain Clark thought he would weigh 500 pounds. For my own part, I think the estimate too small by 100 pounds. He measured 8 feet 7½ inches from the nose to the extremity of the hind feet; 5 feet 10½ inches around the breast; 1 foot 11 inches around the middle of the arm; and 3 feet 11 inches around the neck. His talons, which were five in number on each foot, were 4⅜ inches in length. He was in good order.

We therefore divided him among the party, and made them boil the oil and put it in a cask for future use. The oil is as hard as hog's lard when cool—much more so than that of the black bear.

[May 6] Saw a brown bear swim the river above us; he disappeared before we could get in reach of him. I find that the curiosity of our party is pretty well satisfied with respect to this animal.

from Clark's Journal
[June 12] Saw a number of rattlesnakes today. One of the men caught one by the head, in catching hold of a bush on which his head lay reclined. Three canoes were in great danger today; one dipped water, another very near turned over, &c. The interpreter's woman very sick. One man has a felon rising on his hand; the other, with the toothache, has taken cold in the jaw, &c.

from Lewis's Journal [*He had gone ahead of the main party in search of the Great Falls.*]
[June 13] This morning we set out about sunrise after taking breakfast off our venison and fish. My ears were saluted with the agreeable sound of a fall of water, which soon began to make a roaring too

tremendous to be mistaken for anything but the Great Falls of the Missouri. Here I arrived about 12 o'clock, having traveled about 15 miles. I hurried down the hill to gaze at this sublimely grand spectacle.

. . . The whole body of water passes with incredible swiftness. Immediately at the cascade, the river is about 300 yards wide. About 90 or 100 yards of this is a smooth even sheet of water falling over a precipice of at least 80 feet; the remaining party, about 200 yards wide, on my right, forms the grandest sight I ever beheld. The rocks seem to be most happily fixed to present a sheet of the whitest beaten froth for 200 yards in length and about 80 feet perpendicular. . . . From the reflection of the sun on the spray or mist which arises from these Falls, there is a beautiful rainbow produced which adds not a little to the beauty of this majestically grand scenery.

After writing this imperfect description, I again viewed the Falls, and was disgusted with the imperfect idea which it conveyed of the scene. I wished for the pencil of Salvator Rosa, a Titian, or the pen of Thomson, that I might be enabled to give to the enlightened world some just idea of this truly magnificent and sublimely grand object which has, from the commencement of time, been concealed from the view of civilized man. But this was fruitless and vain. I most sincerely regretted that I had not brought a camera obscura with me.

from Clark's Journal [*His party was carrying the boats up the river to meet Lewis.*]
[June 15] A fair morning, and warm. We set out at the usual time and proceeded with great difficulty, as the river is more rapid. Our Indian woman sick and low-spirited.

The current excessively rapid and difficult to ascend. Great numbers of dangerous places, and the fatigue which we have to encounter is incredible: the men in the water from morning until night, hauling the cord and boats, walking on sharp rocks and slippery stones which alternately cut their feet and throw them down. Notwithstanding all this difficulty, they go with great cheerfulness. Added to those difficulties, the rattlesnakes are innumerable and require great caution.

The Indian woman much worse this evening. She will not take any medicine. Her husband petitions to return, &c. River more rapid.

from Lewis's Journal
[June 25] Captain Clark somewhat unwell today. He made Charbonneau cook for the party against their return. It is worthy of remark that the

winds are sometimes so strong on these plains that the men informed me that they hoisted a sail in the canoe and it had driven her along on the truck wheels. This is really sailing on dry land.

[June 28] The white bear have become so troublesome to us that I do not think it prudent to send one man alone on an errand of any kind, particularly where he has to pass through the brush. They come close around our camp every night but have never yet ventured to attack us, and our dog gives us timely notice of their visits. I have made the men sleep with their arms by them as usual, for fear of accidents.

from Clark's Journal

[June 29] A torrent of rain and hail fell, more violent than ever I saw before. The rain fell like one volley of water from the heavens and gave us time only to get out of the way of a torrent of water which was pouring down the hill into the river with immense force, tearing everything before it, taking with it large rocks and mud.

I took my gun and shot pouch in my left hand and with the right scrambled up the hill, pushing the interpreter's wife—who had her child in her arms—before me, the interpreter himself making attempts to pull up his wife by the hand, much scared and nearly without motion. We at length reached the top of the hill safely. I directed the party to return to the camp, at the run, as fast as possible to get to our load, where clothes could be got to cover the child, whose clothes were all lost; and the woman, who was but just recovering from a severe indisposition and was wet and cold, I was fearful of a relapse.

from Lewis's Journal

[August 8] The Indian woman recognized the point of a high plain to our right, which, she informed us, was not very distant from the summer retreat of her nation, on a river beyond the mountains which runs to the west. She assures us that we shall either find her people on this river, or on the river immediately west of its source.

As it is now all-important with us to meet with those people as soon as possible, I determined to proceed tomorrow with a small party to the source of the principal stream of this river and pass the mountains to the Columbia, and down that river until I found the Indians. In short, it is my resolution to find them or some others who have horses, if it should cause me a trip of one month. For, without horses we shall be obliged to leave a great part of our stores, of which it appears to me that we have

a stock already sufficiently small for the length of the voyage before us.

[August 14] This evening Charbonneau struck his Indian woman, for which Captain Clark gave him a severe reprimand. Joseph and Reuben Fields killed 4 deer and an antelope. Captain Clark killed a buck. Several of the men have lamed themselves by various accidents in working the canoes through this difficult part of the river, and Captain Clark was obliged personally to assist them in this labor.

[August 17] Captain Clark arrived [at the Shoshone camp] with the interpreter, Charbonneau, and the Indian woman, who proved to be a sister of the chief Cameâhwait. The meeting of these people was really affecting, particularly between Sacajawea and an Indian woman who had been taken prisoner with her, and who had afterwards escaped and rejoined her nation.

[August 18] This day I completed my thirty-first year. I reflected that I had as yet done but little, very little, indeed, to further the happiness of the human race, or to advance the information of the succeeding generation. I viewed with regret the many hours I have spent in indolence. But, since they are past and cannot be recalled, I dash from me the gloomy thought, and resolve in future to redouble my efforts . . . to live for mankind, as I have heretofore lived for myself.

[September 18] We marched 18 miles this day and encamped on the side of a steep mountain. We suffered for water this day, passing one rivulet only. This morning we finished the remainder of our last colt. We dine and supped on a scant portion of portable soup, a few canisters of which, a little bear's oil, and about 20 pounds of candles form our stock of provision, the only resources being our guns and pack horses. Our route is along the ridge of a high mountain. Course S. 20 W. 18 miles. Used the snow for cooking.

from Clark's Journal

[November 7] Great joy in camp. We are in view of the ocean, this great Pacific Ocean which we have been so long anxious to see, and the roaring or noise made by the waves breaking on the rocky shores (as I suppose) may be heard distinctly.

from Lewis's Journal

[February 20, 1806] This forenoon we were visited by Tâhcum, a principal chief of the Chinooks, and 25 men of his nation. In the evening at sunset we desired them to depart, as is our custom, and closed our gates. We never suffer parties of such number to remain within the fort all night. We determined always to be on our guard as much as the nature of the situation will permit us, and never place ourselves at the mercy of any savages. We well know that the treachery of the aborigines of America and the too great confidence of our countrymen in their sincerity and friendship has caused the destruction of many hundreds of us.

from Clark's Journal

[March 23] At 1:00 P.M. left Fort Clatsop on our homeward-bound journey. At this place we had wintered and remained from the 7th of December, 1805, to this day, and have lived as well as we had any right to expect, and we can say that we were never one day without three meals of some kind a day, either poor elk meat or roots, notwithstanding the repeated fall of rain which has fallen almost constantly.

from Lewis's Journal

[September 23] We rose early. Descended to the Mississippi and down that river to St. Louis, at which place we arrived about 12 o'clock. We suffered the party to fire off their pieces as a salute to the town. We were met by all the village and received a hearty welcome from its inhabitants.

1. Who was the only person to die on this two-year journey? _____

2. When was the last discipline problem mentioned? _____

3. When did Sacagawea give birth to her baby? _____

4. Lewis said bears were not as dangerous as reported. Did his view change? _____

5. What do the journals usually call Sacagawea? _____

6. Give a date from Clark's journal that shows his concern for Sacagawea. _____

7. When did the exploration party come in view of the Pacific? _____

AMERICAN REPUBLIC

Name _____

CHAPTER 9 ACTIVITY 3

Steps to War

Place these events in the order they appear in the textbook.

Battle of Tippecanoe   Embargo Act   repeal of Milan Decree
British victory at Trafalgar   issue of Orders in Council   repeal of Orders in Council
Chesapeake affair   Madison's declaration of war   Tecumseh's confederation
coalition of War Hawks   Non-Intercourse Act

1805   1. _____   7. _____

1807   2. _____   1811   8. _____

         3. _____   9. _____

         4. _____   1812   10. _____

1809   5. _____   11. _____

1810   6. _____

Major Battles

Complete the chart. For each battle, include the American commander if he is mentioned in the text. Also place an asterisk (*) beside each battle that the United States won.

	Battle	Year	Leader	Significance
Northern Campaigns	Tippecanoe			
	Detroit			
	Fort Niagara			
	Lake Erie			
Eastern Campaigns	Plattsburg			
	Bladensburg			
	Fort McHenry			
	New Orleans			

© BJU Press. Reproduction prohibited.

The Sinking of the *Guerrière*

Moses Smith was a seaman aboard the U.S.S. *Constitution* during its battle with the H.M.S. *Guerrière*. He recorded in detail in his diary how the ship sank. Read Smith's account and answer the questions that follow.

There was something melancholy and grand in the sight. Although the frigate was a wreck floating about, a mastless hulk for the sport of the waves, she bore marks of her former greatness. Much of her ornamental work had been untouched; and her long, high, black sides rose in solitary majesty before us, as we bade her farewell. . . . Her years were now ended; her course was run; she was about to sink into the deep ocean forever.

Captain Dacres stood by our taffrail as we squared away from the *Guerrière*. . . . At the distance of about three miles we hove to and awaited the result. Hundreds of eyes were stretched in that one direction, where the ill-fated *Guerrière* moved heavily on the deep. It was like waiting for the uncapping of a volcano—or the bursting up of a crater. Scarcely a word was spoken on board the *Constitution*, so breathless was the interest felt in the scene.

The first intimation we had that the fire was at work was the discharge of the guns. One after another, as the flame advanced, they came booming toward us. Roar followed roar, flash followed flash, until the whole mass was enveloped in clouds of smoke. We could see but little of the direct progress of the work, and therefore we looked more earnestly for the explosion—not knowing how soon it might occur. Presently there was a dead silence; then followed a vibratory, shuddering motion, and streams of light, like streaks of lightning running along the sides; and the grand crash came! The quarter deck, which was immediately over the magazine, lifted in a mass, broke into fragments, and flew in every direction. The hull, parted in the center by the shock, and loaded with such masses of iron and spars, reeled, staggered, plunged forward a few feet, and sank out of sight.

It was a grand and awful scene. Nearly every floating thing around her went down with the *Guerrière*. . . . We immediately squared away, and were again under a crowd of sail for our native land.

1. What did the *Guerrière* look like as the *Constitution* began to sail away? _____

_____

2. Why do you think the *Constitution* moved three miles away to watch the sinking ship?

_____

3. To what does Smith compare waiting for the explosion? _____

4. What was the first evidence of the *Guerrière*'s being on fire? _____

5. How did Smith describe the final explosion of the *Guerrière*? _____

_____

_____

Chapter Review

Naval Engagements

Place each item from the following list under the category in which it belongs:

deserters
Oliver Hazard Perry
Jenkin Ratford
Philadelphia

Constitution
Embargo Act of 1807
Leopard
Stephen Decatur

Lake Erie
Lawrence
Barbary pirates
Macedonian

Tripolitan War	*Chesapeake* affair	War of 1812
_____	_____	_____
_____	_____	_____
_____	_____	_____
_____	_____	_____
_____	_____	_____

Presidential Administrations

Place each item from the following list under the proper president.

organization of War Hawks
Treaty of Ghent
repeal of Judiciary Act of 1801
Louisiana Purchase
Pike Expedition
burning of Washington, D.C.

defeated Charles C. Pinckney
Tripolitan War
Embargo Act of 1807
Battle of Tippecanoe
decreased national debt by one-half
loss of Fort Dearborn to the British

repeal of Berlin and Milan Decrees
Chesapeake affair
British Orders in Council

Thomas Jefferson	James Madison
_____	_____
_____	_____
_____	_____
_____	_____
_____	_____
_____	_____
_____	_____
_____	_____

Important Individuals

Match the following individuals and descriptions.

a. Shawnee chief

b. naval hero of the Tripolitan War

c. Secretary of the Treasury

d. hero of New Orleans

e. British leader who burned Washington, D.C.

f. Western explorer

g. War Hawk leader

h. Federalist Supreme Court justice

i. French foreign minister

j. Jefferson's second vice president

k. American ambassador to France

l. French fur trapper

_____ 1. Samuel Chase

_____ 2. Albert Gallatin

_____ 3. Stephen Decatur

_____ 4. Robert Livingston

_____ 5. Talleyrand

_____ 6. William Clark

_____ 7. Charbonneau

_____ 8. George Clinton

_____ 9. Tecumseh

_____ 10. Henry Clay

_____ 11. Admiral Cockburn

_____ 12. Andrew Jackson

Comparing Presidential Campaigns

This era marked a major transition in American politics. Summarize each election, based on the information in your textbook. Then answer the questions that follow.

	Election of 1816	Election of 1820	Election of 1824	Election of 1828
Main Candidates				
Main Parties	*Democratic-Republican and Federalist*			
Style of Campaigning		*almost none*	*frequent speeches*	
Voter Participation		*little interest because of caucuses*	*increasing interest*	

1. What campaign marked the end of the Federalist Party? _____

2. During what campaign did a candidate receive all but one electoral vote? _____

3. The caucus system "died" in 1824. Why? _____

_____

4. In what election did the most popular candidate *lose*? _____

5. What party was the predecessor of the Democratic Party? _____

6. Why did the number of voters double between 1824 and 1828? _____

_____

The Year That Changed America

For each of the four important events that took place in 1819, write a short paragraph of *at least* four sentences. Be sure to describe the event and explain its significance for American history.

Adams-Onís Treaty

_____

_____

_____

_____

_____

Panic of 1819

_____

_____

_____

_____

_____

McCulloch v. Maryland

_____

_____

_____

_____

_____

Debate over Slavery Leading to the Missouri Compromise

_____

_____

_____

_____

_____

_____

Map Study

Refer to the maps in the textbook to complete this map.

1. Label these territories: Michigan, Florida, Arkansas, Unorganized.

2. Label these new states: Indiana (1816), Mississippi (1817), Illinois (1818), Alabama (1819), Maine (1820), Missouri (1821).

3. With a colored pencil, draw the boundary between the United States and Mexico according to the Adams-Onís Treaty.

4. With a different colored pencil, draw the boundary between free and slave states as of 1820.

5. Place a star at the site of the Battle of Horseshoe Bend.

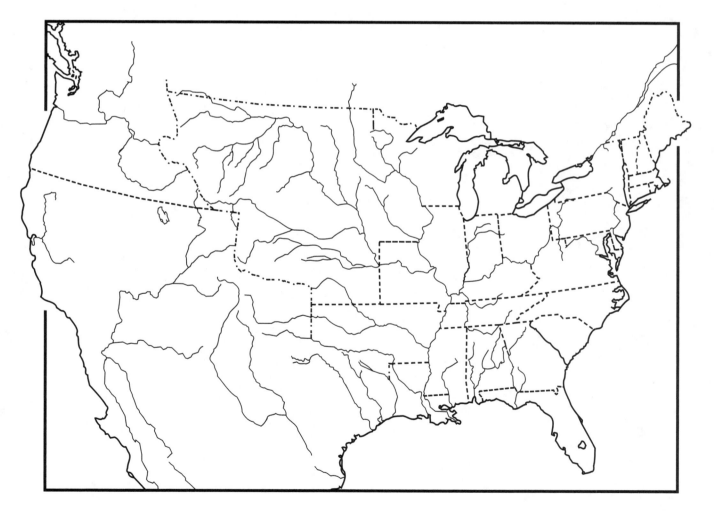

The Missouri Compromise

Answer these questions about the Missouri Compromise. Refer to the maps and information in the textbook.

1. What slave territory applied for statehood in 1819? _____

2. What free territory applied for statehood in 1819? _____

3. What latitude became the northern boundary of slavery in the territories? _____

4. Which five slave states were above this latitude? _____

   _____

5. Compare the number of states eventually created out of northern and southern territories. Did the North or the South eventually get more states from the territories that existed at the time of the Compromise?

   _____

   _____

Chapter Review

Matching

Write a phrase describing each name or term in the list. Then write the letter of the name or term in the blank.

A. John Quincy Adams   D. Andrew Jackson
B. John C. Calhoun   E. James Monroe
C. Henry Clay

_____ 1. _____

_____ 2. _____

_____ 3. _____

_____ 4. _____

_____ 5. _____

A. autocracy   C. incumbent   E. mudslinging
B. caucus   D. interstate commerce   F. tariff of abominations

_____ 6. _____

_____ 7. _____

_____ 8. _____

_____ 9. _____

_____ 10. _____

_____ 11. _____

Short Answer

Write a question for each of the answers below.

Era of Good Feelings   12. _____

_____

Monroe Doctrine   13. _____

_____

McCulloch v. Maryland   14. _____

_____

Missouri Compromise   15. _____

_____

Democratic Party   16. _____

_____

Multiple Choice

Write the letter of the correct choice in the blank.

_____ 17. Andrew Jackson was considered a hero for all these reasons *except* that

    A. he won the Battle of Horseshoe Bend.

    B. he won the Battle of New Orleans.

    C. he invaded Florida and deposed the Spanish governor.

    D. he killed Alexander Hamilton in a duel.

_____ 18. The Monroe Doctrine introduced all of these principles of foreign policy *except* that

    A. European nations could not set up new colonies in America.

    B. the U.S. would avoid European wars unless its rights were menaced.

    C. the U.S. would consider any European intervention in America dangerous.

    D. the U.S. would intervene in Latin American autocracies.

_____ 19. The Missouri Compromise included all of these provisions *except* that

    A. Missouri would come in as a slave state.

    B. Maine would come in as a free state.

    C. slavery would be forbidden in the new territories.

    D. slavery would be protected south of 36° 30′.

_____ 20. During the election of 1824, the Democratic-Republican candidate was

    A. John Quincy Adams.

    B. Henry Clay.

    C. Andrew Jackson.

    D. William Crawford.

_____ 21. John Quincy Adams was accused of making a "corrupt bargain" when he

    A. signed the Missouri Compromise.

    B. agreed to support the "tariff of abominations."

    C. sent southern delegates to the Pan-American Conference.

    D. made Henry Clay the secretary of state.

_____ 22. The election of 1828 differed from most earlier campaigns for all of these reasons *except* that

    A. techniques of mass campaigning appeared.

    B. more voters participated in the election.

    C. the mudslinging was at its worst.

    D. the candidates were selected by caucus.

The Inauguration of President Andrew Jackson, 1829

The following account was written by Margaret Smith, a member of Washington's high society during the time of Andrew Jackson. Read her account and then answer the questions below.

"[Washington] March 11th, Sunday [1829]

Thursday morning. . . . Thousands and thousands of people, without distinction of rank, collected in an immense mass round the Capitol, silent, orderly and tranquil, with their eyes fixed on the front of that edifice, waiting the appearance of the President in the portico.

The door from the Rotunda opens, preceded by the marshals, surrounded by the Judges of the Supreme Court, the old man with his grey locks, that crown of glory, advances, bows to the people, who greet him with a shout that rends the air, the Cannons, from the heights around, from Alexandria and Fort Warburton proclaim the oath he has taken and the hills reverberate the sound. It was grand,—it was sublime!

An almost breathless silence succeeded and the multitude was still,—listening to catch the sound of his voice, tho' it was so low, as to be heard only by those nearest to him. After reading his speech, the oath was administered to him by the Chief Justice. The Marshal presented the Bible. The President took it from his hands, pressed his lips to it, laid it reverently down, then bowed again to the people—Yes, to the people in all their majesty. . . .

The south side of the Capitol was literally alive with the multitude, who stood ready to receive the hero and the multitude who attended him. . . . When the speech was over, and the President made his parting bow, the barrier that had separated the people from him was broken down and they rushed up the steps all eager to shake hands with him. It was with difficulty he made his way through the Capitol and down the hill to the gateway that opens on the avenue. Here for a moment he was stopped. The living mass was impenetrable.

After a while a passage was opened, and he mounted his horse which had been provided for his return (for he had walked to the Capitol) then such a cortege as followed him! Country men, farmers, gentlemen, mounted and dismounted, boys, women and children, black and white. Carriages, wagons and carts all pursuing him to the President's house. . . . [W]e set off to the President's House, but on a nearer approach found an entrance impossible, the yard and avenue was compact with living matter."

[Later, at the President's house:]

"But what a scene did we witness! The Majesty of the People had disappeared, and a rabble, a mob, of boys, negros [*sic*], women, children, scrambling, fighting, romping. What a pity what a pity! No arrangements had been made no police officers placed on duty and the whole house had been inundated by the rabble mob. We came too late.

The President, after having been literally nearly pressed to death and almost suffocated and torn to pieces by the people in their eagerness to shake hands with Old Hickory, had retreated through the back way or south front and had escaped to his lodgings at Gadsby's.

Cut glass and china to the amount of several thousand dollars had been broken in the struggle to get the refreshments, punch and other articles had been carried out in tubs and buckets, but had it been in hogsheads it would have been insufficient, ice-creams, and cake and lemonade, for 20,000 people, for it is said that number were there, tho' I think the number exaggerated.

Ladies fainted, men were seen with bloody noses and such a scene of confusion took place as is impossible to describe,—those who got in could not get out by the door again, but had to scramble out of windows. At one time, the President who had retreated and retreated until he was pressed against the wall, could only be secured by a number of gentleman forming around him and making a kind of barrier of their own bodies, and the pressure was so great that Col. Bomford who was one said that at one time he was afraid they should have been pushed down, or on the President. It was then the windows were thrown open, and the torrent found an outlet, which otherwise might have proved fatal.

This concourse had not been anticipated and therefore not provided against. Ladies and gentlemen only had been expected at this Levee, not the people en masse. But it was the People's day, and the People's President and the People would rule."

1. Describe the crowd's attitude before Jackson's appearance at the Capitol. Contrast this with the crowd later at the President's house. _____

_____

_____

_____

2. What types of people came to see the president?

_____

_____

3. What happened to President Jackson among the crowd at his house?

_____

_____

4. Why were the president's officials unprepared for what happened that day?

_____

_____

5. What does the writer conclude at the end of her account? How does this line up with what you know about Andrew Jackson? _____

_____

_____

_____

_____

AMERICAN REPUBLIC

Name _____

CHAPTER 11 ACTIVITY 2

Nullification Crisis

Why didn't the nullification crisis end in civil war? Complete the chart by writing down the causes of northern actions and the southern reactions. The answers are listed at the bottom.

Cause	Northern Action	Southern Reaction
Federalists want to stay in power.	Alien and Sedition Acts (1798)	*The Virginia and Kentucky Resolutions first assert the right of nullification.*
	"Tariff of Abominations" (1828)	
	Webster-Hayne debate (1830)	
	Tariff of 1832	
	Force Bill (1832)	
	Compromise of 1833	
	no further action	

Causes

S.C. holds only the Force Bill nullified.
S.C. passes the Ordinance of Nullification.
Northerners want protective tariffs.
Northerners offer a slightly revised protective tariff.
S.C. fails to receive support for nullification.
Southerners bargain with the West for a lower tariff.

Southern Reactions

S.C. withdraws nullification of the tariff.
Nullifiers give up hope for a revenue tariff.
Question of states' rights remains unsettled.
S.C. calls a national convention to support nullification.
Calhoun resigns vice-presidency to lead the fight for states' rights.
Fearing for the South's economy, Calhoun first asserts nullification.

Political Cartoons

Although political cartoons existed in colonial days, they began to take their modern form during the Jacksonian era. Political cartoons appeal to the common people. "A picture is worth a thousand words," the saying goes. Look at the following political cartoon from a newspaper of the latter part of the Jacksonian era (Van Buren's reelection campaign in 1840), and then answer the questions that follow.

A HARD ROAD TO HOE!

Or, the **White House Turnpike**, macadamized by the **North Benders**.

SOLD BY HUESTIS & Co. 104 NASSAU-ST, N. Y.

1. What two things block Van Buren's road to the White House? _____

2. Which political figure do those two things symbolize and why? _____

_____

_____

3. Who do you think is pulling Van Buren on his journey to the White House? _____

4. What burden on Van Buren's back makes his trip difficult? _____

5. What alternative does Van Buren have to his trip to the White House? _____

6. Was the cartoonist for or against Van Buren's reelection, and how can you tell? _____

_____

_____

_____

Jackson on the Bank Veto

The following excerpt is drawn from Jackson's message about his veto of the Bank recharter. In it, Jackson's views on government and the states are evident. Read the excerpt and answer the questions that follow.

The Bank is professedly established as an agent of the Executive Branch of the government, and its constitutionality is maintained on that ground. Neither upon the propriety of present action nor upon the provisions of this act was the Executive consulted. It has had no opportunity to say that it neither needs nor wants an agent clothed with such powers and favored by such exemptions. There is nothing in its legitimate functions which makes it necessary or proper. Whatever interest or influence, whether public or private, has given birth to this act, it cannot be found either in the wishes or necessities of the Executive Department, by which present action is deemed premature, and the power conferred upon its agent not only unnecessary but dangerous to the government and country.

It is to be regretted that the rich and powerful too often bend the acts of government to their selfish purposes. Distinctions in society will always exist under every just government. Equality of talents, of education, or of wealth cannot be produced by human institutions. In the full enjoyment of the gifts of heaven and the fruits of superior industry, economy, and virtue, every man is equally entitled to protection by law.

But when the laws undertake to add to these natural and just advantages artificial distinctions, to grant titles, gratuities, and exclusive privileges to make the rich richer and the potent more powerful, the humble members of society—the farmers, mechanics, and laborers—who have neither the time nor the means of securing like favors to themselves, have a right to complain of the injustice of their government.

There are no necessary evils in government. Its evils exist only in its abuses. If it would confine itself to equal protection, and, as heaven does its rains, shower its favors alike on the high and the low, the rich and the poor, it would be an unqualified blessing. In the act before me there seems to be a wide and unnecessary departure from these just principles.

Nor is our government to be maintained or our Union preserved by invasions of the rights and powers of the several states. In thus attempting to make our General Government strong, we make it weak. Its true strength consists in leaving individuals and states as much as possible to themselves—in making itself felt, not in its power, but in its beneficence; not in its control, but in its protection; not in binding the states more closely to the center, but leaving each to move unobstructed in its proper orbit.

Experience should teach us wisdom. Most of the difficulties our government now encounters, and most of the dangers which impend over our Union, have sprung from an abandonment of the legitimate objects of government by our national legislation, and the adoption of such principles as are embodied in this act.

1. Was the president consulted in creating the Bank? According to Jackson, what is the Executive Branch's opinion of the Bank? _____

_____

_____

2. What does Jackson believe the rich and powerful will do with the government?

_____

3. When do the people have a right to complain about their government?

_____

_____

_____

4. When does government become evil? _____

5. Where does the strength of the government lie? _____

6. According to Jackson, where did the government's current problems come from?

_____

7. How is Jackson's support of the common people evident in this message?

_____

_____

_____

Presidents of the Jacksonian Era

Match the presidents with the phrases that are associated with them.

A. Andrew Jackson
B. Martin Van Buren
C. William Henry Harrison
D. John Tyler

_____ 1. "a man without a party"

_____ 2. the Hermitage in Tennessee

_____ 3. annexation of Texas

_____ 4. longest inaugural address

_____ 5. Battle of New Orleans

_____ 6. Webster-Ashburton Treaty

_____ 7. Black Hawk War

_____ 8. independent treasury

_____ 9. appointment of Chief Justice Roger B. Taney

_____ 10. Specie Circular

_____ 11. "pet banks"

_____ 12. "his accidency"

_____ 13. "spoils system"

_____ 14. running mate of old Tippecanoe

_____ 15. "Old Kinderhook" (O.K.)

_____ 16. forcible removal of the Cherokees from Georgia

_____ 17. "Kitchen Cabinet"

_____ 18. land act giving squatters the right to buy land

_____ 19. Force Bill

_____ 20. resignation of his entire cabinet

_____ 21. vetoed the recharter of the Bank of the United States

_____ 22. Compromise Tariff of 1833

_____ 23. died after only one month in office

_____ 24. *Worcester v. Georgia*

_____ 25. plagued by an economic depression

_____ 26. nullification crisis

_____ 27. champion of the "common man"

_____ 28. first Whig president

_____ 29. first president not born a British citizen

_____ 30. first president to die in office

_____ 31. first president born in a log cabin

_____ 32. the hand-picked successor of Andrew Jackson

_____ 33. represented by a log cabin and barrel of cider

_____ 34. "Our Federal Union: it must and shall be preserved!"

_____ 35. "The less government interferes with private pursuits, the better for the general prosperity."

Modified True/False

If the statement is true, write the word *true* in the blank. If it is false, change the underlined words to make the statement true.

_____ 1. Andrew Jackson was the <u>second</u> president from a state west of the original thirteen colonies.

_____ 2. Andrew Jackson <u>ignored</u> John Marshall's order in *Worcester v. Georgia*.

_____ 3. The <u>"Kitchen Cabinet"</u> was Jackson's method of handing out government jobs to loyal followers.

_____ 4. <u>Black Hawk</u> was a Cherokee scholar who developed an alphabet for his people.

_____ 5. A <u>revenue</u> tariff is designed to protect infant industries from foreign competition.

_____ 6. Protective tariffs were unpopular among the <u>northern</u> states.

_____ 7. Most money in the South was invested in slaves and <u>cotton</u>.

_____ 8. John C. Calhoun offered the theory of <u>secession</u> to protect South Carolina from harmful federal tariffs.

_____ 9. <u>Robert Y. Hayne</u> declared, "Liberty and Union, now and forever, one and inseparable!"

_____ 10. Calhoun resigned from the <u>vice-presidency</u> to lead the fight for states' rights.

_____ 11. The Compromise of 1833 gradually <u>lowered</u> tariffs to twenty percent.

_____ 12. Jackson's reelection campaign focused on the future of <u>states' rights</u>.

_____ 13. The <u>Force Bill</u> required anyone who bought government lands to pay for them in specie.

_____ 14. The Whig party ran <u>three</u> presidential candidates in the election of 1836.

_____ 15. Van Buren had the opportunity to change control of the Supreme Court to the <u>Whig</u> Party.

_____ 16. Settlers on western lands without titles to the land are called <u>lame ducks</u>.

_____ 17. <u>Daniel Webster</u> negotiated a settlement of the boundary between Maine and Canada.

Map Study: Growth of Transportation

Refer to the maps in the text to complete the map on the next page.

1. Label these lakes: Michigan, Erie.

2. Label these towns and cities: Portland; Boston; Baltimore; Washington, D.C.; New York City; Philadelphia; Buffalo; Albany; Pittsburgh; Wheeling; Cleveland; Vandalia; Chicago; Boonesboro; St. Louis; Savannah; Augusta; Atlanta; New Orleans.

3. Using a blue pencil, draw and label these roads: Boston Post Road, Great Wagon Road, Wilderness Road, National Road.

4. Using a green pencil, draw these canals: Erie, Illinois and Michigan, Ohio and Erie.

5. Using a red pencil, draw these railroad routes:

   ⋆ the main route on the East Coast from Portland to Savannah

   ⋆ the main route in the West from New Orleans to Chicago

   ⋆ the main route connecting Baltimore and St. Louis

   ⋆ the main route connecting St. Louis, Chicago, Cleveland, Philadelphia, and New York City

Map Questions

Answer these questions based on the textbook and its maps.

1. What series of Indian paths became a wagon road through the Appalachians? _____

2. What pioneer road aided the settlement of Kentucky? _____

3. What federally funded road aided settlement of the Northwest? _____

4. How were turnpikes paid for? _____

5. What was the main purpose of a "post road"? _____

6. What natural pass did Daniel Boone use through the Appalachians? _____

7. Name a city that was both a steamboat *and* a railroad center. _____

8. Why did New York City grow as a result of the Erie Canal? _____

   _____

9. From what Maryland city did Peter Cooper take the *Tom Thumb* on its first trip? _____

10. What were the first two cities linked by telegraph? _____

The Canal Boat

In 1835, the famous New England writer Nathaniel Hawthorne traveled the Erie Canal. His account first appeared in the *New-England Magazine*, December 1835. Read the account and then answer the questions that follow.

I was inclined to be poetical about the Grand Canal. In my imagination, De Witt Clinton [New York's governor] was an enchanter, who had waved his magic wand from the Hudson to Lake Erie, and united them by a watery highway, crowded with the commerce of two worlds, till then inaccessible to each other. . . . I pictured the surprise of the sleepy Dutchmen when the new river first glittered by their doors, bringing them hard cash or foreign commodities, in exchange for their hitherto unmarketable produce. Surely, the water of this canal must be the most fertilizing of all fluids; for it causes towns—with their masses of brick and stone, their churches and theatres, their business and hubbub, their luxury and refinement, their gay dames and polished citizens—to spring up, till, in time, the wondrous stream may flow between two continuous lines of buildings, through one thronged street, from Buffalo to Albany. I embarked about thirty miles below Utica, determining to voyage along the whole extent of the canal, at least twice in the course of the summer.

Behold us, then, fairly afloat, with three horses harnessed to our vessel. . . . Bound to a distant port, we had neither chart nor compass, nor cared about the wind, nor felt the heaving of a billow, nor dreaded shipwreck, however fierce the tempest, in our adventurous navigation of an interminable mud-puddle—for a mud-puddle it seemed. . . . With an imperceptible current, it holds its drowsy way through all the dismal swamps and unimpressive scenery, that could be found between the great lakes and the sea-coast. Yet there is variety enough, both on the surface of the canal and along its banks, to amuse the traveller, if an overpowering tedium did not deaden his perceptions.

Sometimes we met a black and rusty-looking vessel, laden with lumber, salt from Syracuse, or Genesee flour, and shaped at both ends like a square-toed boot; as if it had two sterns, and were fated always to advance backward. On its deck would be a square hut, and a woman seen through the window at her household work, with a little tribe of children, who perhaps had been born in this strange dwelling and knew no other home. Thus, while the husband smoked his pipe at the helm, and the eldest son rode one of the horses, on went the family, travelling hundreds of miles in their own house, and carrying their fireside with them. The most frequent species of craft were the "line boats," which had a cabin at each end, and a great bulk of barrels, bales, and boxes in the midst; or light packets, like our own, decked all over, with a row of curtained windows from stem to stern, and a drowsy face at every one. Once, we encountered a boat, of rude construction, painted all in gloomy black, and manned by three Indians, who gazed at us in silence and with a singular fixedness of eye. . . . Not long after, in the midst of a swamp and beneath a clouded sky, we overtook a vessel that seemed full of mirth and sunshine. It contained a little colony of Swiss, on their way to Michigan, clad in garments of strange fashion and gay colors, scarlet, yellow and bright blue, singing, laughing, and making merry, in odd tones and a babble of outlandish words. . . . These honest Swiss were an itinerant community of jest and fun, journeying through a gloomy land and among a dull race of money-getting drudges . . . yet still retaining the happy lightness of their own spirit.

Had I been on my feet at the time, instead of sailing slowly along in a dirty canal-boat, I should often have paused to contemplate the diversified panorama along the banks of the canal. Sometimes the scene was a forest, dark, dense . . . [and] covered with dismal black stumps, where, on the verge of the canal, might be seen a log-cottage, and a sallow-faced woman at the window. Lean and aguish, she looked like Poverty personified, half clothed, half fed, and dwelling in a desert, while a tide of wealth was sweeping by her door. Two or three miles further would bring us to a lock, where the slight impediment to navigation had created a little mart of trade. Here would be found commodities of all sorts, enumerated in yellow letters on the window-shutters of a small grocery-store, the owner of which had set his soul to the gathering of coppers and small change, buying and selling through the week, and counting his gains on the blessed Sabbath. The next scene might be the dwelling-houses and stores of a thriving village, built of wood or small gray stones, a church-spire rising in the midst, and generally two taverns, bearing over their piazzas the pompous titles of "hotel," "exchange," "tontine," or "coffee-house." Passing on, we glide now into the unquiet heart of an inland city—of Utica, for instance—and find ourselves amid piles of brick, crowded docks and quays, rich warehouses and a busy population. We feel the eager and hurrying spirit of the place, like a stream and eddy whirling us along with it. Through the thickest of the tumult goes the canal, flowing between lofty rows of buildings and arched bridges of hewn stone. Onward, also, go we, till the hum and bustle of struggling enterprise die away behind us, and we are threading an avenue of the ancient woods again.

This . . . was so tiresome in reality, that we were driven to the most childish expedients for amusement. An English traveller paraded the deck with a rifle in his walking-stick, and waged war on squirrels and woodpeckers, sometimes sending an unsuccessful bullet among flocks of tame ducks and geese, which abound in the dirty water of the canal. I, also, pelted these foolish birds with apples, and smiled at the ridiculous earnestness of their scrambles for the prize, while the apple bobbed about like a thing of life. Several little accidents afforded us good-natured diversion. At the moment of changing horses, the tow-rope caught a Massachusetts farmer by the leg, and threw him down in a very indescribable posture, leaving a purple mark around his sturdy limb. A new passenger fell flat on his back, in attempting to step on deck, as the boat emerged from under a bridge. Another, in his Sunday clothes, as good luck would have it, being told to leap aboard from the bank, forthwith plunged up to his third waistcoat button in the canal, and was fished out in a very pitiable plight, not at all amended by our three rounds of applause. Anon, a Virginia school-master, too intent on a pocket Virgil to heed the helmsman's warning—"Bridge! bridge!" was saluted by the said bridge on his knowledge-box. I had prostrated myself, like a pagan before his idol, but heard the dull leaden sound of the contact, and fully expected to see the treasures of the poor man's cranium scattered about the deck. However, as there was no harm done, except a large bump on the head, and probably a corresponding dent in the bridge, the rest of us exchanged glances and laughed quietly. Oh, how pitiless are idle people!

The table being now lengthened through the cabin, and spread for supper, the next twenty minutes were the pleasantest I had spent on the canal. . . . At the close of the meal, it had become dusky enough for lamplight. The rain pattered unceasingly on the deck, and sometimes came with a sullen rush against the windows, driven by the wind, as it stirred through an opening of the forest. The intolerable dullness of the scene engendered an evil spirit in me. Perceiving that the Englishman was taking notes in a memorandum-book, with occasional glances round the cabin, I presumed that we were all to figure in a future volume of travels, and amused my ill-humor by falling into the probable vein of his remarks. . . .

The crimson curtain being let down between the ladies and gentlemen, the cabin became a bed-chamber for twenty persons, who were laid on shelves, one above another. For a long time, our various incommodities kept us all awake, except five or six, who were accustomed to sleep nightly amid the uproar of their own snoring, and had little to dread from any other species of disturbance. It is a curious fact, that these snorers had been the most quiet people in the boat, while awake, and became peace-breakers only when others ceased to be so, breathing tumult out of their repose. . . . Other, though fainter sounds than these, contributed to my restlessness. . . .

Finally, all was hushed in that quarter. Still, I was more broad awake than through the whole preceding day, and felt a feverish impulse to toss my limbs miles apart, and appease the unquietness of mind by that of matter. Forgetting that my berth was hardly so wide as a coffin, I turned suddenly over, and fell like an avalanche on the floor, to the disturbance of the whole community of sleepers. As there were no bones broken, I blessed the accident, and went on deck. A lantern was burning at each end of the boat, and one of the crew was stationed at the bows, keeping watch, as mariners do on the ocean. Though the rain had ceased, the sky was all one cloud, and the darkness so intense, that there seemed to be no world, except the little space on which our lanterns glimmered. Yet, it was an impressive scene.

We were traversing the "long level," a dead flat between Utica and Syracuse, where the canal has not rise or fall enough to require a lock for nearly seventy miles. There can hardly be a more dismal tract of country. The forest which covers it, consisting chiefly of white cedar, black ash, and other trees that live in excessive moisture, is now decayed and death-struck, by the partial draining of the swamp into the great ditch of the canal.

Looking ahead, I discerned a distant light, announcing the approach of another boat, which soon passed us, and proved to be a rusty old scow. . . . Shortly after, our boatman blew a horn, sending a long and melancholy note through the forest avenue, as a signal for some watcher in the wilderness to be ready with a change of horses. We had proceeded a mile or two with our fresh team, when the tow-rope got entangled in a fallen branch on the edge of the canal, and caused a momentary delay, during which I went to examine the phosphoric light of an odd tree, a little within the forest. It was not the first delusive radiance that I had followed. The tree lay along the ground, and was wholly converted into a mass of diseased splendor, which threw a ghastliness around. . . . I called it a frigid fire; a funeral light, illumining decay and death; . . . and was thinking that such ghost-like torches were just fit to light up this dead forest, or to blaze coldly in tombs, when, starting from my abstraction, I looked up the canal. I recollected myself, and discovered the lanterns glimmering far away.

"Boat ahoy!" shouted I, making a trumpet of my closed fists.

Though the cry must have rung for miles along that hollow passage of the woods, it produced no effect. These packetboats make up for their snail-like pace by never loitering day nor night, especially for those who have paid their fare. . . .

"They are gone! Heaven be praised!" ejaculated I; "for I cannot possibly overtake them! Here am I, on the 'long level,' at midnight, with the comfortable prospect of a walk to Syracuse, where my baggage will be left; and now to find a house or shed, wherein to pass the night." So thinking aloud, I took a flambeau from the old tree, burning, but consuming not, to light my steps withal, and, like a Jack-o'-the-lantern, set out on my midnight tour.

1. According to Hawthorne, what happens to land when canal water flows through it? _____

_____

2. What does Hawthorne compare the canal to as it winds its way through the "dismal swamps and

unimpressive scenery"? _____

3. What kinds of goods traveled along the canal? _____

4. What were the most common boats found on the canal? _____

5. Describe the diverse "panorama" through which the canal travels. _____

_____

_____

_____

6. What did the passengers do to entertain themselves? _____

_____

_____

_____

7. What was the most pleasant part of the author's time along the canal? _____

8. Why couldn't Hawthorne sleep on board? What happened when he tried to roll over? _____

_____

_____

9. Why did Hawthorne go into the forest in the middle of the night? _____

_____

_____

10. What happened while Hawthorne was lost in imagination in the forest? Why was he happy about this?

_____

_____

_____

Improvements in Transportation and Communication

Transportation and communication improved dramatically during the 1800s. For each improvement, write the name of the man behind its first success, the date of its success, one advantage, and one disadvantage. Then answer the questions on the back.

Improvement	Supporter	Date	Advantage	Disadvantage
stagecoach		1766		
plank road				
macadamized road				
locomotive				
flatboat				
steamboat				
canal				
clipper				
post roads				
pony express				
telegraph				

Thought Questions

Answer these questions based on the textbook and the chart on the previous page.

1. Why do you think Americans continued to build roads after the locomotive was invented?

   _____

   _____

2. Railroads eventually took the place of canals because railroads were so much cheaper. Why do you think the canal craze continued until 1850, twenty years *after* Peter Cooper proved the value of railroads in 1830?

   _____

   _____

3. The federal government stopped construction of the National Road in the late 1830s before it reached St. Louis.

   ★ Where did it stop? _____

   ★ What changes in transportation during the 1830s and 1840s made the road less practical? _____

   _____

4. Macadamized roads are still being built today. Why do you think this type of road construction became more popular than the smooth plank roads? _____

   _____

5. Why do you think telegraph poles were placed alongside railroad tracks?

   _____

   _____

6. Some improvements in transportation and communication refined old sources of power, such as wind, water, and horses. Other improvements adapted new sources of power, such as steam and electricity. In each example below, give one reason you think the new source of power proved more successful than the old source.

   ★ locomotive over stagecoach _____

   ★ steamboat over clipper _____

   ★ telegraph over pony express _____

7. How did improvements in transportation benefit communication? _____

   _____

   _____

Rev. Henry A. Miles on *Lowell, As It Was and As It Is*

In 1846 Rev. Henry Miles published a detailed history of Lowell, Massachusetts (an early mill town for girls). He said the only purpose of his book was a "careful presentation of the facts." Answer the questions about his "facts" in each excerpt.

The superintendent, from his room, has the whole of the corporation under his eye. On the one side are the boarding-houses, all of which are under his care, and are rented only to known and approved tenants. On the other side are the mills, in each room of which he has stationed some carefully selected overseer, who is held responsible for the work, good order, and proper management of his room. . . . The superintendent's mind regulates all; his plans, matured and decided by the directors of the company, who visit him every week, control all. He presides over one of the most perfect systems of subdivided and yet well-defined responsibility. . . .

Each of the long blocks of boarding-houses is divided into six or eight tenements, and are generally three stories high. These tenements are finished off in a style much above the common farmhouses of the country. . . . These are constantly kept clean, the buildings well painted, and the premises thoroughly whitewashed every spring, at the corporation's expense. The front room is usually the common eating-room of the house, and the kitchen is in the rear. The keeper of the house, (commonly a widow, with her family of children,) has her parlor in some part of the establishment, and in some houses there is a sitting-room for the use of the boarders.

The remainder of the apartments are sleeping-rooms. In each of these are lodged two, four, and in some cases six boarders; and the room has an air of neatness and comfort, exceeding what most of the occupants have been accustomed to in their paternal homes. In many cases, these rooms are not sufficiently large for the number who occupy them; and oftentimes that attention is not paid to their ventilation which a due regard to health demands. These are points upon which a reform is called for. . . . At the same time, it should in justice be added, that the evil alluded to is not peculiar to Lowell, and will not probably appear to be a crying one, if the case should be brought into comparison with many [other] apartments. . . .

Regulations to be observed by persons occupying the boarding-houses:

✶ No disorderly or improper conduct must be allowed in the houses.

✶ The doors must be closed at 10 o'clock in the evening.

✶ Those who keep the houses, when required, must give an account of their boarders with regard to their general conduct, and whether they are in the habit of attending public worship.

1. Who supervises the girls' "good order" in the mill rooms? _____

2. Who supervises the girls' "general conduct" in the boarding houses? _____

3. What health problem is described in this excerpt? What fact does Miles use to excuse this problem?

_____

_____

[The time allowed for meals] is too short for a due regard to health. . . . And yet it is probably as long as most business men allow to themselves; it is probably as long as is spent at the tables of more than half of our public hotels. For the sake of the operatives we wish that the time for meals was lengthened, but we do not see the propriety of calling for reform in those habits of hasty eating which pervade the whole country, and characterize our nation. . . .

4. What health problem is described in this excerpt? What facts does Miles use to excuse this problem?

_____

_____

_____

No fact connected with the manufacturing business has been so often, or so strongly objected to as this, that the average daily time of running the mills is twelve hours and ten minutes. It is no part the object of this book to defend any thing which may be shown to be wrong, its sole purpose being a careful presentation of the facts. Arguments are not needed to prove that toil, if it be continued for this length of time, each day, month after month, and year after year, is excessive and too much for the tender frames of young women to bear. No one can more sincerely desire, than the writer of this book, that they had more leisure time for mental improvement and social enjoyment. It must be remembered, however, that their work is comparatively light. All the hard processes, not conducted by men, are performed by machines, the movements of which female operatives are required merely to oversee and adjust. . . .

The average number of hours in which they are actually employed is not more than ten and a half. They are out to go shopping, to repair their clothes, to take care of themselves in any occasional illness, to see friends visiting the city, to call on sick friends here; nor are reasonable requests of this kind refused. Many of these girls, moreover, in the course of each year, take a vacation of a few weeks, to return to their homes. In these absences the work of the mill is not suspended. The wheels continue their revolutions for the prescribed number of hours. The processes are temporarily superintended by other hands. To suppose that every operative is on duty just as long as the machinery is in motion, is an error of the most deceptive kind.

5. What is the most common objection to the manufacturing? What fact does Miles use to excuse this

problem? Why does Miles call this objection "an error of the most deceptive kind"? _____

_____

_____

_____

6. Do you think the girls' lives were worse at the boarding houses than on the farm? Support your opinion

from these excerpts. _____

_____

_____

_____

_____

American Inventions

American life changed dramatically during the 1800s as a result of inventions and improvements in agriculture and industry. For each invention or improvement below, write who introduced it, how it worked, and what impact it had on American society.

Invention	Inventor	Function of Invention	Impact of Invention on Society
steel plow		cutting of smooth, straight furrows without the soil sticking to the plow blades	
horse-drawn reaper			
cotton gin			
American textile factory system			
hand-cranked sewing machine			
foot-treadle sewing machine			
interchangeable parts			
clipper ships			

Reforming America

Match each of the following people or movements with the reform with which he or she was most directly connected. Beside each match, write a brief description of how that person influenced that particular reform effort.

A. William Ellery Channing   E. Charles Finney

B. Dorothea Dix   F. Horace Mann

C. Timothy Dwight   G. Elizabeth Cady Stanton

D. Ralph Waldo Emerson

_____ 1. Unitarianism

_____

_____

_____ 2. Transcendentalism/Romanticism

_____

_____

_____ 3. Second Great Awakening

_____

_____

_____ 4. Revivalism

_____

_____

_____ 5. Education

_____

_____

_____ 6. Seneca Falls Convention/women's rights

_____

_____

_____ 7. Mental illness

_____

_____

Chapter Review

Who Am I?

Read each statement and decide who it describes. Write your answer in the blank.

1. I left England to build factories in America. _____

2. My revivals attracted crowds through new publicity measures and attractive theology. _____

3. I patented the sewing machine with the foot treadle. _____

4. I was the first to successfully test a locomotive on the railroad. _____

5. My invention for water travel on the Mississippi and the Hudson became very popular because it had the proper financial and political backing. _____

6. I opened trade with Japan. _____

7. I was the first to patent the sewing machine. _____

8. My invention for speeding up water travel did not become popular because the stagecoach still traveled faster. _____

9. My *Flying Cloud* set the record for sailing between New York and San Francisco. _____

10. We wanted to end slavery. _____

11. I was the first postmaster general under the Constitution. _____

12. My mill town for girls in Massachusetts provided room and board for the workers and a model for industry. _____

13. I improved the factory system through the development of interchangeable parts. _____

14. My invention expanded communication by sending signals through wires. _____

What Am I?

Read each statement and decide what it describes. Write your answer in the blank.

15. This system brought many workers to one place to produce goods. _____

16. These water compartments open and shut to raise and lower ships traveling by canal. _____

17. These groups called for shorter workdays, free education, and the end of child labor. _____

18. This one machine cut and harvested grain as fast as six working men. _____

19. Attendees of this meeting wanted more rights for women. _____

20. This route, the first federally funded highway, reached from Cumberland, Maryland, to Vandalia, Illinois.

_____

21. The changes in technology and transportation brought this time of great innovation and production of manufactured goods. _____

22. This invention, developed by John Deere, fixed the problems with the old iron plows.

_____

23. This manmade water highway made water transportation possible between the Atlantic Ocean and the Great Lakes. _____

24. This service carried mail by horseback between St. Joseph, Missouri, and Sacramento, California.

_____

25. This route, which used to be an Indian path, led settlers from Philadelphia to Augusta, Georgia, along the Appalachian Mountains. _____

Where Am I?

Read each statement and decide where it describes. Write your answer in the blank.

26. The revivals of the Second Great Awakening began at this university. _____

27. This region was most affected by the invention of the cotton gin. _____

28. The Wilderness Road leads through this natural passage through the Appalachian Mountains.

_____

29. This city received the first telegraph message from Washington, D.C. _____

30. Large numbers of immigrants came from this country in the early 1800s. _____

31. Americans traded for tea, spices, silk, and dishware in this new market. _____

32. The Industrial Revolution did not take hold in this region as it did elsewhere. _____

33. This was the first state to form public schools, led by Horace Mann. _____

34. This state was the first to have a regularly scheduled railroad service. _____

35. Revivals in this region took the form of camp meetings. _____

36. These regions combined had more than two-thirds of the nation's total railroad mileage.

_____

Map Study: Manifest Destiny

Refer to the maps in your textbook (including those at the back of the book) to complete the map on the next page.

1. Label these rivers: Missouri, Platte, Snake, Columbia, Willamette, Rio Grande, Nueces, Colorado.

2. Label these territories: Iowa, Oregon, Indian.

3. Label these new states: Texas, California.

4. Label Mexico.

5. Label these cities with a dot: Independence, St. Joseph, Council Bluffs, Santa Fe, Salt Lake City, Astoria, San Francisco, New Orleans.

6. Label these trails on the key: Oregon, Mormon, Santa Fe, California.

7. Label these forts with a diamond: Ft. Leavenworth, Ft. Kearney, Ft. Hall, Bent's Fort.

Map Questions: Rivers and Forts

Answer these questions with the help of the textbook and maps.

1. What major rivers did the Oregon Trail follow? _____

2. What river did the Mormon Trail share with the Oregon Trail? _____

3. What river did the California Trail follow? _____

4. Give two reasons the trails ran close to rivers. _____

5. What fort was built at the base of the Santa Fe and Oregon trails? _____

6. What fort was located at the major turn in the Santa Fe Trail? _____

7. What fort was located at the split of the Oregon and California trails? _____

8. How do you think it was decided where to place the forts? _____

_____

9. What three rivers aided the settlement of Oregon? _____

10. Why do rivers make good boundaries? _____

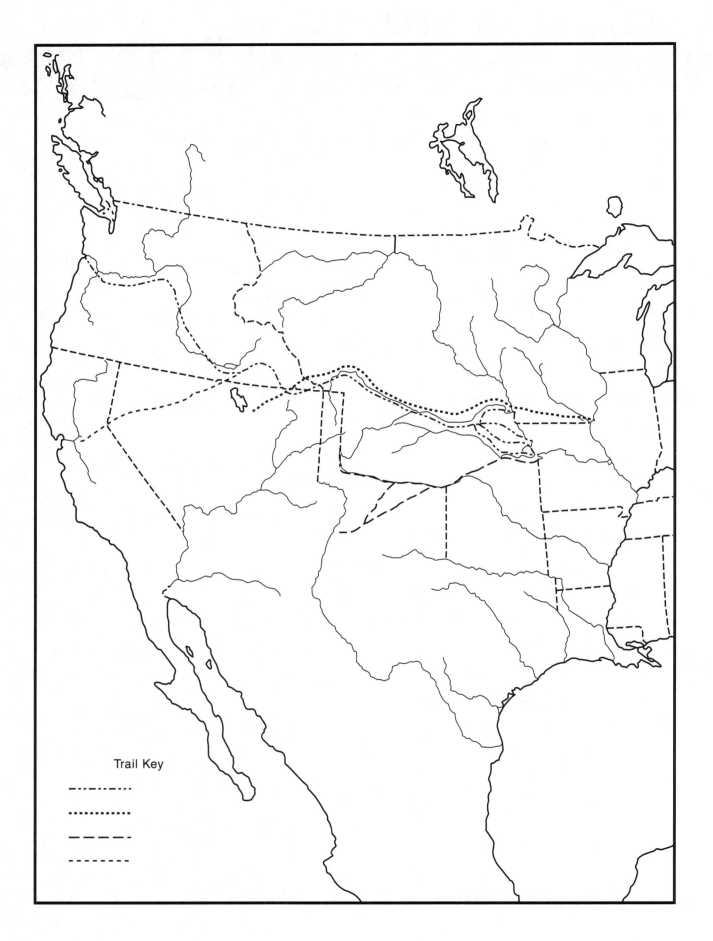

Trail Key

Name _____

Trails to the West

A. Using your textbook, fill in the following chart about the four major trails to the West.

	Santa Fe Trail	Oregon Trail	Mormon Trail	California Trail
Date (of Its First Use)				early 1840s
Town(s) at the Starting Point				same as Oregon Trail
Forts and Landmarks on the Trail				same as Oregon Trail
Destination				
Original Purpose				
Main Advantages			use of Oregon Trail; safe, isolated valley	
Main Weaknesses			cold weather; dry regions	
Significance in Western Settlement	▓			
Significance in Mexican War		▓	▓	▓

B. Identify the following people and places, and explain how each was instrumental in the westward movement in American history.

1. Jedediah Smith _____

    _____

    _____

2. William and Charles Bent _____

    _____

    _____

3. Stephen Austin _____

    _____

    _____

4. Sam Houston _____

    _____

    _____

5. The Alamo _____

    _____

    _____

6. San Jacinto _____

    _____

    _____

7. James K. Polk _____

    _____

    _____

8. John Jacob Astor _____

    _____

    _____

9. Joseph Smith and Brigham Young _____

    _____

    _____

10. John Sutter _____

    _____

    _____

Oregon Trail Diary

In March 1836, Narcissa Whitman and her husband, Dr. Marcus Whitman, left New York State for the Oregon Territory. Their goal in traveling west was to set up a mission to reach the Indians. They arrived in September 1836 at the site of present-day Walla Walla, Washington. Narcissa gave birth to the first white American in the Oregon Territory. Although their child died at a young age, Narcissa and Marcus took in many children at their mission. Sadly, the Indians did not prove to be receptive to the gospel and soon resented the Whitmans. To the Indians, the Whitmans represented the other whites who soon took over their lands. When disease broke out among the Indians, the Indians blamed Dr. Whitman for spreading it. Not as many white people had fallen sick because of their previous exposure to the disease. In 1847, the Indians murdered the Whitmans. Following are portions of Narcissa's Oregon Trail diary, which are mostly in the form of letters to her family back home. Read the selection, and then answer the questions at the end.

PLATTE RIVER, JUST ABOVE THE FORKS, JUNE 3RD, 1836. . . . Friday eve, six o' clock. We have just encamped for the night near the bluffs over against the river. The bottoms are a soft, wet plain, and we were obliged to leave the river yesterday for the bluffs. The face of the country yesterday afternoon and today has been roll-ing sand bluffs, mostly barren, quite unlike what our eyes have been satiated with for weeks past. No timber nearer than the Platte, and the water tonight is very bad—got from a small ravine. We have usually had good water previous to this.

Our fuel for cooking since we left timber (no timber except on rivers) has been dried buffalo dung; we now find plenty of it and it answers a very good purpose, similar to the kind of coal used in Pennsylvania (I suppose now Harriet will make up a face at this, but if she was here she would be glad to have her supper cooked at any rate in this scarce timber country). The present time in our journey is a very important one. The hunter brought us buffalo meat yesterday for the first time. Buffalo were seen today but none have been taken. We have some for supper tonight. Husband is cook-ing it—no one of the company professes the art but himself. I expect it will be very good. Stop—I have so much to say to the children that I do not know in what part of my story to begin. I have very little time to write. I will first tell you what our com-pany consists of. We are ten in number; five missionaries, three Indian boys and two young men employed to assist in packing animals.

Saturday, 4th. Good morning, H. and E. I wrote last night till supper; after that it was dark I could not see. I told you how many bipeds there was in our company last night; now for the quadrupeds: Fourteen horses, six mules and fifteen head of cattle. We milk four cows. We started with seventeen, but we have killed one calf, and the Fur Company, being out of provision, have taken one of our cows for beef. *[Along the route, their group joined with a group of fur traders.]* It is usually pinching times with the Company before they reach the buffalo. We have had plenty because we made ample provision at Liberty. We purchased a barrel of flour and baked enough to last us, with killing a calf or two, until we reached the buffalo.

The Fur Company is large this year; we are really a moving village—nearly 400 ani-mals, with ours, mostly mules, and 70 men. The Fur Company have seven wagons drawn by six mules each, heavily loaded, and one cart drawn by two mules, which carries a lame man, one of the proprietors of the Company. We have two wagons in our company. Mr. and Mrs. S., husband and myself ride in one, Mr. Gray and the baggage in the other. Our Indian boys drive the cows and Dulin the horses. Young Miles leads our forward horses, four in each team. Now E., if you want to see the camp in motion, look away ahead and see first the pilot and the captain, Fitzpatrick, just before him, next the pack animals, all mules, loaded with great packs; soon after you will see the wagons, and in the rear, our company. We all cover quite a space. The pack mules always string one after the other just like Indians. . . .

✪✪✪

I wish I could describe to you how we live so that you can realize it. Our manner of living is far preferable to any in the States. I never was so contented and happy before neither have I enjoyed such health for years. In the morning as soon as the day breaks the first that we hear is the words, "Arise! Arise!"—then the mules set up such a noise as you never heard, which puts the whole camp in motion. We encamp in a large ring, baggage and men, tents and wagons on the outside, and all the animals except the cows, which are fastened to pickets, within the circle. This arrangement is to accommodate the guard, who stand regularly every night and day, also when we are in motion, to protect our animals from the approach of Indians, who would steal them. As I said, the mules' noise brings every man on his feet to loose them and turn them out to feed.

Now, H. and E., you must think it very hard to have to get up so early after sleeping on the soft ground, when you find it hard work to open your eyes at seven o'clock. Just think of me—every morning at the word, "Arise!" we all spring. While the horses are feeding we get breakfast in a hurry and eat it. By this time the words, "Catch up! Catch up," ring through the camp for moving. We are ready to start usually at six, travel till eleven, encamp, rest and feed, and start again about two; travel until six, or before, if we come to a good tavern, then encamp for the night. . . .

Tell mother I am a very good housekeeper on the prairie. I wish she could just take a peep at us while we are sitting at our meals. Our table is the ground, our table-cloth is an India-rubber cloth used when it rains as a cloak; our dishes are made of tin-basins for teacups, iron spoons and plates, each of us, and several pans for milk and to put our meat in when we wish to set it on the table. Each one carries his own knife in his scabbard, and it is always ready to use. When the table things are spread, after making our own forks or sticks and helping ourselves to chairs, we gather around the table. Husband always provides my seat, and in a way that you would laugh to see. It is the fashion of all this country to imitate the Turks. . . . We take a blanket and lay down by the table, and those whose joints will let them follow the fashion; others take out some of the baggage (I suppose you know that there is no stones in this country, not a stone have I seen of any size on the prairie). For my part I fix myself as gracefully as I can, sometimes on a blanket, sometimes on a box, just as it is convenient. Let me assure you of this, we relish our food none the less for sitting on the ground while eating. We have tea and a plenty of milk, which is a luxury in this country. Our milk has assisted us very much in making our bread since we have been journeying. . . . I never saw any thing like buffalo meat to satisfy hunger. We do not want any thing else with it. I have eaten three meals of it and it relishes well. Supper and breakfast we eat in our tent. We do not pitch it at noon. Have worship immediately after supper and breakfast.

✪✪✪

. . . I wish you were all here with us going to the dear Indians. I have become very much attached to Richard Sak-ah-too-ah. 'Tis the one you saw at our wedding; he calls me mother; I love to teach him—to take care of him, and hear them talk. There are five Nez Perces in the company, and when they are together they chatter finely. Samuel Temoni, the oldest one, has just come into the camp with the skin and some of the meat of a buffalo which he has killed himself. He started this forenoon of his own accord. It is what they like dearly, to hunt buffalo. So long as we have him with us we shall be supplied with meat.

✪✪✪

Friday eve. [Aug. 12, entering the mountains] - Dear Harriet, the little trunk you gave me has come with me so far, and now I must leave it here alone. Poor little trunk, I am sorry to leave thee; thou must abide here alone, and no more by thy presence remind me of my dear Harriet. Twenty miles below the falls on Snake river this shall be thy place of rest. Farewell, little trunk, I thank thee for thy faithful services, and that I have been cheered by thy presence so long. Thus we scatter as we go along. The hills are so steep and rocky that husband thought it best to lighten the wagon as much as possible and take nothing but the wheels, leaving the box with my trunk. I regret leaving anything that came from home, especially that trunk, but it is best. It would have been better for me not to have attempted to bring any baggage whatever, only what was necessary to use on the way. It costs so much labor, besides the expense of animals. If I were to make the journey again I would make quite different preparations. To pack and unpack so many times, and cross so many streams where the packs frequently get wet, requires no small amount of labor, besides the injury of the articles. Our books, what few we have, have been wet several times. In going from Elmira to Williamsport this trunk fell into the creek and wet all my books, and Richard's, too, several times. The sleigh box came off and all of us came near a wetting likewise. The custom of the country is to possess nothing, and then you will lose nothing while traveling. Farewell for the present.

✪✪✪

The river is divided by two islands into three branches, and is fordable. The packs are placed upon the tops of the highest horses and in this way we crossed without wetting. Two of the tallest horses were selected to carry Mrs. Spalding and myself over. Mr. McLeod gave me his and rode mine. The last branch we rode as much as half a mile in crossing and against the current, too, which made it hard for the horses, the water being up to their sides. Husband had considerable difficulty in crossing the cart. Both cart and mules were turned upside down in the river and entangled in the harness. The mules would have been drowned but for a desperate struggle to get them ashore. Then after putting two of the strongest horses before the cart, and two men swimming behind to steady it, they succeeded in getting it across. I once thought that crossing streams would be the most dreaded part of the journey. I can now cross the most difficult stream without the least fear. . . .

✪✪✪

20th. - Saturday. Last night I put my clothes in water and this morning finished washing before breakfast. This is the third time I have washed since I left home— once at Fort Williams and once at Rendezvous. Mr. McLeod called this evening to see if we were ready to leave. He observed we had been so engaged in labor as to have no time for rest, and proposed for ourselves to remain over Sabbath. This I can assure you was a favor for which we can never be too thankful, for our souls need the rest of the Sabbath as well as our bodies.

✪✪✪

22d. - Left the [Snake] Fort yesterday; came a short distance to the crossing of Snake river, crossed and encamped for the night. The river had three branches, divided by islands, as it was when we crossed before. The first and second places were very deep, but we had no difficulty in crossing on horseback. The third was deeper still; we dare not venture horseback. This being a fishing post of the Indians, we easily found a canoe, made of rushes and willows, on which we placed ourselves and our saddles (Sister Spalding and myself), when two Indians on horseback, each with a rope attached to the canoe, towed us over. (O! if father and mother and the girls could have seen us in our snug little canoe, floating on the water.) We were favorites of the company. No one else was privileged with a ride on it. I wish I could give you a correct idea of this little bark. It is simply bunches of rushes tied together, and attached to a frame made of a few sticks of small willows. It was just large enough to hold us and our saddles. Our baggage was transported on the top of our tallest horses, without wetting.

As for the wagon, it is left at the Fort, and I have nothing to say about crossing it at this time. Five of our cattle were left there also, to be exchanged for others at Walla Walla. Perhaps you will wonder why we have left the wagon, having taken it so nearly through. Our animals were failing, and the route in crossing the Blue Mountains is said to be impassable for it. We have the prospect of obtaining one in exchange at Vancouver. If we do not we shall send for it, when we have been to so much labor in getting it thus far. It is a useful article in the country.

❂❂❂

August 27th. . . . Girls, how do you think we manage to rest ourselves every noon, having no house to shelter us from the scorching heat, or sofa on which to recline? Perhaps you think we always encamp in the shade of some thick wood. Such a sight I have not seen, lo, these many weeks. If we can find a few small willows or a single lone tree, we think ourselves amply provided for. But often our camping places are in some open plain and frequently a sand plain, but even here is rest and comfort. My husband, who is one of the best the world ever knew, is always ready to provide a comfortable shade, with one of our saddle-blankets spread upon some willows or sticks placed in the ground. Our saddles, fishamores and the other blankets placed upon the ground constitute our sofa where we recline and rest until dinner is ready. How do you think you would like this? Would you not think a seat by mother, in some cool room preferable? Sometimes my wicked heart has been disposed to murmur, thinking I should have no rest from the heat when we stopped, but I have always been reproved for it by the comfort and rest received. Under the circumstances I have never wished to go back. Such a thought never finds a place in my heart. "The Lord is better to us than our fears." I always find it so.

[August] 28th. This morning lingered with husband on the top of the hill that overlooks the Grande Ronde, for berries until we were some distance behind camp. We have now no distressing apprehensions the moment we are out of sight of the camp, for we have entirely passed the dangerous country. I always enjoy riding alone with him, especially when we talk about home friends. It is then the tedious hours are sweetly decoyed away.

❂❂❂

After dinner we left the plain and ascended the Blue Mountains. Here a new and pleasing scene presented itself—mountains covered with timber, through which we rode all the afternoon; a very agreeable change. The scenery reminded me of the hills in my native country of Streuben.

29th. - Had a combination of the same scenery as yesterday afternoon. Rode over many logs and obstructions that we had not found since we left the states. Here I frequently met old acquaintances in the trees and flowers, and was not a little delighted; indeed, I do not know as I was ever so much affected with any scenery in my life. The singing of birds, the echo of voices of my fellow travelers, as they were scattered through the woods, all had a strong resemblance to bygone days. But this scenery was of short duration—only one day.

We had no sooner gained the foot of this mountain than another more steep and dreadful was before us. After dinner and rest we descended it. Mount Pleasant, in Prattsburg, would not compare with these Mount Terribles. Our ride this afternoon exceeded anything we have had yet, and what rendered it the more aggravating was the fact that the path all the way was very stony, resembling a newly macadamized road. Our horses' feet were very tender, all unshod, so that we could not make the progress we wished. The mountain in many places was covered with this black broken basalt. We were very late in making camp to-night. After ascending the mountain we kept upon the main divide until sunset, looking in vain for water and a camping place. While upon this elevation we had a view of the Valley of the Columbia River. It was beautiful. Just as we gained the highest elevation and began to descend the sun was dipping his disk behind the western horizon. Beyond the valley we could see two distinct mountains—Mount Hood and Mount St. Helens. These lofty peaks were of a conical form, separated from each other by a considerable distance. Behind the former the sun was hiding part of his rays, which gave us a more distinct view of this gigantic cone. The beauty of this extensive valley contrasted well with the rolling mountains behind us, and at this hour of twilight was enchanting and quite diverted my mind from the fatigue under which I was laboring. We had yet to descend a hill as long, but not as steep or as stony as the other. By this time our horses were in haste to be in camp, as well as ourselves, and mine made such lengthy strides in descending that it shook my sides surprisingly. It was dark when we got into camp, but the tent was ready for me, and tea also, for Mr. McLeod invited us to sup with him.

Dearest mother, let me tell you how I am sustained of the Lord in all this journey. For two or three days past I have felt weak, restless and scarcely able to sit on my horse—yesterday in particular. But see how I have been diverted by the scenery, and carried out of myself in conversation about home and friends. . . . This morning my feelings were a little peculiar; felt remarkably strong and well—so much so as to mention it—but could not see any reason why I should feel any more rested than on the morning previous. Then I began to see what a day's ride was before me, and I understood it. If I had had no better health to-day than yesterday I should have fainted under it. Then the promise appeared in full view: "As thy day, so shall thy strength be," and my soul rejoiced in God, and testifies to the truth of another evidently manifest, "Lo, I am with you always."

1. What did the travelers use for fuel when they could not find wood? What did Narcissa compare it to?

_____

2. How many people did they start out with in their group? What people were in their group?

_____

_____

3. Was the Fur Company a larger or smaller group than the missionaries'? Describe the Fur Company.

_____

_____

_____

4. How did the settlers protect their animals at night? _____

_____

_____

5. How were mealtimes on the wagon train different from mealtimes at home?

_____

_____

_____

6. Who hunted for their buffalo meat? _____

7. Why did Narcissa have to leave behind some of her possessions? _____

_____

_____

8. How many times did Narcissa wash their clothes during the journey? _____

9. Why did they have to leave their wagon and animals behind? _____

_____

_____

10. Give evidence of Narcissa's faith in the Lord throughout her journey. _____

_____

_____

_____

AMERICAN REPUBLIC

Name _____

Map Study: Mexican War and Western Expansion

Refer to the maps in the textbook to complete the map on the next page.

1. Label these rivers: Rio Grande, Nueces, Arkansas, Colorado, Gila.

2. Label these cities with a dot: New Orleans, San Diego, Los Angeles, San Francisco, Salt Lake City, Santa Fe.

3. Label these battle sites with a star: Alamo, San Jacinto, Palo Alto, Monterrey, Buena Vista, Veracruz, Resaca de la Palma, Mexico City.

4. Using two colored pencils, draw a line for these military routes with an arrow at the end:

   ★ Zachary Taylor's advance from the mouth of the Nueces River to Buena Vista

   ★ Winfield Scott's advance from New Orleans to Mexico City

5. Label these territory borders: 54°40′, 49°, 42°.

6. Label the following areas: the Oregon Territory acquired in 1846, the Mexican Cession of 1848, and the Gadsden Purchase of 1853.

Map Questions

Answer these questions with the help of the textbook and maps.

1. What two rivers formed the disputed borders of Texas? _____

2. Were more battles of the Mexican War fought on U.S. soil or Mexican soil? Explain.

   _____

   _____

   _____

   _____

3. Which American general was present at the Battle of Veracruz? Buena Vista? _____

4. List five states that were formed from parts of the Mexican Cession. _____

   _____

5. Before the Gadsden Purchase, which river formed the southern border of the New Mexico territory?

   _____

6. Which western cities (on the map) had Americans settled in before they became part of U.S. territory?

   _____

7. Which country kept a larger portion of the Oregon Territory after 1846, Great Britain or the United States?

   _____

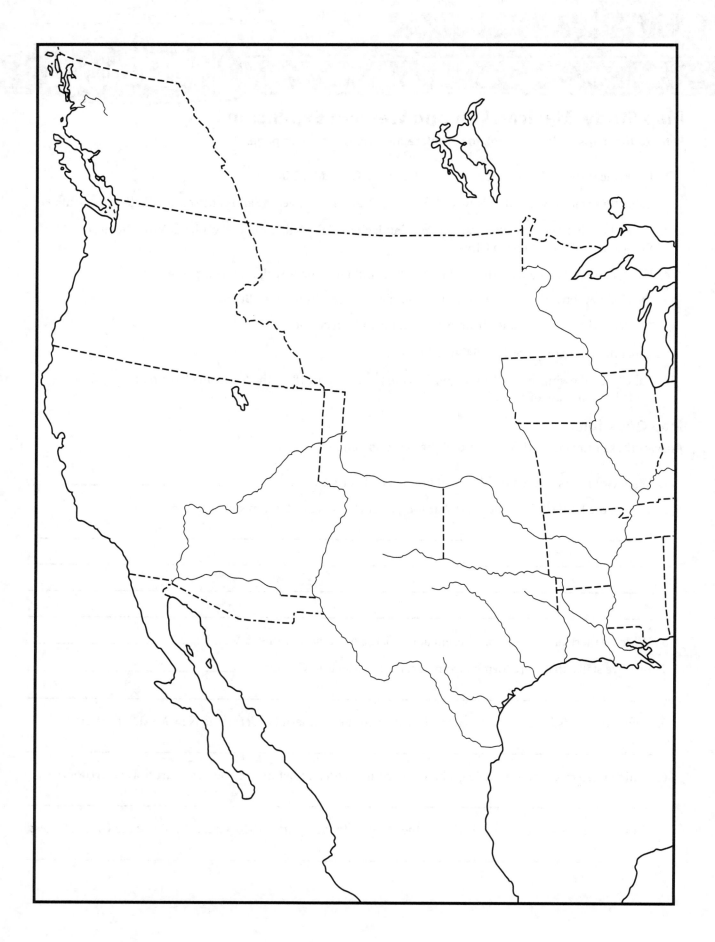

Chapter Review

A. With the help of your textbook, fill in the following blanks to complete a timeline of the Mexican War. Use the list of events provided at the bottom of the page.

October 1835	
January 1845	(1) _____ (2) _____
May 1846	(1) _____ (2) _____
July 1846	
August 1846	*Colonel Stephen Kearny takes Santa Fe.*
September 1846	
February 1847	
March 1847	*General Winfield Scott assaults Veracruz.*
September 1847	
February 1848	
1850	(1) _____ (2) _____
1852	
1853	

Bear Flag Revolution takes place and the U.S. claims California.
Congress passes the Compromise of 1850.
Mexico breaks relations with the U.S.
Mexicans attack General Zachary Taylor at Palo Alto.
Franklin Pierce wins the presidential election.
Taylor marches toward Monterrey.
Mexico and the U.S. sign the Treaty of Guadalupe Hidalgo.
Texas becomes a U.S. state.
Texans fight the Mexicans at the Alamo in San Antonio.
Taylor defeats Santa Anna at Buena Vista.
The U.S. makes the Gadsden Purchase, fulfilling the dream of Manifest Destiny.
Congress declares war on Mexico.
Mexico City surrenders to Winfield Scott.
California becomes a state.

B. The year 1846 was a pivotal year in American history. The Mexican War brought new opportunities and problems. Complete this essay about the war's causes and consequences.

By 1840, Americans believed they had a God-given (1) _____ to expand to the Pacific, including the Southwest. Led by (2) _____, families began to settle in Texas because of cheap land, no taxes, and protection from (3) _____ they owed in the states. As settlers poured in, Mexico's president, (4) _____, tried to regain control by force. The Texans declared independence and elected (5) _____ as their new president. The provisional government, called the (6) _____, spent nine years seeking formal (7) _____ as a new state in the Union. When Congress delayed because it feared war with (8) _____, the dark horse candidate (9) _____ ran for president on the popular pledge, "All of (10) _____, All of Texas." He appealed to both southerners and northerners who dreamed of western expansion.

The brief Mexican War, settled by the Treaty of (11) _____ in 1848, fulfilled America's dreams of Manifest Destiny. The settlement of Oregon's boundary at (12) _____ parallel and the (13) _____ Purchase in the Southwest completed America's acquisition of contiguous territory. The western trappers, known as (14) _____, were overrun by settlers with "Oregon fever." The Mormons, led by (15) _____, settled in Utah. The discovery of gold in 1848 by (16) _____, who was preparing a sawmill for (17) _____, started the famous (18) _____ Gold Rush. In just over one year, this former Mexican territory had enough citizens to apply for statehood.

The request for statehood sparked a raging debate in Congress. Many northerners had opposed the Mexican War because they did not want the South to extend (19) _____ to the territories. Congressman (20) _____ pushed through five separate bills to settle the debate. The bills, known as the (21) _____, were signed by the Whig president (22) _____. California was admitted as a free state, while the territories of New Mexico and (23) _____ were allowed to decide whether they wanted slavery, according to a principle known as (24) _____. America entered the 1850s as a sharply divided nation, held together by the moderate Northern Democrats, called (25) _____, and their president, (26) _____.

AMERICAN REPUBLIC

Name _____

Differences Between the North and the South

Complete the following chart by writing a brief explanation showing the major differences between the North and the South. (Some of the answers you will find in your text; consult outside sources for the others.)

	Topic/issue	North	South
Economic differences	**Agriculture**		
	Industry		
	Source of labor		
Social differences	**Main occupations**		
	Population centers		
	Ruling class		
	Education		
Political differences	**Role of government**		
	Tariffs		
	Rights of states		
	Constitution		
	Basis for beliefs about government		

Who Has the Greater Authority?

Read the following excerpts from Article VI and Amendment X of the U.S. Constitution, which address the issue of governmental authority. Identify which side (North or South) emphasized each doctrine, and explain the reasoning behind each argument. Then identify the position with which you agree and state why.

The Constitution says	This position was emphasized by	This position explained
Article VI: "This Constitution, and the laws of the United States . . . ; and all treaties made . . . under the authority of the United States, shall be the supreme law of the land; and the judges in every state shall be bound thereby, anything in the constitution or laws of any state to the contrary notwithstanding."		
Amendment X: "The powers not delegated to the United States by the Constitution, nor prohibited by it to the states, are reserved to the states respectively, or to the people."		

I agree with the position of the North / South (circle one) because _____

_____

_____

_____

_____

_____

Frederick Douglass's Escape from Slavery

Read the following account of how Frederick Douglass escaped from slavery and then answer the questions that follow.

Frederick Douglass lived a remarkable life. Born in 1818 on Maryland's Eastern Shore, his mother was a slave, and his father was an unknown white man. Eventually he was sent to Baltimore where he worked as a ship's caulker in the thriving seaport. He made his dash to freedom from there in 1838. His ability to eloquently articulate the plight of the slave through his various publications and public speeches brought him international renown. Toward the end of his life, Douglass served his country as Consul General to Haiti and Charge d'Affaires for Santo Domingo. He died in 1895.

Freeman's Papers

Douglass began his life in bondage working the fields on Maryland's Eastern Shore. At age 18, he was sent to Baltimore where he learned to caulk ships. He worked in the local shipyards earning a wage that was not given to him, but to his master. His first step to freedom was to borrow the identity papers of a freed slave:

It was the custom in the State of Maryland to require the free colored people to have what were called free papers. These instruments they were required to renew very often, and by charging a fee for this writing, considerable sums from time to time were collected by the State. In these papers the name, age, color, height, and form of the freeman were described, together with any scars or other marks upon his person which could assist in his identification. This device in some measure defeated itself—since more than one man could be found to answer the same general description. Hence many slaves could escape by personating the owner of one set of papers; and this was often done as follows: A slave, nearly or sufficiently answering the description set forth in the papers, would borrow or hire them till by means of them he could escape to a free State, and then, by mail or otherwise, would return them to the owner. The operation was a hazardous one for the lender as well as for the borrower. A failure on the part of the fugitive to send back the papers would imperil his benefactor, and the discovery of the papers in possession of the wrong man would imperil both the fugitive and his friend.

Hopping a Northbound Train

Armed with these papers, and disguised as a sailor, Douglass nervously clambors aboard a train heading North on a Monday morning:

I was not so fortunate as to resemble any of my free acquaintances sufficiently to answer the description of their papers. But I had one friend—a sailor—who owned a sailor's protection, which answered somewhat the purpose of free papers—describing his person and certifying to the fact that he was a free American sailor. The instrument had at its head the American eagle, which gave it the appearance at once of an authorized document. This protection, when in my hands did not describe its bearer very accurately. Indeed, it called for a man much darker than myself, and close examination of it would have caused my arrest at the start.

In order to avoid this fatal scrutiny on the part of railroad officials, I arranged with Isaac Rolls, a Baltimore hackman, to bring my baggage to the Philadelphia train just on the moment of starting, and jumped upon the car myself when the train was in motion. Had I gone into the station and offered to purchase a ticket, I should have been instantly and carefully examined, and undoubtedly arrested. In choosing this plan I considered the jostle of the train, and the natural haste of the conductor, in a train crowded with passengers and relied upon my skill and address in playing the sailor, as described in my protection to do the rest. One element in my favor was the kind feeling which prevailed in Baltimore and other sea-ports at the time, toward "those who go down to the sea in ships." "Free trade and sailors' rights" just then expressed the sentiment of the country. In my clothes I was rigged out in sailor style. I had on a red shirt and a tarpaulin hat, and a black cravat tied in sailor fashion carelessly and loosely about my neck. My knowledge of ships and sailor's talk came much to my assistance, for I knew a ship from stem to stem, and from keelson to cross-trees, and could talk sailor like an "old salt."

I was well on the way to Havre de Grace before the conductor came into the negro car to collect tickets and examine the papers of his black passengers. This was a critical moment in the drama. My whole future depended upon the decision of this conductor. Agitated though I was while this ceremony was proceeding, still, externally, at least, I was apparently calm and self-possessed. He went on with his duty—examining several colored passengers before reaching me. He was somewhat harsh in tone and peremptory in manner until he reached me, when, strange enough, and to my surprise and relief, his whole manner changed. Seeing that I did not readily produce my free papers, as the other colored persons in the car had done, he said to me, in friendly contrast with his bearing toward the others:

"I suppose you have your free papers?" To which I answered,

"No, sir; I never carry my free papers to sea with me."

"But you have something to show that you are a freeman, haven't you?"

"Yes sir," I answered: "I have a paper with the American eagle on it, and that will carry me around the world."

With this I drew from my deep sailor's pocket my seaman's protection, as before described. The merest glance at the paper satisfied him, and he took my fare and went on about his business. This moment of time was one of the most anxious I ever experienced. Had the conductor looked closely at the paper, he could not have failed to discover that it called for a very different looking person from myself, and in that case it would have been his duty to arrest me on the instant and send me back to Baltimore from the first station. When he left me with the assurance that I was all right, though much relieved, I realized that I was still in great danger: I was still in Maryland, and subject to arrest at any moment. I saw on the train several persons who would have known me in any other clothes, and I feared they might recognize me, even in my sailor "rig," and report me to the conductor, who would then subject me to a closer examination, which I knew well would be fatal to me.

Though I was not a murderer fleeing from justice, I felt perhaps quite as miserable as such a criminal. The train was moving at a very high rate of speed for that epoch of railroad travel, but to my anxious mind it was moving far too slowly. Minutes were hours, and hours were days during this part of my flight. After Maryland, I was to pass through Delaware—another slave State, where slave-catchers generally awaited their prey, for it was not in the interior of the State, but on its borders, that these human hounds were most vigilant and active. The borderlines between slavery and freedom were the dangerous ones for the fugitives. The heart of no fox or deer, with hungry hounds on his trail in full chase, could have beaten more anxiously or noisily than did mine from the time I left Baltimore till I reached Philadelphia.

New York City and Temporary Refuge

My free life began on the third of September, 1838. On the morning of the fourth of that month, after an anxious and most perilous but safe journey, I found myself in the big city of New York, a free man—one more added to the mighty throng which, like the confused waves of the troubled sea, surged to and fro between the lofty walls of Broadway.

But my gladness was short-lived, for I was not yet out of the reach and power of the slave-holders.

Final Safety—New Bedford, Massachusetts

Fleeing New York City, Douglass makes his way north to the sea town of New Bedford where he experiences the exhilaration of freedom.

The fifth day after my arrival, I put on the clothes of a common laborer, and went upon the wharves in search of work. On my way down Union Street I saw a large pile of coal in front of the house of Rev. Ephraim Peabody, the Unitarian minister. I went to the kitchen door and asked the privilege of bringing in and putting away this coal.

"What will you charge?" said the lady.

"I will leave that to you, madam."

"You may put it away," she said.

I was not long in accomplishing the job, when the dear lady put into my hand two silver half-dollars. To understand the emotion which swelled my heart as I clasped this money, realizing that I had no master who could take it from me—that it was mine—that my hands were my own, and could earn more of the precious coin—one must have been in some sense himself a slave.

1. What documents did Maryland require free colored people to possess, what types of information did they contain, and why did that present a problem for both free colored people and runaway slaves who used forged documents? _____

_____

_____

_____

2. What disguise was Douglass able to use to make a successful escape from slavery? _____

3. When Douglass was confronted without those documents, what response did he give that satisfied the questioner? _____

_____

_____

_____

4. What job did Douglass find in New Bedford that finally gave him the feeling that he was truly a free man? _____

5. Why do you think that Douglass's account of escaping slavery had a greater impact on people than the speeches of white abolitionists? _____

_____

_____

_____

Differing Viewpoints: The Sumner-Brooks Episode

Read the following newspaper reports of the Sumner-Brooks episode. As you read, note the names, locations, and political party affiliations of each newspaper. (The first selection is out of chronological order because it provides a more complete—though not an unbiased—account of what happened. Note also that some of them had no headline or title.) Then answer the questions that follow the selections.

[No Title]

Charleston, S.C., Mercury [Democratic], 28 May 1856

Sumner . . . delivered a coarse and malignant Abolition speech, in which he assailed South Carolina and Judge BUTLER with great bitterness. The speech was so coarse and insulting, that even his own faction condemned it, and the Southern men freely said he should be chastised. His peculiar friends tauntingly declared that he was armed during its delivery, and that he was prepared for all responsibility. Col. BROOKS, who is a relative of Judge BUTLER, and from his immediate district, deemed it his duty to chastise Mr. Sumner for his insolence, and his slanders against Judge BUTLER and the State. He sought Mr. SUMNER on Wednesday, but could not find him except in the Senate Chamber. He had determined to postpone the punishment no longer, and therefore he remained in the Senate until it adjourned.

After the adjournment, a number of ladies . . . loitered there for some time. Col. BROOKS waited about an hour after the adjournment, until all the ladies had left, Mr. SUMNER having remained in his seat. . . . As soon as the last lady had left the hall, Col. BROOKS went up to Mr. SUMNER, and facing him, said: "Mr. SUMNER, I have read your speech with great care, and all the impartiality in my power, and I have come to tell you that you have libeled my State, and slandered my relative, who is old and absent, and I deem it my duty to punish you, which I shall now proceed to do." Col. BROOKS thereupon struck Mr. SUMNER, who was rising, across the face with a gutta percha cane. He continued repeating the blows until Mr. SUMNER fell upon the floor, crying out for help. Col. Brooks then desisted voluntarily. . . .

Sumner was well and elegantly whipped, and he richly deserved it. Senator TOOMBS, of Georgia, who was in the midst of it, said, "BROOKS, you have done the right thing, and in the right place." Gallant old Governor FITZPATRICK, of Alabama, who was in the midst of it, warmly sustained BROOKS also.

❂❂❂

The whole South sustains BROOKS, and a large part of the North also. All feel that it is time for freedom of speech and freedom of cudgel to go together.

(Source: http://history.furman.edu/editorials/see.py?sequence=sumenu&location=Sumner%20 Caning&ecode=sccmsu560528a)

The Attack Upon Mr. Sumner

Boston, Mass., Courier [Whig], 23 May 1856

The telegraph gives us an account of an unmanly personal attack by a Representative of South Carolina upon Senator Sumner of Massachusetts, while our Senator was sitting at his desk. . . . Mr. Sumner was writing at his desk, after the closing of the Senate session, and was brutally assaulted by a South Carolina member of the House. There is no excuse for brutalism—there is no excuse for the man who assaults another at disadvantage anywhere, and the Senators of the United States will without doubt take care of their privileges and prerogatives.

✪✪✪

The speech of Mr. Sumner was exceedingly insulting towards some gentlemen who sit with him upon the Senate floor. It was not in consonance with the sort of arguments which people expect to hear from U.S. Senators upon a grave question. They do not want flowery adjectives or far-fetched allusions to, or illustrations from Greece and Rome, to give them an opinion as to how they shall act with regard to a practical question which is now before them. When Mr. Sumner compares Senator Butler of South Carolina and Senator Douglas of Illinois to Don Quixote and Sancho Panza, assimilating one to the character of a crazy man and the other to that of a fool, he takes a ground which Massachusetts, in her dignity and her ability, never presented before.

✪✪✪

The member from South Carolina transgressed every rule of honor which should animate or restrain one gentleman in his connections with another, in his ruffian assault upon Mr. Sumner. There is no chivalry in a brute. There is no manliness in a scoundrel. If Mr. Brooks is a nephew to Senator Butler, as it is said that he is, the Senator has only cause to regret that his blood runs through such ignoble veins.

(Source: http://history.furman.edu/editorials/see.py?sequence=sumenu&location=Sumner%20 Caning&ecode=mabcsu560523a)

Attack on Mr. Sumner

Boston, Mass., Bee [American], 23 May 1856

. . . Hon. Chas. Sumner, M.C. [Member of Congress], of this city, was ferociously and brutally assaulted in the National Senate Chamber yesterday, by a cowardly scoundrel named Brooks. An outrage so gross and villainous was never before committed within the walls of the Capitol. It is rendered additionally infamous and barbaric from the fact that fiendish bystanders prevented persons who were disposed from interfering. This bully Brooks who has disgraced the name of *man*, ought to be branded as a villain of the blackest dye, and then mercilessly kicked from one end of the continent to the other. The black mark of Cain will stand out on his brow to the last moment of his disgraced life.

(Source: http://history.furman.edu/editorials/see.py?sequence=sumenu&location=Sumner%20 Caning&ecode=mabbsu560523a)

[No Title]

Boston, Mass., Atlas [Republican], 23 May 1856

Hon. Charles Sumner . . . was yesterday brutally assaulted by a ruffian named Brooks, who represents South Carolina in the lower House. Those who know Mr. Sumner will readily believe that nothing in his conduct or conversation could have provoked the outrage, and that it must be attributed to the bold and vigorous demonstration of the Kansas inequity, which he has just uttered in the Senate. The reign of terror, then, is to be transferred to Washington, and the mouths of the representatives of the North are to be closed by the use of bowie-knives, bludgeons, and revolvers. Very well; the sooner we understand this the better. If violence must come, we shall know how to defend ourselves. We hope, for the credit of the State, that every man in it will feel this outrage upon Mr. Sumner as a personal indignity, no less than an insult to the Commonwealth of Massachusetts, and that there will be such a general and spontaneous expression of opinion, as will fully manifest our deep disinclination to submit to any repetition of the contumely.

(Source: http://history.furman.edu/editorials/see.py?sequence=sumenu&location=Sumner%20 Caning&ecode=mabasu560523a)

[No Title]

Wilmington, N.C., Daily Herald [American], 26 May 1856

The uppermost topic in the papers, North and South, now, is the recent chastisement of Senator Sumner, by Mr. Brooks, of South Carolina. As was expected, the affair has been a perfect Godsend to the Abolitionists, and they evidently intend to make the most of it. In Massachusetts, especially, public opinion is at fever heat. . . . The affair has assumed a party aspect already. Freesoilism, languishing for an excitement, has received a sudden impetus, and Sumner will be glorified into the dignity of a persecuted patriot, if not a martyr in the cause of freedom.

✪✪✪

We think Sumner deserved what he got, but we do not approve the conduct of Brooks. Sumner had not insulted *him*, and he was not called upon to resent an indignity offered to Senator Butler, even though the latter was his relative and absent. Again, he attacked Sumner under very reprehensible circumstances. He caned him in the Senate chamber, and took him, moreover, at an advantage—while sitting in his chair. The Senate Chamber is not the arena for exhibitions of this character. It is disgraceful that scenes of violence like these should be permitted to occur within it. If Congress is to be leveled to a mere ring for bullying and fighting, we had best amend the Constitution and abolish the Congress. We should at least preserve more respectability at home and abroad.

✪✪✪

Granting that the prevocation [*sic*] was sufficient, [Brooks] has yet given a good handle for the Northern people to seize, in denunciation of his course, and deprived the South of the opportunity of justification.

(Source: http://history.furman.edu/editorials/see.py?sequence=sumenu&location=Sumner%20 Caning&ecode=ncwhsu560526a)

Public Approval of Mr. Brooks

Columbia, S.C., South Carolinian [Democratic], 27 May 1856

[T]he Hon. Preston S. Brooks had not only the approval, but the hearty congratulations of the people of South Carolina for his summary chastisement of the abolitionist Sumner.

Immediately upon the reception of the news on Saturday last, a most enthusiastic meeting was convened in the town of Newberry, at which Gen. Williams, the Intendant, presided. Complimentary resolutions were introduced by Gen. A.C. Garlington, and ardent speeches made by him, Col. S. Fair, Maj. Henry Sumner, and others. The meeting voted him a handsome gold-headed cane. . . . At Anderson . . . a meeting was called, and complimentary resolutions adopted. We heard one of Carolina's truest and most honored matrons from Mr. Brooks' district send a message to him by Maj. Simpson, saying "that the ladies of the South would send him *hickory* sticks, with which to chastise Abolitionists and Red Republicans whenever he wanted them."

Here in Columbia, a handsome sum, headed by the Governor of the State, has been subscribed, for the purpose of presenting Mr. Brooks with a splendid silver pitcher, goblet and stick. . . . In Charleston similar testimonials have been ordered by the friends of Mr. Brooks.

And, to add the crowning glory to the good work, the slaves of Columbia have already a handsome subscription, and will present an appropriate token of their regard to him who has made the first practical issue for their preservation and protection in their rights and enjoyments as the happiest laborers on the face of the globe.

Meetings of approval and sanction will be held, not only in Mr. Brooks' district, but throughout the State at large, and a general and hearty response of approval will re-echo the words, "Well done," from Washington to the Rio Grande.

The Washington Difficulty

Laurensville, S.C., Herald [Democratic], 30 May 1856

[W]e can only give our most hearty indorsement of the conduct of Mr. Brooks, and call upon his constituents in Laurens District to meet here on Monday to give him a testimonial of their determination to sustain him. Our Representatives have been heretofore quietly submitting to the vile calumnies and slanders that have of late years, at every opportunity, been heaped upon the South by our enemies, and we have often wondered at the calmness and discretion of Southern members, under such circumstances; but there is a point when forbearance ceases to be a virtue, and . . . Sumner's speech . . . brought upon him the merited chastisement, it must be evident the fanatical fool had passed that boundary, and it was not in the nature of such a man as Preston S. Brooks to submit to it. Argument, reason, courtesy and conciliation had long since proved ineffectual to silence the wild calumniators.

The only means left untried has now been made use of by Mr. B., and we sincerly hope it will prove a salutary lesson to others who may have the temerity to provoke a like act.

1. What conclusions can one make based on these newspaper editorials? _____

_____

_____

_____

_____

2. List some of the negative terms the newspapers used to refer to Sumner and his speech.

_____

_____

3. List some of the negative terms the newspapers used to refer to Brooks and his attack on Sumner.

_____

_____

4. Write a short paragraph stating your opinion of this incident. In your answer, address these issues: whether Sumner was justified in his speech; whether Brooks was justified in taking matters into his own hands, especially given the fact that he was not directly mentioned in Sumner's speech; whether Sumner invited such violence; and what alternatives each man had.

_____

_____

_____

_____

_____

Map Work: The Divided Nation

On the map, label each of the states that seceded from the Union. Color the Confederate States of America gray. Label each of the border states that remained in the Union, and color them yellow.

Account of the Firing on Fort Sumter

Mary Chesnut was the wife of James Chesnut Jr., an aide to President Jefferson Davis and a brigadier general in the Confederate Army. During the war, she kept a diary that became the most famous diary of the era. In the following excerpt, she is in Charleston, S.C., writing of her experience as a witness to the bombardment of Fort Sumter. Her husband was at the time attempting to negotiate the peaceful surrender of the fort.

April 12th.—I do not pretend to go to sleep. How can I? If Anderson [Union commander at Fort Sumter] does not accept terms at four, the orders are, he shall be fired upon. I count four, St. Michael's bells chime out and I begin to hope. At half-past four the heavy booming of a cannon. I sprang out of bed, and on my knees prostrate I prayed as I never prayed before.

There was a sound of stir all over the house, pattering of feet in the corridors. All seemed hurrying one way. I put on my double-gown and a shawl and went, too. It was to the housetop. The shells were bursting. In the dark I heard a man say, "Waste of ammunition." I knew my husband was rowing about in a boat somewhere in that dark bay, and that the shells were roofing it over, bursting toward the fort. If Anderson was obstinate, Colonel Chesnut [Mary's husband] was to order the fort on one side to open fire. Certainly fire had begun. The regular roar of the cannon, there it was. And who could tell what each volley accomplished of death and destruction?

The women were wild there on the housetop. Prayers came from the women and imprecations [prayers for hurt to befall the enemy] from the men. And then a shell would light up the scene. To-night they say the forces are to attempt to land. We watched up there, and everybody wondered that Fort Sumter did not fire a shot. . . . Do you know, after all that noise and our tears and prayers, nobody has been hurt; sound and fury signifying nothing—a delusion and a snare.

1. What was Chesnut's immediate reaction to hearing the beginning of the bombardment?

   _____

2. What was the reaction of everyone else, including Chesnut (after her reaction in Question 1)?

   _____

3. Why was Chesnut concerned about her husband at the time? _____

   _____

   _____

4. What was the difference between the prayers of the women and those of the men who were watching the

   bombardment? _____

   _____

   _____

   _____

5. Through it all, what, according to Chesnut, was the great wonder when the bombardment was over?

   _____

Chapter Review

Write the name of the person described by or responsible for each of the following things.

1. Founded the abolitionist newspaper *The Liberator* _____

2. Former slave; lectured against slavery in Great Britain and the North _____

3. Associated with the Underground Railroad _____

4. Wrote *Uncle Tom's Cabin* _____

5. Did not believe states had the right to secede but did nothing to prevent their doing so _____

6. Slave who sued for his freedom in what became a famous Supreme Court case _____

7. Radical abolitionist who believed in using violence in his cause; tried to spark a slave rebellion by capturing the federal arsenal at Harpers Ferry _____

8. The commanding officer who was responsible for the capture of the person who attacked Harpers Ferry

_____

9. Ran for president in 1860 as a Southern Democrat _____

10. Ran for president in 1860 as a Northern Democrat _____

11. Ran for president in 1860 as a Republican _____

12. Ran for president in 1860 as a Constitutional Unionist _____

13. Elected to be the first president of the Confederate States of America _____

Identify the following terms based on the description given.

14. Someone who opposed slavery and wanted to end the practice completely _____

15. Act of Congress that introduced the idea of popular sovereignty _____

16. Radical Southerners who advocated immediate secession if the Republicans won the election of 1860

_____

17. The act whereby a state withdraws itself from the Union _____

18. Slave states that divided the Northern states from the states of the Deep South _____

AMERICAN REPUBLIC

Name _____

CHAPTER 15 ACTIVITY 1

Comparing Lincoln and Davis

Using your book (and maybe other outside sources), complete the following chart on Abraham Lincoln and Jefferson Davis.

Category	Lincoln	Davis
Birthplace		
Birth date		
Name of wife/wives		
Number of children		
Prior occupation(s)		
Political party		
Vice president(s)		
Commander(s) under his presidency		
Book(s) authored		
Date of death		
Views on national and state government		

Major Battles of the War Between the States

Complete the chart for each of these major battles as you study this chapter. In the column labeled "Victor," write a *C* if the South won, a *U* if the North won, or *Indecisive* if neither side won a clear victory.

Battle	Year	Commanders	Significance	Victor
First Battle of Bull Run (Manassas)				
Monitor v. *Merrimac*	1862			
Second Battle of Bull Run (Manassas)				
Antietam (Sharpsburg)				
Vicksburg				
Chancellorsville	1863			
Gettysburg	1863			

Political Cartoons of the Civil War

Examine the following political cartoons from the period of the War Between the States. Choose one of them and explain what the artist is trying to communicate through it.

Lincoln's Attitude Toward the Constitution

1. Lincoln's Attitude Toward the Constitution

   _____

   _____

   _____

   _____

   _____

Lincoln's Problem with McClellan

2. Lincoln's Problem with McClellan

_____

_____

_____

Lincoln's Issuing of the Emancipation Proclamation

3. Lincoln's Issuing of the Emancipation Proclamation

_____

_____

_____

_____

_____

Soldiers' Accounts of the War

Read these writings by soldiers in the War Between the States. Then answer the questions that follow.

Alex Cressler in a Letter to Henry A. Bitner

Alex Cressler was a Union soldier from Pennsylvania.

Chambersburg
June 10th 1861

Dear Henry:—
There were fifty wagons brought up on Saturday night, and by seven O'Clock Sunday morning they were all unloaded. I received a letter from D. R. P. Shoemaker on Saturday. I must answer it to day or to-morrow, he is yet at Pleasant Hill and says that if anything would induce him to sholder a musket it would be an invasion of old Franklin, good for him he seems to be a Union man: even to the point of his nose, and [so] he should be.

You seemed to think that some other Nation might join with the South but I believe our cause is a just one, and if, all the other nations of the earth should join with their teeming millions and come to our shores in battle array against us, that by trusting in the god of battles, who I believe is superintending our movements, that triumph must be ours, but we must do our share of the work and stand right up to the mark, whether death be our lot a not Henry, I have no fear of the result, we may lose many good men, but if we go to the work right I feel confident of success. I am sorry that I have not time to answer your letter fully but if you knew how often I have been called away from my writing I know [you] would excuse me, there has been about eight person in here bothering me all the time, and no person in the office to be bothered but myself as Messrs. Carlisle & Stewart have not reached yet, if I have time I [will] try and do better the next time. [Give] my respects to all inquiring friends if any there be.

Yours very Respectfully
Alex. Cressler

P.S. [illeg.] Wright soon but come up sooner or I will pull your ears.

Milton Asbury Ryan in His Memoirs, *Experience of a Confederate Soldier in Camp and Prison in the Civil War, 1861–1865*

I left my home (near Rose Hill, Jasper County, Mississippi) and loved ones with three other companions on the second day of June, 1861 and went to Corinth, Mississippi where the Miss. Troops were rendezvoused and being drilled for the conflict. I was so afraid that the Yankees would be whipped before I could get there. I would not wait for a company to be formed at home. After looking around a day or two we decided to join the Enterprise Guard, which was designated Company B., and was one of ten companies composing the Fourteenth Mississippi Regiment. I was small for my age, not weighing over a hundred pounds, and tender looking, with not a sign of beard on my face.

R.S. Weir was Captain of Company B, when I made application to join his company. He looked at me as though he doubted the propriety of receiving me. He doubtless would have rejected me had it not been for my companions who were with me and older than I. They testified that my parents were willing for me to join the army. However, it was not long before he found that I was made of good tough stuff. I was often detailed to perform some difficult task because I did not give out as some did who were much stouter than I. I suppose we remained at Corinth for two or three months drilling every day. Finally to our great joy we received orders to go to Russellville in East Tennessee. The Union men and Southern sympathizers were having a hot time. The Southern sympathizers were in the minority and were being terribly persecuted by the Union men. We soon restored order and gave all who wanted to join the Confederate Army a chance to do so. We were next ordered to Bowling Green, Kentucky, where we thought we were going into winter quarters. Some time in January 1862 we were ordered to Russellville, Ky. We remained there a short time and were ordered to Fort Donelson. On arrival we were ordered in the breast works surrounding the fort.

1. Why does Alex refer to Shoemaker as "a Union man"?

   _____

2. How strongly does Alex feel about the rightness of his side's cause?

   _____

   _____

3. What does Alex say he will do to Henry if he doesn't write or visit soon?

   _____

4. What was Milton's greatest fear when he first joined the Mississippi militia?

   _____

5. What, to Milton, proved that he was made of "good tough stuff"?

   _____

6. Why does Milton say his unit was ordered to go to East Tennessee?

   _____

   _____

7. What is the significance of Milton's being assigned to Fort Donelson?

   _____

   _____

8. What is the danger of assuming that God is on our side in a struggle such as occurred in the Civil War?

   _____

   _____

Lincoln's Gettysburg Address

On November 19, 1863, a little more than four months after the bloody Battle of Gettysburg, a cemetery was dedicated there for those who died on that battlefield. Many dignitaries attended and spoke, including Sen. Edward Everett. Before becoming a senator, Everett had been a Unitarian pastor, a Greek literature professor at Harvard, a U.S. representative, governor of Massachusetts, diplomat to Great Britain, and Secretary of State. With such credentials, he overshadowed another guest speaker, President Abraham Lincoln. Lincoln's "few appropriate remarks," however, are still remembered, but Everett's lengthy oration has long since been forgotten. Read Lincoln's address. Then answer the questions that follow.

Four score and seven years ago, our fathers brought forth upon this continent a new nation: conceived in liberty, and dedicated to the proposition that all men are created equal.

Now we are engaged in a great civil war, testing whether that nation or any nation so conceived and so dedicated can long endure. We are met on a great battlefield of that war. We have come to dedicate a portion of that field as a final resting place for those who here gave their lives that that nation might live. It is altogether fitting and proper that we should do this.

But, in a larger sense, we cannot dedicate—we cannot consecrate—we cannot hallow—this ground. The brave men, living and dead, who struggled here have consecrated it, far above our poor power to add or detract. The world will little note, nor long remember what we say here, but it can never forget what they did here.

It is for us the living, rather, to be dedicated here to the unfinished work which they who fought here have thus far so nobly advanced. It is rather for us to be here dedicated to the great task remaining before us—that from these honored dead we take increased devotion to that cause for which they gave the last full measure of devotion—that we here highly resolve that these dead shall not have died in vain—that this nation, under God, shall have a new birth of freedom—and that government of the people, by the people, for the people, shall not perish from the earth.

1. How long is "fourscore and seven years," and what year was Lincoln referring to? _____

2. What was the great proposition on which Lincoln said the nation was founded, and to what document was he referring? _____

3. Why did Lincoln say the people meeting for the dedication of that cemetery could not dedicate, consecrate, or hallow that ground? _____
_____

4. Was Lincoln correct in assuming that the world would not remember what he said on that occasion?
_____

5. Memorize the speech, and recite it in class.

Lincoln's Second Inaugural Address

When Lincoln delivered his second inaugural address on March 4, 1865, the end of the war was a foregone conclusion. It was only a matter of time—a little more than a month—before the Confederate armies surrendered. Lincoln was looking beyond military victory, however, and was seeking to reunite the states in a way that would bring healing to the nation and avoid bitterness and hatred between the sections of the country. Read his address with these thoughts in mind. Then answer the questions that follow.

Fellow-Countrymen:

At this second appearing to take the oath of the presidential office there is less occasion for an extended address than there was at the first. Then a statement somewhat in detail of a course to be pursued seemed fitting and proper. Now, at the expiration of four years, during which public declarations have been constantly called forth on every point and phase of the great contest which still absorbs the attention and engrosses the energies of the nation, little that is new could be presented. The progress of our arms, upon which all else chiefly depends, is as well known to the public as to myself, and it is, I trust, reasonably satisfactory and encouraging to all. With high hope for the future, no prediction in regard to it is ventured.

On the occasion corresponding to this four ago all thoughts were anxiously directed to an impending civil war. All dreaded it, all sought to avert it. While the inaugural address was being delivered from this place, devoted altogether to *saving* the Union without war, urgent agents were in the city seeking to *destroy* it without war—seeking to dissolve the Union and divide effects by negotiation. Both parties deprecated war, but one of them would *make* war rather than let the nation survive, and the other would *accept* war rather than let it perish, and the war came.

One-eighth of the whole population were colored slaves, not distributed generally over the Union, but localized in the southern part of it. These slaves constituted a peculiar and powerful interest. All knew that this interest was somehow the cause of the war. To strengthen, perpetuate, and extend this interest was the object for which the insurgents would rend the Union even by war, while the Government claimed no right to do more than to restrict the territorial enlargement of it. Neither party expected for the war the magnitude or duration which it has already attained. Neither anticipated that the cause of the conflict might cease with or even before the conflict itself should cease. Each looked for an easier triumph, and a result less fundamental and astounding. Both read the same Bible and pray to the same God, and each invokes His aid against the other. It may seem strange that any men should dare to ask a just God's assistance in wringing their bread from the sweat of other men's faces, but let us judge not, that we be not judged. The prayers of both could not be answered. That of neither has been answered fully. The Almighty has His own purposes. "Woe unto the world because of offenses; for it must needs be that offenses come, but woe to that man by whom the offense cometh." If we shall suppose that American slavery is one of those offenses which, in the providence of God, must needs come, but which, having continued through His appointed time, He now wills to remove, and that He gives to both North and South this terrible war as the woe due to those by whom the offense came, shall we discern therein any departure from those divine attributes which the believers in a living God always ascribe to Him? Fondly do we hope, fervently do we pray, that this mighty scourge of war may speedily pass away. Yet, if God wills that it continue until all the wealth piled by the bondsman's two hundred and fifty years of unrequited toil shall be sunk, and until every drop of blood drawn with the lash shall be paid by another drawn with the sword, as was said three thousand years ago, so still it must be said "the judgments of the Lord are true and righteous altogether."

With malice toward none, with charity for all, with firmness in the right as God gives us to see the right, let us strive on to finish the work we are in, to bind up the nation's wounds, to care for him who shall have borne the battle and for his widow and his orphan, to do all which may achieve and cherish a just and lasting peace among ourselves and with all nations.

1. Do you believe that Lincoln was accurate in saying of the impending war that "All dreaded it, all sought to avert it"? Why or why not? _____

_____

_____

_____

_____

_____

2. Identify Scripture allusions in Lincoln's speech. _____

_____

_____

_____

3. What words in the speech indicate that Lincoln probably intended to deal kindly with the South following the war? _____

_____

_____

_____

Lee's Farewell to His Troops

On April 9, 1865, General Robert E. Lee surrendered the Army of Northern Virginia, the main army of the Confederacy, to Union general Ulysses S. Grant at Appomattox Courthouse, Virginia. He had done everything in his power to achieve victory for the South by defending it against the Union armies. He had held out as long as he could, hoping in the end to link forces with General Joseph Johnston's army in North Carolina. In the end, however, he saw that further attempts to resist the overwhelming forces of the Union were hopeless. He surrendered the army rather than shed more blood in a lost cause. On April 10, he humbly addressed his troops in his last communication as their commander. His words were few but powerful and meaningful. Read his farewell address. Then answer the questions that follow.

Headquarters, Army of Northern Virginia, April 10, 1865

After four years of arduous service, marked by unsurpassed courage and fortitude, the Army of Northern Virginia has been compelled to yield to overwhelming numbers and resources. I need not tell the survivors of so many hard-fought battles, who have remained steadfast to the last, that I have consented to this result from no distrust of them; but, feeling that valor and devotion could accomplish nothing that could compensate for the loss that would have attended the continuation of the contest, I have determined to avoid the useless sacrifice of those whose past services have endeared them to their countrymen. By the terms of the agreement, officers and men can return to their homes and remain there until exchanged. You will take with you the satisfaction that proceeds from the consciousness of duty faithfully performed; and I earnestly pray that a merciful God will extend to you His blessing and protection. With an increasing admiration of your constancy and devotion to your country, and a grateful remembrance of your kind and generous consideration of myself, I bid you an affectionate farewell.

R. E. Lee, General

✪✪✪

Lee returned to Lexington, Virginia, after the war and kept a low profile, saying little about either the late war or the problems of Reconstruction. When people tried to coax a response from him, his reply was always calm and measured, as in the following letter to Mrs. Jefferson Davis, who had asked him what he thought of an unflattering speech by Speaker of the House Schuyler Colfax.

Lexington, Virginia, February 23, 1866

My Dear Mrs. Davis: Your letter of the 12th inst. reached Lexington during my absence at Washington. I have never seen Mr. Colfax's speech, and am, therefore ignorant of the statements it contained. Had it, however, come under my notice, I doubt whether I should have thought it proper to reply. I have thought, from the time of the cessation of hostilities, that silence and patience on the part of the South was the true course; and I think so still. Controversy of all kinds will, in my opinion, only serve to continue excitement and passion, and will prevent the public mind from the acknowledgment and acceptance of the truth. These considerations have kept me from replying to accusations made against myself, and induced me to recommend the same to others. . . . I have felt most keenly the sufferings and imprisonment of your husband, and have earnestly consulted with friends as to any possible mode of affording him relief and consolation. . . . With sincere prayers for his health and speedy restoration to liberty, and earnest supplications to God that He may take you and yours under His guidance and protection, I am, with great respect,

Your obedient servant,

R. E. Lee

✪✪✪

Yet, a few years later, Lee had begun to reflect on the events following the war. Although he still refused to make public statements, he did allow himself to express some of his opinions in letters to friends. An example is the following excerpt from a letter to Governor Fletcher Stockdale in September 1870 (quoted in *The Life and Letters of Robert Lewis Dabney*, pp. 497–500).

"Governor, if I had foreseen the use those people designed to make of their victory, there would have been no surrender at Appomattox Courthouse; no sir, not by me. Had I foreseen these results of subjugation, I would have preferred to die at Appomattox with my brave men, my sword in my right hand."

1. What reasons did Lee offer his men for his decision to surrender the Confederate army and end the war?

   _____

   _____

   _____

2. What consolation did Lee tell his men they could have as they returned to their homes?

   _____

3. What did he tell them he had come increasingly to admire about the men in the Confederate army?

   _____

   _____

4. Why did Lee remain silent in the face of repeated attacks and accusations against both the South generally and himself in particular? _____

   _____

   _____

5. How did Lee's opinion about the surrender at Appomattox change during the early years of Reconstruction? _____

   _____

   _____

   _____

6. Do you think that Lee was right in his decision to remain silent and refuse to defend himself and the South? Why or why not? Should he have allowed his later opinions to be given public exposure? Why or why not? _____

   _____

   _____

   _____

Chapter Review

The study of wars involves several different types of history, including the following:

    A. **Military history**—the study of armies, navies, commanders, soldiers, battles, and campaigns

    B. **Political history**—the study of government relations, unfair laws, riots, elections, and foreign affairs

    C. **Economic history**—the study of trade, industry, workers, farming, and new technology, including weaponry

    D. **Social history**—the study of family life, personal hardships, race relations, immigrants, and photography

I. Read carefully each of the following statements. Then identify the type of history under which each statement falls. (Some of the statements might fit into more than one type of history.)

_____ 1. The Civil War split families throughout the United States, including the families of Senator John Crittendon and President Abraham Lincoln.

_____ 2. Soldiers spent 60 percent of their time in camp, 5 percent fighting.

_____ 3. Northerners often hired immigrants to serve as substitutes for them in the draft.

_____ 4. Northerners were angry at the government's unfair draft laws, and a four-day riot occurred in New York City.

_____ 5. The Confederate "Twenty-Negro Law" exempted from the draft those who owned twenty or more slaves.

_____ 6. Northern white people did not treat black people fairly. They kept them out of the army until 1863, and even then they gave black soldiers the worst tasks.

_____ 7. Northern businesses relied on women and a large pool of immigrants to work in their factories.

_____ 8. The Union blockade cut off most of the South's trade. As a result, the South could not get money for its cotton, and basic items became scarce and very expensive.

_____ 9. Daily life in the South became increasingly difficult as the war progressed, and the people had to live without many basic foods.

_____ 10. Southerners had to make unusual substitutes for food they could not buy. For instance, they used peanuts and sweet potatoes to make coffee.

_____ 11. The Confederate government became so desperate toward the end of the war that it used taxes in kind. Tax collectors demanded corn and hogs, not dollars and cents.

_____ 12. For the first time in history, modern industry and technology became a critical factor in war. Both sides used telegraphs, trains, mines, rifled guns, and ironclad ships.

_____ 13. Mathew Brady, the most famous photographer of the Civil War, captured images from the war for people back home.

_____ 14. General Winfield Scott created the "Anaconda Plan," the North's strategy of strangling the South with a naval blockade while capturing and controlling the Mississippi River.

_____ 15. Southern businessmen relied on blockade runners to carry goods in and out of the Confederate ports. The daring captains and crews of such ships made the ship owners huge profits, but they could not meet all of the South's needs.

_____ 16. Sailors in the Union blockade received little glory for their work, but they were a great help to the war effort.

_____ 17. The Union army in the East had five different commanders in 1863.

_____ 18. Pickett's charge during the Battle of Gettysburg shows the courage of Lee's army against hopeless odds.

_____ 19. One reason for Lincoln's Emancipation Proclamation was a diplomatic effort to keep Great Britain from joining the South.

_____ 20. The wanton destructiveness of civilian property during Sherman's March to the Sea created bitterness in the South and hurt relations between the two regions for generations to come.

_____ 21. The presidential election of 1864 was perhaps the greatest opportunity the South had to win the war. More important than Southern military victories were the Northern voters, who could choose a new president with a "peace ticket."

_____ 22. One evidence of Lincoln's political skill was his selection of Andrew Johnson, a Southern Democrat, as his vice president in 1864.

_____ 23. Grant's generous terms of surrender at Appomattox helped to reunite the people into one nation again. Grant gave the Confederate soldiers supplies and let them keep their side arms and their horses for farm work.

_____ 24. Union armies destroyed Southern farms, businesses, and railroads in the war. It took almost a century for the Southern economy to recover completely.

_____ 25. A great personal and national tragedy of the war was Lincoln's assassination by John Wilkes Booth.

II. Match each of the following people with their significance during the Civil War.

_____ 26. Union general who excelled at organization but was slow to act; challenged Lincoln for president in 1864

_____ 27. Confederate general in chief

_____ 28. President of the United States; first Republican to hold that office

_____ 29. Union naval commander who captured lower Mississippi River area, including New Orleans

_____ 30. Union general at Battle of Fredericksburg

_____ 31. President of the Confederate States of America

_____ 32. Confederate general who worked mainly under Lee but whose division produced Confederate victory at Chickamauga

_____ 33. Confederate general famed for his "foot cavalry"; accidentally shot by his own men at Chancellorsville

_____ 34. Union general under Grant whose policy of total war on his "March to the Sea" embittered Southerners for generations

_____ 35. Union general who captured upper Mississippi River area and became Lincoln's general in chief

A. Gen. Ambrose Burnside
B. Jefferson Davis
C. Adm. David Farragut
D. Gen. Ulysses S. Grant
E. Gen. Thomas "Stonewall" Jackson
F. Gen. Robert E. Lee
G. Abraham Lincoln
H. Gen. James Longstreet
I. Gen. George McClellan
J. Gen. William T. Sherman

III. On the following map, color seceding states *gray* and border states remaining in the Union *orange*. Locate and label the following places, marking the major battles with an X at the appropriate locations. Draw *red arrows* showing the major strategic routes followed by the Union armies.

Atlanta	Chickamauga	New Orleans	Vicksburg
Chancellorsville	Fort Donelson	Petersburg	Washington, D.C.
Charleston	Gettysburg	Richmond	
Chattanooga	Manassas	Savannah	

Lee and Johnson: Their Postwar Attitudes

Robert E. Lee seldom wrote his opinions about the war, but when he did, they were worth serious consideration. Essentially, his advice was for Southerners to accept the results of the war and move on with their lives, restoring the South rather than creating more problems by opposing Reconstruction. Andrew Johnson, although an enemy of secession and a supporter of the war against the South, was committed to pursuing Lincoln's compassionate Reconstruction plan. Read the following letter that Lee wrote, discussing the reason the South fought and how he thinks Reconstruction could best be accomplished. Then read excerpts from Johnson's December 3, 1866, message to Congress on the restoration of the Southern states to the Union. Answer the questions that follow.

Lexington, Virginia
January 5, 1866

Mr. C. Chauncey Burr.

My Dear Sir: I am very much obliged to you for your letter of the 27th ult., and for the number of the "Old Guard" which you kindly sent me. I am glad to know that the intelligent and respectable people at the North are true and conservative in their opinions, for I believe by no other course can the right interests of the country be maintained. All that the South has ever desired was that the Union, as established by our forefathers, should be preserved, and that the government as originally organized should be administered in purity and truth. If such is the desire of the North, there can be no contention between the two sections, and all true patriots will unite in advocating that policy which will soonest restore the country to tranquility and order, and serve to perpetuate true republicanism. Please accept my thanks for your advocacy of right and liberty and the kind sentiments which you express toward myself, and believe me to be, with great respect,

Your obedient servant,
R.E. Lee

Fellow-Citizens of the Senate and House of Representatives:

. . . I deem it a subject of profound regret that Congress has thus far failed to admit to seats loyal Senators and Representatives from the other States whose inhabitants, with those of Tennessee, had engaged in the rebellion. Ten States—more than one-fourth of the whole number—remain without representation; the seats of fifty members in the House of Representatives and of twenty members in the Senate are yet vacant, not by their own consent, not by a failure of election, but by the refusal of Congress to accept their credentials. Their admission, it is believed, would have accomplished much toward the renewal and strengthening of our relations as one people and removed serious cause for discontent on the part of the inhabitants of those States. It would have accorded with the great principle enunciated in the Declaration of American Independence that no people ought to bear the burden of taxation and yet be denied the right of representation. It would have been in consonance with the express provisions of the Constitution that "each State shall have at least one Representative" and "that no State, without its consent, shall be deprived of its equal suffrage in the Senate." These provisions were intended to secure to every State and to the people of every State the right of representation in each House of Congress; and so important was it deemed by the framers of the Constitution that the equality of the States in the Senate should be preserved that not even by an amendment of the

Constitution can any State, without its consent, be denied a voice in that branch of the National Legislature.

It is true it has been assumed that the existence of the States was terminated by the rebellious acts of their inhabitants, and that, the insurrection having been suppressed, they were thenceforward to be considered merely as conquered territories. The legislative, executive, and judicial departments of the Government have, however, with great distinctness and uniform consistency, refused to sanction an assumption so incompatible with the nature of our republican system and with the professed objects of the war. Throughout the recent legislation of Congress the undeniable fact makes itself apparent that these ten political communities are nothing less than States of this Union. At the very commencement of the rebellion each House declared, with a unanimity as remarkable as it was significant, that the war was not "waged upon our part in any spirit of oppression, nor for any purpose of conquest or subjugation, nor purpose of overthrowing or interfering with the rights or established institutions of those States, but to defend and maintain the supremacy of the Constitution and all laws made in pursuance thereof, and to preserve the Union, with all the dignity, equality, and rights of the several States unimpaired; and that as soon as these objects" were "accomplished the war ought to cease." . . .

The action of the executive department of the Government upon this subject has been equally definite and uniform, and the purpose of the war was specifically stated in the proclamation issued by my predecessor on the 2nd day of September, 1862. It was then solemnly proclaimed and declared "that hereafter, as heretofore, the war will be prosecuted for the object of practically restoring the constitutional relation between the United States and each of the States and the people thereof in which States that relation is or may be suspended or disturbed."

. . . In our efforts to preserve "the unity of government which constitutes us one people" by restoring the States to the condition which they held prior to the rebellion, we should be cautious, lest, having rescued our nation from perils of threatened disintegration, we resort to consolidation, and in the end absolute despotism, as a remedy for the recurrence of similar troubles. The war having terminated, and with it all occasion for the exercise of powers of doubtful constitutionality, we should hasten to bring legislation within the boundaries prescribed by the Constitution and to return to the ancient landmarks established by our fathers for the guidance of succeeding generations. . . .

1. What did Lee consider the one unifying purpose that would help the nation avoid further sectional conflict? _____

2. What Revolutionary War–era argument does Johnson raise in connection with Congress's refusal to readmit the Southern states? _____

3. Instead of treating the Southern states as disciplined wayward children, how does Johnson say Congress is treating them? _____

4. Against what peril does Johnson warn Congress? _____
_____

5. What course of action does he propose Congress should take? _____
_____
_____

Major Events of Reconstruction

Identify each of the phases of Reconstruction, the time period that each covered, and the predominant person(s) or group(s) involved in each. Then write each of the following events in the correct order and state their significance.

Civil Rights Act (first)   General Amnesty Act   Disputed election
Ten Percent Plan   Fourteenth Amendment   Freedmen's Bureau
Tenure of Office Act   Wade-Davis Bill   Reconstruction Act
Johnson's plan   Fifteenth Amendment   Troops withdrawn from the South

Reconstruction phase name:
Years:
Predominant person(s) or group(s) involved:

Year	Event	Significance
1863		
1864		
1865		Congress rejected Johnson's plan because it was too lenient.
1865	Thirteenth Amendment	

Reconstruction phase name:
Years:
Predominant person(s) or group(s) involved:

Year	Event	Significance
1865		
1866		
1866		
1867		
1867		
1870		

| Reconstruction phase name: |
| Years: |
| Predominant person(s) or group(s) involved: |

Year	Event	Significance
1872		
1876		
1877		

Saved by One Vote: An Eyewitness Account of the Trial of Andrew Johnson

The House of Representatives presented to the Senate eleven articles of impeachment against President Andrew Johnson. Articles 1–8 dealt with his alleged violation of the Tenure of Office Act. Article 9 accused him of issuing orders that violated the Army Act. Articles 10 and 11 accused Johnson of criticizing Congress using "inflammatory and scandalous harangues." The trial began March 5 and lasted until late May. William H. Crook was Andrew Johnson's bodyguard. He was in the Senate gallery on May 16 when the crucial vote was taken. Read his eyewitness account, then answer the questions that follow.

Every one who by any possible means could get a ticket of admission to the Senate chamber produced it early that morning [May 16] at the Capitol. The floor and galleries were crowded.

The journal was read: the House of Representatives was notified that the Senate, "sitting for the trial of the President upon the articles of impeachment," was ready to receive the other House in the Senate chamber. The question of voting first upon the eleventh article was decided.

While the clerk was reading the legal statement of those crimes of which, in the opinion of the House of Representatives, the President was guilty, some people fidgeted and some sat with their hands tensely clasped together. At the end, the Chief Justice directed that the roll be called. The clerk called out:

"Mr. Anthony." Mr. Anthony arose.

"Mr. Anthony"—the Chief Justice fastened his eyes upon the senator—"how say you? Is the respondent, Andrew Johnson, President of the United States, guilty or not guilty of a high misdemeanor as charged in this article?"

"Guilty," answered Mr. Anthony.

A sigh went round the assemblage. Yet Mr. Anthony's vote was not in doubt. A two-thirds vote of thirty-six to eighteen was necessary to convict. Thirty-four of the Senators were pledged to vote against the President. Mr. Fowler, of Tennessee, it was known, would probably vote for acquittal, although there was some doubt. Senator Ross was the sphinx; no one knew his position.

The same form was maintained with each Senator in turn. When Fowler's name was reached, every one leaned forward to catch the word.

"Not guilty," said Senator Fowler.

The tension grew. There was a weary number of names before that of Ross was reached. When the clerk called it, and Ross stood forth, the crowd held its breath.

"Not guilty," called the Senator from Kansas.

It was like the bubbling over of a caldron. The Radical Senators, who had been laboring with Ross only a short time before, turned to him in rage; all over the house people began to stir. The rest of the roll-call was listened to with lessened interest, although there was still the chance for a surprise. When it was over, and the result—thirty-five to nineteen—was announced, there was a wild outburst, chiefly groans of anger and disappointment, for the friends of the President were in the minority.

I ran all the way from the Capitol to the White House. I was young and strong in those days, and I made good time. When I burst into the library, where the President sat with Secretary Welles and two other men whom I cannot remember, they were quietly talking. Mr. Johnson was seated at a little table on which luncheon had been spread in the rounding southern end of the room. There were no signs of excitement.

"Mr. President," I shouted, too crazy with delight to restrain myself, "you are acquitted!"

All rose. I made my way to the President and got hold of his hand. The other men surrounded him, and began to shake his hand. The President responded to their congratulations calmly enough for a moment, and then I saw that tears were rolling down his face. I stared at him; and yet I felt I ought to turn my eyes away.

✪✪✪

In a few minutes came a message of congratulation from Secretary Seward to "my dear friend." By that time the room was full of people, and I slipped away.

1. How many articles of impeachment were brought against Johnson? _____

2. Approximately how long did the impeachment trial last? _____

3. In general, what was the sole reason the House of Representatives had impeached Johnson?

_____

4. What role did William Crook play in the Johnson Administration? _____

5. What percentage of the Senate was required for conviction? How many votes did that mean?

_____

6. Which senator cast the deciding vote, and what state did he represent? _____

7. Do you think Johnson had committed any impeachable offenses? Why or why not? _____

_____

_____

_____

_____

Interpreting a Reconstruction-Era Political Cartoon

During Reconstruction, elections saw the House and Senate seats of many former Confederate leaders being filled by carpetbaggers, scalawags, and even freedmen. One such person was Jefferson Davis, who had resigned his Senate seat when Mississippi seceded. During Reconstruction, his seat was filled by a freedman, Hiram Revels. Study the following pictorial editorial by famed political cartoonist Thomas Nast. Then write your own interpretation of the cartoon's meaning. (Pay particular attention to the Shakespeare quotation beneath the cartoon.)

"TIME WORKS WONDERS."

IAGO. (JEFF DAVIS.) "FOR THAT I DO SUSPECT THE LUSTY MOOR
HATH LEAP'D INTO MY SEAT: THE THOUGHT WHEREOF
DOTH LIKE A POISONOUS MINERAL GNAW MY INWARDS." — OTHELLO.

_____

_____

_____

_____

_____

_____

Writing a History Essay

Writing an essay for a history class will be much easier if you follow some basic procedures. The first step is to break the topic down into logical parts. For example, suppose that the essay topic is "The Difficulties of the United States in Trying to Solve the South's Postwar Problems." How can you break down this topic? A good way is to discuss each major problem separately, creating a basic outline.

I. Meeting basic needs for food, services, and industry

II. Giving freedmen a new place in a changed society

III. Establishing new state governments

After you choose a basic outline, you should decide what things to discuss under each main point. Northerners and Southerners had completely different ideas about how to solve each problem. Perhaps under each point you could discuss (A) the solutions that the federal government and Northerners adopted in the early years of Reconstruction and (B) the solutions that Southerners adopted under the Redeemers. The first point of your outline then would look something like this:

I. Meeting basic needs for food, services, and industry

   A. Northern ideas

   B. Southern ideas

Now all that is left for you is to fill in the details! Look for key terms and concepts. Following is a list of the key terms under each main point in the outline:

I. Meeting basic needs for food, services, and industry

   A. Northern ideas: the Freedmen's Bureau

   B. Southern ideas: mill towns

II. Giving freedmen a new place in a changed society

   A. Northern ideas: constitutional amendments, civil rights acts

   B. Southern ideas: black codes, the Ku Klux Klan, sharecropping

III. Establishing new state governments

   A. Northern ideas: the Reconstruction Act of 1867, carpetbaggers

   B. Southern ideas: scalawags, Redeemers, the Solid South

Write a short paragraph on each of these main ideas (three paragraphs total). To complete your essay, write a brief introductory paragraph stating your topic. Then write a brief concluding paragraph. Ask your teacher for help if you do not know how to write an introduction and a conclusion.

Sandhog: Building the Brooklyn Bridge, 1871

Residents of Brooklyn needed a bridge over the East River to connect them with New York City. The winter of 1867–68 was bitterly cold. The East River froze, giving them no easy way to get to their jobs in the city. Politicians finally agreed to build a bridge. It was the first project on such a large scale that the city had ever undertaken. It was to be the longest suspension bridge in the world—more than a mile long. The first task was to anchor the bridge's two towers on solid bedrock under the layers of mud at the bottom of the East River. Engineers designed and built a huge wooden box, towed it to the site where the first tower was to be built, and sunk it. Next, they pumped compressed air into the chamber to keep water from leaking in. Finally, they ripped out the temporary floor of the box to allow workers to dig down through the river mud until they reached bedrock. Working in the box was extremely hazardous. Because of the high air pressure required and the intense heat, lack of oxygen, and deafening noise, workers could actually work for only about two hours. The bridge was completed and opened in 1883.

The following excerpt is the account of a fifteen-year-old Irish immigrant, Frank Harris. With a friend's help, he got a job—on trial—as a "sandhog," performing one of the most dangerous tasks in the construction of the Brooklyn Bridge. The pay was five dollars a day. Read his description of the work. Then answer the questions that follow.

In the bare shed where we got ready, the men told me no one could do the work for long without getting the "bends"; the "bends" were a sort of convulsive fit that twisted one's body like a knot and often made you an invalid for life. They soon explained the whole procedure to me. We worked, it appeared, in a huge bell-shaped caisson of iron that went to the bottom of the river and was pumped full of compressed air to keep the water from entering it from below: the top of the caisson is a room called the "material chamber," into which the stuff dug out of the river passes up and is carted away. On the side of the caisson is another room, called the "air-lock," into which we were to go to be "compressed." As the compressed air is admitted, the blood keeps absorbing the gasses of the air till the tension of the gasses in the blood becomes equal to that in the air. When this equilibrium has been reached, men can work in the caisson for hours without serious discomfort, if sufficient pure air is constantly pumped in. It was the foul air that did the harm, it appeared. "If they'd pump in good air, it would be O.K.; but that would cost a little time and trouble, and men's lives were cheaper." I saw that the men wanted to warn me, thinking I was too young, and accordingly I pretended to take little heed.

When we went into the "air-lock" and they turned on one air-lock after another of compressed air, the men put their hands to their ears and I soon imitated them, for the pain was very acute. Indeed, the drums of the ears are often driven in and burst if the compressed air is brought in too quickly. I found that the best way of meeting the pressure was to keep swallowing air and forcing it up into the middle ear, where it acted as an air-pad on the inner side of the drum. . . .

When the air was fully compressed, the door of the air-lock opened at a touch and we all went down to work with pick and shovel on the gravelly bottom. My headache soon became acute. The six of us were working naked to the waist in a small iron chamber with a temperature of about 80 degrees Fahrenheit: in five minutes the sweat was pouring from us, and all the while we were standing in icy water that was only kept from rising by the terrific air pressure. No wonder the headaches were blinding. The men didn't work for more than ten minutes at a time, but I plugged on steadily, resolved to prove myself and get constant employment; only one man, a Swede named Anderson, worked at all as hard.

The amount done each week was estimated, he told me, by an inspector. Anderson was known to the contractor and received half a wage extra as head of our gang. He assured me I could stay as long as I liked, but he advised me to leave at the end of a month: it was too unhealthy: above all, I mustn't drink and should spend all my spare time in the open. He was kindness itself to me, as indeed were all the others. After two hours' work down below we went up into the air-lock room to get gradually "decompressed," the pressure of air in our veins having to be brought down gradually to the usual air pressure. The men began to put on their clothes and passed round a bottle of schnapps; but though I was soon as cold as a wet rat and felt depressed and weak to boot, I would not touch the liquor. In the shed above I took a cupful of hot cocoa with Anderson, which stopped the shivering, and I was soon able to face the afternoon's ordeal.

For three or four days things went fairly well with me, but on the fifth day or sixth we came on a spring of water, or "gusher," and were wet to the waist before the air pressure could be increased to cope with it. As a consequence, a dreadful pain shot through both my ears: I put my hands to them tight and sat still for a little while. Fortunately, the shift was almost over and Anderson came with me to the horse-car. "You'd better knock off," he said. "I've known 'em go deaf from it."

. . . One day, just as the "decompression" of an hour and a half was ending, an Italian named Manfredi fell down and writhed about, knocking his face on the floor till the blood spurted from his nose and mouth. When we got him into the shed, his legs were twisted like plaited hair. The surgeon had him taken to the hospital. I made up my mind that a month would be enough for me.

1. Why do you think Frank was so desperate that he would take such a dangerous job?

_____

2. What about the job made it so dangerous? _____

_____

_____

_____

3. What physical symptom did the workers experience that caused all of them but Frank and a Swede to stop

working? _____

4. Why did Frank refuse to stop working in spite of this physical problem? _____

_____

5. What was the longest amount of time the supervisor advised Frank to stay at that job? _____

6. What advice did the supervisor give him concerning his time off the job? _____

_____

7. Why was the building of the Brooklyn Bridge so important? _____

_____

_____

_____

_____

148

Eyewitness to Ku Klux Klan Violence, 1868

Less than a year following the end of the war, a group of Confederate veterans met in Pulaski, Tennessee. Seeking to relieve their boredom, they decided to form a club with secret rituals, elaborate ceremonies, and unusual costumes. One purpose of their organization was to intimidate freedmen, carpetbaggers, and scalawags to prevent them from voting. They named their group the Ku Klux Klan. By 1868, the organization had spread across the South and even into the Midwest. Most importantly, they became increasingly more violent in their tactics. The following excerpt is the recollection of a former slave who saw the Klan violence firsthand. He was interviewed by the Federal Writers' Project in 1933. Read his account and then answer the questions that follow.

I was born in Orange County [North Carolina] and I belong to Mr. Gilbert Gregg near Hillsboro. I don't known nothin' 'bout my mammy and daddy, but I had a brother Jim who was sold to dress young misses fer her weddin'. The tree is still standing where I set under an' watch them sell Jim. I set dar an' I cry an' cry, especially when they puts the chains on him an' carries him off, an' I ain't never felt so lonesome in my whole life. I ain't never hear from Jim since an' I wonder now sometimes if'en he's still living.

I knows that the master was good to us an' he fed an' clothed us good. We had our own garden an' we was gitten long all right.

I seed a whole heap of Yankees when they comed to Hillsboro an' most of them ain't got no respect for God, man, nor the devil. I can't remember so much about them though cause we lives in town . . . an' we has a gyard.

The most that I can tell you 'bout is the Klu Klux. I never will forget when they hung Cy Guy. They hung him for a scandalous insult to a white woman an' they comed after him a hundred strong.

They tries him there in the woods, an' they scratches Cy's arm to get some blood, an' with that blood they writes that he shall hang 'tween the heavens and the earth till he is dead, dead, dead, and that any [black man] what takes down the body shall be hanged too.

Well sir, the next morning there he hung, right over the road an' the sentence hanging over his head. Nobody would bother with that body for four days an' there it hung, swinging in the wind, but the fourth day the sheriff comes an' takes it down.

There was Ed an' Cindy, who before the war belonged to Mr. Lynch an' after the war he told them to move. He gives them a month and they' ain't gone, so the Ku Kluxes gets them.

It was on a cold night when they came and dragged the [blacks] out of bed. They carried them down in the woods an' whup them, then they throes them in the pond, their bodies breakin' the ice. Ed comes out an' come to our house, but Cindy ain't been seen since.

Sam Allen in Caswell County was told to move an' after a month the hundred Ku Klux came a-totin' his casket an' they tells him that his time has come an' if he wants to tell his wife goodbye an' say his prayers, hurry up.

They set the coffin on two chairs an' Sam kisses his old woman who's a-crying, then he kneels down beside his bed with his head on the pillar an' his arms thrown out in front of him.

He sits there for a minute an' when he rose he had a long knife in his hand. Before he could be grabbed, he done kill two of the Klu Kluxes with the knife, an' he done gone out of the door. They ain't catch him neither, and the next night when they came back, determined to get him, they shot another [black man] by accident.

Bob Boylan falls in love with another woman, so he burns his wife an' four youngsters up in their house.

The Ku Kluxes gets him, of course, an' they hangs him high on the old red oak on the Hillsboro Road. After they hanged him, his lawyer says to us boys, "Bury him good, boys, just as good as you'd bury me if I was daid."

I shook hands with Bob before they hanged him an' I helped bury him too an' we bury him nice an' we all hopes that he done gone to glory.

1. Who is the only member of his immediate family that Ben Johnson remembered, and what happened to that relative? _____

2. How did Ben remember his master treating him and the other slaves? _____

_____

3. What was Ben's attitude toward Yankee soldiers? _____

_____

4. Why did the Ku Klux Klan hang Cy Guy? _____

5. What did the KKK do as a warning to other blacks who might be tempted to insult a white woman?

_____

6. What happened to the black woman Cindy? _____

_____

7. What instances of black resistance to the KKK did Ben cite? _____

_____

8. Several times in his recollections, Ben refers to the KKK coming after blacks in a mob of a hundred. Why do you think so many people came after single individuals? _____

_____

_____

_____

9. Why do you think that many whites who were not members of the KKK remained silent while such violence against fellow human beings was being committed? _____

_____

_____

_____

10. How could one apply the parable of the Good Samaritan in Luke 10:30–37 to the KKK violence during Reconstruction? _____

_____

_____

Chapter Review

Match the presidents with the problems associated with them. Then complete the chart on the next page.

A. Abraham Lincoln   C. Ulysses S. Grant

B. Andrew Johnson   D. Rutherford B. Hayes

_____ 1. To ensure his election, he bargained away much of his presidential power.

_____ 2. He became president when the elected president was assassinated.

_____ 3. Congress refused to accept his Ten Percent Plan.

_____ 4. He vetoed the Wade-Davis Bill.

_____ 5. A former general, he succeeded Andrew Johnson as president.

_____ 6. He was the first president to be impeached.

_____ 7. He became president even though his opponent won the popular vote.

_____ 8. He did not prosecute the many corrupt politicians in government.

_____ 9. An assassin killed him soon after the president called for "charity for all."

_____ 10. He was elected by eight Republicans in a special electoral commission.

_____ 11. The Republican Party never accepted him because he was a Southern Democrat who did not want to treat the Southern states too harshly.

_____ 12. He was ridiculed for spending $7 million to purchase "Seward's Folly."

_____ 13. His presidency was marked by corruption.

_____ 14. Congress accused him of exceeding his presidential powers during the war.

_____ 15. His unwillingness to compromise drove moderate Republicans into the Radical camp.

_____ 16. Troops were removed from the South during his term in office.

_____ 17. The Radicals gained control of Congress and Reconstruction during his term.

_____ 18. He proposed Civil Service reforms that were unpopular in the Senate.

_____ 19. Congress passed the Reconstruction Act in spite of his veto.

_____ 20. During his elections, the Radicals stirred up war hatred by "waving the bloody shirt."

Complete the following chart.

	Ten Percent Plan	Johnson's Plan	Wade-Davis Bill	Reconstruction Act
Percentage of voters swearing oath				
Conditions for pardons				
Extra conditions new states must accept				

AMERICAN REPUBLIC

Name _____

Emma Lazarus's Most Famous Poem

Read the following brief biographical sketch of Emma Lazarus and answer the questions that follow.

The Lazarus family was among the earliest Jewish immigrants to America in the early nineteenth century. They were in the upper class of the Spanish and Portuguese Jews who came to America from the Iberian Peninsula. Moses Lazarus sought to help his family assimilate into American life, so he cultivated friendships and business connections with wealthy Christians, including the Vanderbilts and the Astors.

Moses and Esther Lazarus had seven children, and Emma was their fourth child. Emma grew up in New York City and received a good classical education. She began writing poetry and self-published her first book of poems when she was only seventeen. She became part of the literary elite in New York City. In her later years, she wrote poems and essays supporting the rights of Russian immigrants and promoting the founding of a Jewish state in Palestine.

Emma wrote her most famous poem, "The New Colossus," in 1883. It captured the attitude of the nation and offered hope and inspiration to all foreigners who dreamed of coming to the United States and becoming Americans. It was immortalized for future generations when it was placed on a plaque at the base of the Statue of Liberty, less than half a mile from Ellis Island, the most famous port of entry for immigrants to America.

Not like the brazen giant of Greek fame,
With conquering limbs astride from land to land;
Here at our sea-washed, sunset gates shall stand
A mighty woman with a torch, whose flame
Is the imprisoned lightning, and her name
Mother of Exiles. From her beacon-hand
Glows world-wide welcome; her mild eyes command
The air-bridged harbor that twin cities frame.
"Keep, ancient lands, your storied pomp!" cries she
With silent lips. "Give me your tired, your poor,
Your huddled masses yearning to breathe free,
The wretched refuse of your teeming shore.
Send these, the homeless, tempest-tost to me,
I lift my lamp beside the golden door!"

1. Of what religion was the Lazarus family? _____

2. From what region did the Lazarus family come? _____

3. How did Emma's father try to encourage his family's assimilation into American society?

_____

_____

4. What was Emma's special talent? _____

5. How old was she when her first book was published? _____

6. What causes did she promote? _____

_____

7. What is the title of her most famous work? Why did it become so famous? _____

_____

_____

_____

8. Write a brief essay explaining the meaning of that work to immigrants then and now. _____

_____

_____

_____

_____

_____

_____

_____

_____

_____

_____

_____

_____

_____

_____

_____

_____

_____

AMERICAN REPUBLIC

Name _____

Eyewitness Tells of "Last Spike" Driving

The May 1926 issue of *Southern Pacific Bulletin* contained an article by associate editor Earle Health about Amos L. Bowsher, a retired locomotive engineer on the Southern Pacific Railroad and an eyewitness of the driving of the "golden spike." Read the article and then answer the questions that follow.

It was the tapping of an ordinary iron hammer in the hands of Governor Leland Stanford on an ordinary iron spike that formed the electric contact which flashed the telegraphic message over the country, May 10, 1869, that the last link had been made in the rail lines of the first transcontinental railroad.

The famous gold spike and other spikes of precious metals, also the silver hammer, which were the gifts of Western states, took only an honorary part in the memorable ceremonies held at Promontory, Utah, when the Central Pacific (now Southern Pacific) and Union Pacific were connected, uniting the Pacific and Atlantic seaboards.

While all this is contrary to historical writings about the "Driving of the Last Spike," they are facts, nevertheless, according to Amos L. Bowsher, retired Southern Pacific locomotive engineer and one of the few persons living who witnessed the event.

"I don't want to detract from the fine sentiment that has been attached to the 'gold spike,'" said Mr. Bowsher, "but the last spike driven was a regular iron spike, and not the glistening gold one given by David Hewes of Sacramento. The special spikes and silver hammer were all presented to either Governor Stanford of the Central Pacific or C.T. Durant of the Union Pacific, but were never touched with a hammer. During the ceremonies the gold spike rested in a place of honor in a hole in the last tie.

Mr. Bowsher was at that time general foreman of telegraph construction work. By dropping extensions from the Central Pacific and Union Pacific overhead wires he made the telegraphic connection which sent the word out over the wires that the last spike had been driven. He wrapped [the] extension of the Central Pacific wire around the handle of the hammer and connected it to the copper plate which had been fastened to the face of the hammer. To the spike which had been partly driven into the tie Bowsher attached the extension of the Union Pacific wire. [The] head of the spike had been carefully polished so there would be no interference in completing the electric circuit when the hammer and spike met.

"It was a very pleasant day," Mr. Bowsher recalled, "but I was so busy with my crew perfecting the telegraph circuits that I didn't pay a great deal of attention to what was going on. The first special train of the Central Pacific arrived about 9 o'clock and a little later two trains arrived from the East bringing Union Pacific officers and their guests. Governor Stanford's special train arrived about 11 o'clock and soon after the crowd began to congregate around the spot where the last spike was to be driven.

"It was certainly a cosmopolitan gathering. Irish and Chinese laborers who had set records in track laying that have never since been equaled joined with the cowboys, Mormons, miners and Indians in celebrating completion of the railroad. There were even some high silk hats among the distinguished visitors from the East and West.

"A little after noon all was in readiness. The Union Pacific locomotive No. 119 and the Central Pacific locomotive 'Jupiter,' with Engineer Bill Sippy and Fireman Dick Murphy, were placed about 100 feet apart. On one side of the track was lined up a company of soldiers that came with the Union Pacific people. There was much speechmaking, the speakers standing in the middle of the track. When the spike was about to be driven the crowd moved in close to the tracks and the engines were brought nearer together."

At 12:47 Louie Jacobs, who was Central Pacific telegrapher at the end of track ticked out this message. "Almost ready. Hats off: prayer is being offered."

Through telegraphic communication had preceded the railroad, and all over the country groups of people gathered in telegraph offices to hear the bulletins from Promontory. The building of this railroad over snow-covered, granite peaks of the Sierra Nevada mountains and across barren plains, was recognized as the greatest engineering achievement of the day. Its completion was made the occasion for celebrations in many cities.

At Washington, D.C., a ball was suspended outside the capitol building which was detached and dropped at the first tap of the hammer at Promontory. Wires were extended to the bell in the capitol dome and each tap of the hammer more than 2000 miles away was repeated on the great bell.

The wires in San Francisco were connected with the alarm bell in [the] Fire Department tower, and also so adjusted that the first tap of the hammer on the last spike fired a parapet gun at Fort Point at the entrance of the Golden Gate.

"Governor Stanford tapped the spike very lightly with the hammer," Mr. Bowsher continued. "Just the slightest touch was all that was necessary to carry the 'tapping' message over the wires. After several taps were telegraphed, the wires were disconnected and I understand several people took a swing at the spike, including Mrs. J.H. Strobridge, wife of the Central Pacific construction foreman. Mrs. Strobridge and Mrs. Mary L. Ryan, wife of 'E. Black' Ryan, who was the first secretary to Governor Stanford, were women present at the driving of the last spike.

"I don't remember whether the last spike was placed in the highly polished laurel tie from California. This tie was there some place but I don't think I saw it. I understand that several ties had to be put down after the ceremony, for no sooner was one placed than it was pounced on and cut to pieces by treasure hunters. There were probably enough pieces of wood to make a dozen ties taken away from Promontory as coming from the 'original' last tie.

"Also there was a 'shark' from San Francisco who signed up purchasers of watch charms to be cast from the original gold spike. I was one of those who 'bit' at $5 a charm. Of course our charms were knocked out of far different stuff than the real gold spike."

Pictures taken on the scene show Mr. Bowsher on the telegraph pole just a few feet from where the spike was driven. He was high above the crowd and could see all that was going on.

The original gold spike and one of [the] silver spikes presented that day are now in the museum at Stanford University. The laurel tie was destroyed in the San Francisco fire of 1906.

Mr. Bowsher is a veteran of the Civil War serving in the First United States Cavalry. He was struck by Horace Greely's [sic] advice to young men to go West and took advantage of an opportunity to join a detachment of troops bound for San Francisco. His service expired while he was on the government transport at sea in the Pacific, and, when the ship reached San Francisco in January, 1866, he was free to go his own way.

Through his friendship with Major A.G. Brackett he was given a letter to R.P. Hammond, who was then superintendent of the railroad from Valencia Street to San Jose. He went to work on this road as telegraph repairer and when the Central Pacific took over the line he was transferred to Sacramento Division in the same capacity. This was in October 1867. Soon afterward he became general foreman of telegraph construction working under F.L. VanDenberg, and was in the front lines of construction work until the rails reached Promontory. Later he was general foreman of telegraph construction work over the entire system.

When the Central Pacific's telegraph lines were leased to the Western Union in 1880, Mr. Bowsher transferred to engine service and, after firing for several months, became a locomotive engineer. At the time he was retired on pension, in March 1911, after 43 years 5 months' service he was engineer on the Oregon Express.

On April 5 this year Mr. and Mrs. Bowsher, who are now living at Sacramento, celebrated their 54th wedding anniversary. Before her marriage Mrs. Bowsher (Della Cassidy) was telegraph operator in the office at West Oakland roundhouse.

Mr. Bowsher is now 86 years old and one of the ranking veterans of Central Pacific and Southern Pacific service.

1. What were the names of the two railroad companies whose tracks were joined at Promontory Point?

   _____

2. What kind of spike was the last to be driven on the railroad? _____

   _____

3. By what means did the rest of the nation learn of the completion of the railroad? _____

   _____

4. Where was Mr. Bowsher at the time the spike was driven? _____

   _____

5. Who tapped the spike that sent the message throughout the country? _____

   _____

6. What was the significance of this event to the rest of American history? _____

   _____

   _____

   _____

   _____

   _____

   _____

Ways of Doing Business

Complete the following chart. For each type of business listed, write a definition, an example, its advantages, and its disadvantages. (Some sections are completed for you.)

Type of business	Definition	Example	Advantages	Disadvantages
Sole proprietorship		Edison's Menlo Park laboratory		
Partnership				
Corporation		Bell Telephone Company		loss of individual control and large profits for one owner
Trust				
Holding company		James Hill's Northern Securities		

Andrew Carnegie: The Gospel of Wealth, 1889

Andrew Carnegie went from being a poor immigrant to the world's wealthiest man, but he never forgot his roots among the common people. He sensed an obligation to help others. He also sensed hypocrisy among those who amassed large fortunes, many of them as a direct result of selling goods to the common people, but who never did anything to help society at large. He shared his ideas for resolving that contradiction in a work called "The Gospel of Wealth." In the following excerpt from that work, Carnegie discusses his ideas about how the wealthy can best fulfill their obligation to the communities in which the wealthy have gained their wealth. Read the excerpt and answer the questions that follow.

There are but three modes in which surplus wealth can be disposed of. It can be left to the families of the decedents; or it can be bequeathed for public purposes; or, finally, it can be administered during their lives by its possessors. Under the first and second modes most of the wealth of the world that has reached the few has hitherto been applied. Let us in turn consider each of these modes. The first is the most injudicious. In monarchial countries, the estates and the greatest portion of the wealth are left to the first son, that the vanity of the parent may be gratified by the thought that his name and title are to descend to succeeding generations unimpaired. The condition of this class in Europe today teaches the futility of such hopes or ambitions. The successors have become impoverished through their follies or from the fall in the value of land. . . . Why should men leave great fortunes to their children? If this is done from affection, is it not misguided affection? Observation teaches that, generally speaking, it is not well for the children that they should be so burdened. Neither is it well for the state. Beyond providing for the wife and daughters moderate sources of income, and very moderate allowances indeed, if any, for the sons, men may well hesitate, for it is no longer questionable that great sums bequeathed oftener work more for the injury than for the good of the recipients. Wise men will soon conclude that, for the best interests of the members of their families and of the state, such bequests are an improper use of their means.

❂❂❂

As to the second mode, that of leaving wealth at death for public uses, it may be said that this is only a means for the disposal of wealth, provided a man is content to wait until he is dead before it becomes of much good in the world. . . . The cases are not few in which the real object sought by the testator is not attained, nor are they few in which his real wishes are thwarted. . . .

The growing disposition to tax more and more heavily large estates left at death is a cheering indication of the growth of a salutary change in public opinion. . . . Of all forms of taxation, this seems the wisest. Men who continue hoarding great sums all their lives, the proper use of which for public ends would work good to the community, should be made to feel that the community, in the form of the state, cannot thus be deprived of its proper share. By taxing estates heavily at death, the state marks its condemnation of the selfish millionaire's unworthy life.

. . . This policy would work powerfully to induce the rich man to attend to the administration of wealth during his life, which is the end that society should always have in view, as being that by far most fruitful for the people. . . .

There remains, then, only one mode of using great fortunes: but in this way we have the true antidote for the temporary unequal distribution of wealth, the reconciliation of the rich and the poor—a reign of harmony—another ideal, differing, indeed from that of the Communist in requiring only the further evolution of existing conditions, not the total overthrow of our civilization. It is founded upon the present most intense individualism, and the race is prepared to put it in practice by degrees whenever it pleases. Under its sway we shall have an ideal state, in which the surplus wealth of the few will become, in the best sense, the property of the many, because administered for the common good, and this wealth, passing through the hands of the few, can be made a much more potent force for the elevation of our race than if it had been distributed in small sums to the people themselves. Even the poorest can be made to see this, and to agree that great sums gathered by some of their fellow citizens and spent for public purposes, from which the masses reap the principal benefit, are more valuable to them than if scattered among them through the course of many years in trifling amounts.

1. Based on this reading, what do you think was Carnegie's attitude toward inherited wealth?

_____

_____

_____

_____

2. Do you agree or disagree with that position? Why? _____

_____

_____

_____

3. What do you think would be Carnegie's attitude toward the modern welfare system in this country if he were alive today? Why? _____

_____

_____

4. What are the consequences when wealthy people hoard their fortunes or flaunt their wealth rather than following Carnegie's principles of giving? _____

_____

_____

_____

_____

5. What is conspicuously missing in Carnegie's principles of giving?

_____

_____

_____

6. Study the life of Andrew Carnegie, perhaps by reading a biography, to see how Carnegie practiced his philosophy of philanthropy.

Chapter Review

Answer the following questions as you review the chapter in preparation for the test.

1. What is the business practice of combining small rail lines? _____

2. Who created a railroad empire from New York to the Great Lakes? _____

3. In what year was the first transcontinental railroad completed? _____

4. Which line of the first transcontinental railroad crossed the Sierra Nevada and used Chinese laborers?

   _____

5. Which line of the first transcontinental railroad crossed the plains and used Irish laborers?

   _____

6. Where did the two lines of the first transcontinental railroad meet? _____

7. What 1862 law helped settlers buy cheap land beside western railroads? _____

8. Who built the Great Northern Railroad? _____

9. What made the Great Northern Railroad different from the other railroads of the time?

   _____

10. What was America's first major act to regulate business? _____

11. What did the Interstate Commerce Commission regulate? _____

12. Who invented the air brake in 1869? _____

13. What standard gauge of track did U.S. railroads finally adopt in 1886? _____

14. How many transcontinental railroads did the United States have in 1900? _____

15. Before 1880, from which region of the world did most immigrants come? _____

16. Of what nationality was the largest group of immigrants between 1890 and 1914? _____

17. What was the main port of entry for immigrants to the United States? _____

18. Which immigrant group made up the largest number of immigrants on the West coast? _____

19. What act in 1882 severely limited legal immigration by the group in question 18? _____

20. What is investment money called? _____

21. What new form of business arrangement did industrialists develop in the late 1800s that obtained a charter from the government to raise investment money by selling stock to people who hoped to make a profit?

   _____

22. Which industrial giant wrote "The Gospel of Wealth"? _____

23. Which industrial giant and his associates organized the first trust? _____

24. What term means an economic system in which people are free to invest in businesses and make profits on those investments? _____

25. What 1890 act of Congress was designed to regulate business combinations? _____

26. What was the name of the first labor union in the United States? _____

27. Who was the founder of the American Federation of Labor? _____

28. What is the term used for the practice of unions representing workers in negotiations with owners and managers? _____

29. What is the term used for a court order forbidding or ending a strike? _____

30. What term means putting a higher value on money and possessions than on the more important things in life, such as one's spiritual needs? _____

Mining Methods in the Old West

Read the following descriptions of various methods used to mine in the American West. Then answer the questions that follow.

Thousands of people went west in the latter half of the nineteenth century to seek their fortune in gold, silver, or other minerals. They used several ways to get the object of their dreams from the soil. Some of those ways were quicker and more effective than others. Some of the methods, even if they were effective, were not very good for the environment in the long term.

Placer Mining

Whenever the mineral sought was deposited in sand, gravel, or loose soil, the most effective way to extract it was placer mining. This type of mining could be done by several different methods without drilling or dynamiting. Three common methods of placer mining were panning, sluicing, and cradling.

- **Panning**

  This is generally the first method one thinks of when discussing gold miners of the Old West. It involved putting a handful of soil or gravel into an almost flat pan, adding water, and then swirling it around in the pan, allowing the water to gradually wash the lighter soil out of the pan. The heavier metal ore would stay in the bottom of the pan. This method was very time consuming.

- **Sluicing**

  This method involved constructing a long wooden trough that was elevated on one end and the bottom of which was filled with slats called riffles. The trough was called a sluice [SLOOS]. First, the miner poured soil into the upper end of the trough. Then he poured water—generally from a stream—into that end of the trough. The water would force the dirt down the trough. The lighter material would be carried over the riffles and out the other end, forming tailings. The heavier metals would be trapped by the riffles. Sluicing was much faster than panning.

- **Cradling**

  To use this method, the miner would dredge, or drag, sediment from the bottom of a stream and dump it into a table-like piece of equipment called a cradle. Then he would jostle, or rock, the cradle back and forth, forcing the lighter and larger material to fall over the edge and retaining the heavier metal material. This method, too, was labor and time intensive.

Hydraulic Mining

The use of hydraulic mining was fast and efficient, but it was also an unwise method of mining when one considers stewardship of natural resources. Water under high pressure was sprayed directly onto an area of rock or soil that contained metal or mineral deposits. The water broke up the rock or hardened soil and washed out the ore. Then the mixture was milled. This method left the soil eroded and destroyed plant life, so it was not good for the environment in the long run. It eventually was made illegal in most areas.

Hard Rock Mining

This method of mining involved drilling or digging into solid rock to find the desired mineral or metal. At first, miners using this method used picks and shovels. Later, they used drills and dynamite to blast away rock and expose the veins of metal. Sometimes they dug straight back into a hillside, creating a tunnel. They had to reinforce the walls and ceiling of the tunnels to prevent cave-ins. If the mine proved to be very rich in the desired ore, they sometimes laid track inside the tunnels on which they could run ore cars carrying the ore outside for extraction of the metal or mineral. In other instances, the miners dug a shaft straight down into the ground until they discovered a vein. They would then lift the ore to the surface to be processed. Hard rock mining was obviously the only way to get the metals from deep within the earth, but it was also very dangerous work for miners. In addition to cave-ins, miners were in danger of floods when they hit the water table. If they went very deep into the earth, lack of oxygen also became a problem. The mines sometimes filled with toxic gases.

Regardless of the method the miners chose, mining involved a lot of hard work and varying degrees of danger and risk. But the miners valued the potential riches to be gained more than they feared the risks involved in obtaining them.

1. Which of the mining methods used in the Old West was the most destructive to the environment?

_____

2. Which method was the most dangerous? _____

3. What dangers did that method involve? _____

_____

4. What are the three variations of placer mining? _____

5. If you were a miner in the Old West, which of these methods would you use and why? _____

_____

_____

_____

_____

A Cowboy in Dodge City, 1882

In 1882, twenty-three-year-old Andy Adams got a job as a drover on a cattle drive. His journal of the drive was published in 1903 as *The Log of a Cowboy: A Narrative of the Old Trail Days*. Read the following excerpt, which tells of their arrival in Dodge City, Kansas, three months after the drive began. Then answer the questions that follow.

On reaching Dodge, we rode up to the Wright House [a general store, hotel, and restaurant], where Flood [the trail boss] met us and directed our cavalcade across the railroad to a livery stable. . . . We unsaddled and turned our horses into a large corral and while we were in the office of the livery, surrendering our artillery [firearms], Flood came in and handed each of us twenty-five dollars in gold [about $420 in today's money], warning us that when that was gone no more would be advanced. On receipt of the money, we scattered like partridges before a gunner. Within an hour or two, we began to return to the stable by ones and twos, and were stowing into our saddle pockets our purchases which ran from needles and thread to .45 cartridges, every [man] reflecting the art of the barber, while John Officer has his blond mustache blackened, waxed, and curled like a French dancing master.

✪✪✪

[The Texans made the rounds of the gambling houses, stopped at the Long Branch saloon, and then back to the Wright House for dinner. They filled their afternoon with much of the same. When night fell, they congregated at the Lone Star dance hall where months on the trail and a day of drinking led to confrontation.]

Quince Forrest was spending his winnings as well as drinking freely, and at the end of a quadrille [a type of dance] gave vent to his hilarity in an old-fashioned Comanche yell. The bouncer of the dance hall of course had his eye on our crowd, and at the end of a change, took Quince to task. He was a surly brute, and instead of couching his request in appropriate language, threatened to throw him out of the house. Forrest stood like one absent-minded and took the abuse, for physically he was no match for the bouncer, who was armed, moreover, and wore an officer's star. . . . At the conclusion of the dance, Quince and The Rebel [left the dance hall], giving the rest of us the word to remain as though nothing was wrong. [Half an hour later], Priest returned and asked us to take our leave one at a time without attracting any attention, and meet at the stable.

I remained until the last. . . . [The Rebel and I left] . . . together shortly afterward and found the other boys mounted and awaiting our return, it being now about midnight. It took but a moment to secure our guns, and once in the saddle, we rode through the town in the direction of the herd. On the outskirts of the town, we halted. "I'm going back to that dance hall," said Forrest, "and have one round at least with that [bouncer]. No man who walks this old earth can insult me, as he did, not if he has a hundred stars on him. If any of you don't want to go along, ride right on to camp, but I'd like to have you all go. And when I take his measure, it will be the signal to the rest of you to put out the lights. All that's going come on."

There were no dissenters to the program. I saw at a glance that my Bunkie was heart and soul in the play, and took my cue and kept my mouth shut. We circled round the town to a vacant lot within a block of the rear of the dance hall. Honeyman was left to hold the horses; then, taking off our belts and hanging them on the pommels of our saddles, we secreted our six-shooters inside the waistbands of our trousers. The hall was still crowded with the revelers when we entered, a few at a time, Forrest and Priest being the last to arrive. Forrest had changed hats with the

Rebel, who always wore a black one, and as the bouncer circulated around, Quince stopped squarely in front of him. There was no waste of words, but a gun-barrel flashed in the lamplight, and the bouncer, struck with the six-shooter, fell like a beef. Before the bewildered spectators could raise a hand, five six-shooters were turned into the ceiling. The lights went out at the first fire, and amidst the rush of men and the screaming of women, we reached the outside, and within a minute were in our saddles. All would have gone well had we returned by the same route and avoided the town; but after crossing the railroad track, anger and pride having not been properly satisfied, we must ride through the town.

On entering the main street, leading north and opposite the bridge on the river, somebody of our party in the rear turned his gun loose into the air. The Rebel and I were riding in the lead, and at the clattering of hoofs and shooting behind us, our horses started on the run, the shooting by this time having become general. At the second street crossing, I noticed a rope of fire belching from a Winchester in the doorway of a store building. There was no doubt in my mind but we were the object of the manipulator of that carbine, and as we reached the next cross street, a man kneeling in the shadow of a building opened fire on us with a six-shooter. Priest reined in his horse, and not having wasted cartridges in the open-air shooting, returned the compliment until he emptied his gun. By this time every officer in the town was throwing lead after us, some of which cried a little too close for comfort. When there was no longer any shooting on our flanks, we turned into a cross street and soon left the lead behind us. At the outskirts of the town we slowed up our horses and took it leisurely for a mile or so, when Quince Forrest halted us and said, "I'm going to drop out here and see if any one follows us. I want to be alone, so that if any officers try to follow us up, I can have it out with them."

[They returned to their camp, but the next morning Forrest was not back. He finally returned, however, riding in a buggy with two other men. He then explained the situation to his fellow cowboys.]

"Well, that horse of mine got a bullet plugged into him last night as we were leaving town, and before I could get him to Duck Creek, he died on me. I carried my saddle and blankets until daylight. . . . [A]ll of a sudden here comes this livery rig along with that drummer [traveling salesman]. . . . I explained [that I needed a ride], but he decided that his business was more important than mine, and refused me. I referred the matter to Judge Colt, and the judge decided that it was more important that I overtake this herd."

1. Why do you think the trail boss did not give the cowboys all of their pay when they arrived in Dodge City?

_____

2. Why did the cowboys have to "surrender" their "artillery" at the livery stable before going into town?

_____

_____

3. What part of the account indicates that not every cowboy spent his money foolishly?

_____

_____

4. What more than anything else was responsible for the cowboys' bad behavior?

_____

5. From this story, what three things do you think were the cowboy's most important possessions?

_____

Ranchers and Farmers Collide in Nebraska, 1884

Public lands in the West offered excellent opportunities for cattlemen to graze their cattle without expense. Later, they began to erect barbed wire fences to control their herds. The government, however, had promised excited pioneers that they could each have 160 acres of public land free of charge if they could homestead it for five years. The life was hard, but thousands of pioneers, spurred by the promise of free land, gave it their best shot. When many of them arrived at their claims, however, they found them fenced off. Confrontations between the cattlemen and the homesteaders were bound to occur. Solomon Butcher kept a diary of his life as a homesteader. Read the following excerpt, which describes one confrontation between the two groups. Then answer the questions that follow.

Early in the fall of 1884, a few settlers located homesteads in the northeast corner of the Brighton Ranch Company's pasture on Ash Creek. This pasture was about fifteen miles square and extended several miles south of the Loup River almost to Broken Bow, and was enclosed with a wire fence. The land being government land, and subject to entry, these settlers served notice on the ranch company to remove their fence from about their claims within thirty days.

The company paid no attention to this request, and at the expiration of the time the settlers made a raid on the fence and appropriated the posts to make roofs for their sod houses. . . .

In a short time after the appropriation of these posts the foreman of the ranch had the settlers arrested and taken to Broken Bow for trial. The sheriff had no sooner departed with the prisoners than the second foreman of the ranch rigged up two large wagons, drawn by four mules each, and proceeded to the houses of the settlers, accompanied by a number of the cowboys. They drove up to a house, took a team and large chain, hitched onto the projecting end of the ridge log, and in about three seconds the neat little home was a shapeless mass of sod, hay, brush and posts mixed up in almost inextricable confusion. The ranchmen then culled their posts from the wreck and loaded them into the wagons, when they went to the next house and repeated the operation, leaving the occupants to pick their few household goods out of the ruins at their leisure. The boys were having great fun at the expense of the settlers, cracking jokes and making merry as the work of destruction went on. After destroying several houses in this manner, they proceeded to the claim of a Mr. King, and Mrs. King, seeing them approaching, met them with a shotgun and dared them to come on. Had it been Mr. King, the invitation would possibly have been accepted, but the cowboys were too gallant to enter into a quarrel with a lady, and withdrew without molesting her.

In the meantime, a boy of the settlement had been dispatched to Broken Bow on the fastest pony that could be produced, to secure help, and quite a posse of men from the town started for the scene of action. The foreman of the ranch, who was in Broken Bow at the time as complaining witness against the settlers, heard of this and sent one of his cowboys in haste to warn the second foreman of the impending invasion. This messenger arrived at the settlement in advance of the citizens and gave the alarm. The housewreckers were thoroughly scared, and turning the heads of their mule teams towards the South Loup, applied the whip freely. As the mules began to run over the rough prairie the posts began to fall off the wagons, and as the teams began to show signs of weariness the cowboys began to heave off more posts to lighten the load as they bumped along, leaving a trail behind them like that of a railroad construction gang.

Arriving at the ranch, they turned out their mules, secured their Winchesters and made a break for the hills on the south side of the river to await developments. When the posse of rescuers arrived at the little settlement and found the invaders gone, they did not follow them, but returned to Broken Bow. The cowboys remained in the hills two days, watching for the approach of the enemy in vain.

The ranch company failed to make any case against the settlers, it being shown that the ranch pasture was government land and that the claims were lawfully held by the homesteaders, who had a perfect right to remove the fence which enclosed their property. The prisoners were accordingly released and were not again molested. The second foreman of the ranch was subsequently arrested for tearing down the houses of the settlers, tried at Broken Bow, found guilty, fined $25 and costs and confined one day in the county jail.

1. Who was legally right in this incident, the cattlemen or the homesteaders? _____

2. What steps did they take that were the legally correct procedure for dealing with the situation?

_____

_____

_____

3. What did they *not* do that they should have done? _____

_____

_____

_____

_____

4. Did the cattlemen have a legitimate argument against the homesteaders' demands to remove the fences? If so, what? _____

_____

_____

_____

5. Imagine that you are the chairman of a government committee assigned the task of developing an agreement that would protect the rights of both the cattlemen and the homesteaders and that would be acceptable to both sides. What would be the ingredients of your plan? _____

_____

_____

_____

_____

_____

_____

The Death of Billy the Kid, 1881

Pat Garrett published the following account one year after he killed Billy the Kid. Read the selection and then answer the questions that follow.

. . . [W]e found a man in camp and stopped. . . . We unsaddled here, got some coffee, and, on foot, entered an orchard which runs from this point down to a row of old buildings, some of them occupied by Mexicans, not more than sixty yards from Maxwell's house. We approached these houses cautiously, and when within earshot, heard the sound of voices conversing in Spanish. We concealed ourselves quickly and listened; but the distance was too great to hear words, or even distinguish voices. Soon a man arose from the ground, in full view, but too far away to recognize. He wore a broad-brimmed hat, a dark vest and pants, and was in his shirtsleeves. With a few words, which fell like a murmur on our ears, he went to the fence, jumped it, and walked down towards Maxwell's house. Little as we then suspected it, this man was the Kid. We learned, subsequently, that, when he left his companions that night, he went to the house of a Mexican friend, pulled off his hat and boots, threw himself on a bed, and commenced reading a newspaper. He soon, however, hailed his friend, who was sleeping in the room, told him to get up and make some coffee, adding: "Give me a butcher knife and I will go over to Pete's and get some beef; I'm hungry." The Mexican arose, handed him the knife, and the Kid, hatless and in his stocking feet, started to Maxwell's which was but a few steps distant.

When the Kid, by me unrecognized, left the orchard, I motioned to my companions, and we cautiously retreated a short distance, and, to avoid the persons whom we had heard at the houses, took another route, approaching Maxwell's house from the opposite direction. When we reached the porch in front of the building, I left Poe and McKinney at the end of the porch, about twenty feet from the door of Pete's room, and went in. It was near midnight and Pete was in bed. I walked to the head of the bed and sat down on it, beside him, near the pillow. I asked him as to the whereabouts of the Kid. He said that the Kid had certainly been about, but he did not know whether he had left or not. At that moment a man sprang quickly into the door, looking back, and called twice in Spanish, "Who comes there?" No one replied and he came on in. He was bareheaded. From his step I could perceive he was either barefooted or in his stocking-feet, and held a revolver in his right hand and a butcher knife in his left.

He came directly towards me. Before he reached the bed, I whispered, "Who is it, Pete?" but received no reply for a moment. It struck me that it might be Pete's brother-in-law, Manuel Abreu, who had seen Poe and McKinney, and wanted to know their business. The intruder came close to me, leaned both hands on the bed, his right hand almost touching my knee, and asked, in a low tone: "Who are they, Pete?" At the same instant Maxwell whispered, "That's him!" Simultaneously, the Kid must have seen, or felt, the presence of a third person at the head of the bed. He raised quickly his pistol, a self-cocker, within a foot of my breast. Retreating rapidly across the room he cried: "Quien es? Quien es?" ("Who's that? Who's that?") All this occurred in a moment. Quickly as possible I drew my revolver and fired, threw my body aside, and fired again. The second shot was useless; the Kid fell dead. He never spoke. A struggle or two, a little strangling sound as he gasped for breath, and the Kid was with his many victims.

1. Where do you think William Bonney got the nickname Billy the Kid? _____

_____

_____

_____

2. Why do you think Garrett was slow in pursuing Bonney? _____

_____

_____

_____

3. Why did Garrett throw himself aside after he fired the first shot? _____

_____

_____

_____

4. Find a Bible reference that says in effect that those who live by violent means will die violent deaths, just as Bonney did. _____

_____

_____

5. List other criminals who lived a life of violence and ended up dying violent deaths. _____

_____

_____

_____

_____

Massacre at Wounded Knee, 1890

By 1890, the Sioux Indian nation was in desperate straits. The buffalo were gone, the Sioux were confined to reservations, and they were dependent on the U.S. Army and Indian agents of the U.S. government. Many of them began listening to the voice of a Paiute Indian named Wovoka, who said that a day was coming when the dead would join the living in a land where game was plentiful and Indians could live as they had before the white men came. They could bring the event about faster by dancing the Ghost Dance. The dancers wore brightly colored and decorated clothing that, according to Wovoka, made them immune to the soldiers' bullets. The Ghost Dance spread among the various Indian tribes, revitalizing the Indians to resist the white men and spreading fear among whites. Troop "K" of the U.S. Army, comprising about 500 soldiers, intercepted a band of Sioux (including both warriors and women and children) led by an Indian named Big Foot on December 28, 1890, and brought them to Wounded Knee to negotiate with them. Philip Wells, a mixed-race Sioux who was an interpreter for the Army, wrote the following account of what happened next. Read the account and then answer the questions that follow.

I was interpreting for [Colonel] Forsyth just before the battle of Wounded Knee, December 29, 1890. The captured Indians had been ordered to give up their arms, but Big Foot replied that his people had no arms. Forsyth said to me, "Tell Big Foot he says the Indians have no arms, yet yesterday they were well armed when they surrendered. He is deceiving me. Tell him he need have no fear in giving up his arms, as I wish to treat him kindly." Big Foot replied, "They have no guns, except such as you have found." Forsyth declared, "You are lying to me in return for my kindness."

During this time a medicine man, gaudily dressed and fantastically painted, executed the maneuvers of the ghost dance, raising and throwing dust into the air. He exclaimed, "Ha! Ha!" as he did so, meaning he was about to do something terrible, and said, "I have lived long enough," meaning he would fight until he died. Turning to the young warriors who were squatted together, he said, "Do not fear, but let your hearts be strong. Many soldiers are about us and have many bullets, but I am assured their bullets cannot penetrate us. The prairie is large, and their bullets will fly over the prairies and will not come toward us. If they do come toward us, they will float away like dust in the air." I turned to Major Whitside and said, "That man is making mischief," and repeated what he had said. Whitside replied, "Go direct to Colonel Forsyth and tell him about it," which I did.

Forsyth and I went to the circle of warriors where he told me to tell the medicine man to sit down and keep quiet, but he paid no attention to the order. Forsyth repeated the order. Big Foot's brother-in-law answered, "He will sit down when he gets around the circle." When the medicine man came to the end of the circle, he squatted down. A cavalry sergeant exclaimed, "There goes an Indian with a gun under his blanket!" Forsyth ordered him to take the gun from the Indian, which he did. Whitside then said to me, "Tell the Indians it is necessary that they be searched one at a time." The young warriors paid no attention to what I told them. I heard someone on my left exclaim, "Look out! Look out!" I saw five or six young warriors cast off their blankets and pull guns out from under them and brandish them in the air. One of the warriors shot into the soldiers, who were ordered to fire into the Indians. I looked in the direction of the medicine man. He or some other medicine man approached to within three or four feet of me with a long cheese knife, ground to a sharp point and raised to stab me. He stabbed me during the melee and nearly cut off my nose. I held him off until I could swing my rifle to hit him, which I did. I shot and killed him in self-defense.

Troop "K" was drawn up between the tents of the women and children and the main body of the Indians, who had been summoned to deliver their arms. The Indians began firing into Troop "K" to gain the canyon of Wounded Knee creek. In doing so they exposed their women and children to their own fire. Captain Wallace was killed at this time while standing in front of his troops. A bullet, striking him in the forehead, plowed away the top of his head. I started to pull off my nose, which was hung by the skin, but Lieutenant Guy Preston shouted, . . . "Don't do that! That can be saved!" He then led me away from the scene of the trouble.

The initial shooting prompted a general firefight. Indians ran to retrieve their discarded rifles. Soldiers fired repeatedly into the Sioux camp. The soldiers fired grapeshot into the Indians' teepees with their Hotchkiss guns (rapid-firing artillery that used a 3.2-inch shell). When the firing was over, about three hundred Sioux lay dead, as did twenty-five soldiers.

1. What role did Wells play in the drama at Wounded Knee? _____

_____

_____

2. What about the Ghost Dance tended to reinvigorate and animate the warriors against the soldiers?

_____

_____

3. Several accounts of the incident at Wounded Knee reported that many of the Indians killed were cut down by "friendly fire." Why might this have been true? _____

_____

_____

_____

4. Why did the massacre at Wounded Knee later become a focal point of the twentieth-century American Indian Movement? _____

_____

_____

_____

5. Write a short essay tracing the mistreatment of Indians in this country and proposing what might have been done to avoid many of the abuses that occurred. _____

_____

_____

_____

_____

_____

_____

_____

Chapter Review

Answer each of the following questions as a general review for this chapter.

1. For thirty years, what mining area yielded more than $400 million worth of gold and silver, becoming the nation's richest source of those two metals? _____

2. What was the name of the world's richest single gold mine? _____

3. What significance does the ratio 16:1 have in relation to the Bland-Allison Act?

_____

_____

_____

4. What kind of cattle did the cattlemen of Texas raise? _____

5. Of the several cattle trails from Texas to northern railhead cities, which was the busiest? _____

6. Who ultimately had the responsibility of getting a herd of cattle to market safely? _____

7. Which trail hand generally was paid the least and was in charge of all of the horses and riding equipment?

_____

8. Which two men boosted the profits and prolonged the life of the cattle industry by developing meat processing plants? _____

9. What did one of those men invent that allowed the transportation of fresh meat to distant eastern cities and further increased the profitability of the cattle industry? _____

10. It was said that meatpackers used every part of the pig except what? _____

11. What animal began to encroach on the cattlemen's lands late in the nineteenth century? _____

12. What act in 1862 had opened western lands for free settlement, granting 160 acres to anyone who would live on and improve it for at least five years? _____

13. What name was applied to homesteaders who "jumped the gun" at the beginning of the Oklahoma Land Rush? _____

14. Of what material did the homesteaders on the plains have to make their houses? _____

15. What did James Glidden invent that revolutionized the settlement of the West? _____

16. Which outlaw killed a sheriff, a deputy, and two prison guards before being chased down and killed by Sheriff Pat Garrett? _____

17. One member of which outlaw band forsook his life of crime, became a successful businessman, and was outspoken in his condemnation of lawlessness? _____

18. Which unpopular lawman participated in a shootout with outlaws at the O.K. Corral in Tombstone, Arizona? _____

19. Which former gambler and sheriff of Tombstone was appointed a deputy U.S. marshal by Theodore Roosevelt? _____

20. Which organization established the first Rogues Gallery for identifying known outlaws?

_____

21. What Indian ritual stirred fear in whites and led indirectly to the last of the Indian battles?

_____

22. On what animal of the American West did the nomadic Indians depend? _____

23. What term is used to refer to tracts of land that were set aside for Indians? _____

24. What U.S. officer lost his army and his life at the Battle of Little Big Horn? _____

25. Name one of the Sioux chiefs who fought at the Battle of Little Big Horn. _____

26. What Nez Perce chief tried to lead his people to Canada but was captured? _____

27. What term describes Indians who were placed under federal protection and support? _____

28. Which act in 1887 tried to assimilate the Indians into mainstream America? _____

29. Which Sioux chief and medicine man inspired the attack at Little Big Horn? _____

30. Where did the last major confrontation between the Indians and U.S. soldiers occur?

_____

Match each statement with the person who would have said it.

    A. miner   B. cowboy   C. homesteader   D. Indian

_____ 31. I wish I could find my own Comstock Lode!

_____ 32. The U.S. Cavalry attacked our camp yesterday, killing many of my brothers.

_____ 33. I just bought a hundred-pound roll of Glidden's miracle "yarn."

_____ 34. Many of my friends have been going to the Ghost Dance.

_____ 35. My next stop will probably be the Black Hills of South Dakota.

_____ 36. We spent a rowdy night in Abilene after our trip was over!

_____ 37. My trail boss is the best in the business.

_____ 38. In my opinion, our sod house is no better than a hole in the ground.

_____ 39. Everyone is joining the Grange, which promises us a better life.

_____ 40. "Pike's Peak or bust!" is my dream.

"The White Man's Burden"

Rudyard Kipling became known as the poet of British imperialism after he penned the following poem. This and many of his other works were about or had their setting in colonies of Great Britain. "The White Man's Burden" was published in *McClure's Magazine* in 1899, days before the Spanish-American War ended. Kipling considered the poem his personal advice to the United States to help the people of the Philippines develop individually, politically, and economically. It also provides a warning of what Americans were getting into by becoming an imperialist power. Read the poem carefully, looking especially for both the responsibilities of colonial powers and the problems an imperialist power should expect. Then answer the questions that follow.

Take up the White Man's burden—
Send forth the best ye breed—
Go bind your sons to exile
To serve your captives' need;
To wait in heavy harness,
On fluttered folk and wild—
Your new-caught, sullen peoples,
Half-devil and half-child.

Take up the White Man's burden—
In patience to abide,
To veil the threat of terror
And check the show of pride;
By open speech and simple,
An hundred times made plain
To seek another's profit,
And work another's gain.

Take up the White Man's burden—
The savage wars of peace—
Fill full the mouth of Famine
And bid the sickness cease;
And when your goal is nearest
The end for others sought,
Watch sloth and heathen Folly
Bring all your hopes to nought.

Take up the White Man's burden—
No tawdry rule of kings,
But toil of serf and sweeper—
The tale of common things.
The ports ye shall not enter,
The roads ye shall not tread,
Go mark them with your living,
And mark them with your dead.

Take up the White Man's burden—
And reap his old reward:
The blame of those ye better,
The hate of those ye guard—
The cry of hosts ye humour
(Ah, slowly!) toward the light:—
"Why brought he us from bondage,
Our loved Egyptian night?"

Take up the White Man's burden—
Ye dare not stoop to less—
Nor call too loud on Freedom
To cloke your weariness;
By all ye cry or whisper,
By all ye leave or do,
The silent, sullen peoples
Shall weigh your gods and you.

Take up the White Man's burden—
Have done with childish days—
The lightly proferred laurel,
The easy, ungrudged praise.
Comes now, to search your manhood
Through all the thankless years
Cold, edged with dear-bought wisdom,
The judgment of your peers!

1. List phrases from Kipling's poem that show the responsibilities of imperialist powers to their colonial subjects. _____

_____

2. List phrases or terms that can be interpreted as warnings of problems imperialist powers should expect.

_____

_____

_____

3. List any phrases or terms that might be interpreted as being condescending to colonial peoples.

_____

_____

_____

4. From your reading of the poem, do you think Kipling was more a supporter or a critic of imperialism? Why? _____

_____

_____

_____

_____

_____

_____

American Imperialism

For each foreign territory, give the nature of America's involvement (financial, diplomatic, or military), the president involved, and a major consequence of America's involvement (either a benefit or a problem).

Territory	Date	U.S. Involvement	President	Consequence
Early Gains				
Alaska	1867		Johnson	
Hawaii	1898			
Spanish-American War				
Cuba	1898			
Puerto Rico	1898			
Philippines	1898			
Latin America				
Venezuela	1902			
Panama	1903			
Asia				
China	1899, 1900			
Japan	1853, 1905		Fillmore, Roosevelt	

Name _____

Sensationalism, Jingoism, and Impartiality

After the Spanish-American War in 1898, Joseph Pulitzer encouraged impartiality in his paper and tried to avoid sensationalism and jingoism. Read the definitions of each of those terms. Then read each statement that follows and decide whether it shows *sensationalism*, *jingoism*, or *impartiality*.

Impartiality—"not favoring one side of an issue."
Sensationalism—"the use of exaggeration or shocking details to arouse curiosity."
Jingoism—"extreme nationalism; loud support for aggressive action toward other countries."

_____ 1. The Cubans have rebelled because they believe their Spanish rulers have mistreated them.

_____ 2. The Spanish devils have painted the town squares red with the blood of Cubans fighting for freedom.

_____ 3. American honor demands swift action against Spain because de Lôme dared to insult our president.

_____ 4. Clara Barton was one of the many nurses who rushed to the Havana harbor to care for the wounded American sailors.

_____ 5. The American army in Cuba has been almost wiped out by the dreaded yellow fever. Everywhere you look you can see dead bodies and feverish soldiers waiting to die.

_____ 6. Unless Congress ratifies the Treaty of Paris and takes its share of new territories, America is doomed to become a second-rate nation.

_____ 7. Dr. Walter Reed has proved that mosquitoes carry the deadly yellow fever.

_____ 8. If pip-squeak Colombia thinks it can blackmail America for $25 million, we'll show them who calls the shots around here!

_____ 9. The day before Panama declared its independence, American warships moved into position off the coast.

_____ 10. Before Gorgas went to work clearing the swamps, the rats were so thick that you couldn't take a step without touching one, and the mosquitoes were so thick they blocked the sun.

The United States Declares War on Spain, 1898

H. H. Kohlsaat, editor of the *Chicago Times-Herald*, was summoned to the White House in 1898 when President William McKinley was considering the prospect of going to war with Spain. Read Kohlsaat's account of the meeting carefully. Then answer the questions.

There was a piano recital in the Blue Room of the White House. Mrs. McKinley was seated near the pianist, looking very frail and ill. The President was in the center of the room on an S-shaped settee. There were eighteen or twenty guests present. As I stood in the doorway someone said: "The President is trying to catch your eye." He motioned me to sit by him, and whispered: "As soon as she is through this piece go and speak to Mrs. McKinley and then go to the Red Room door. I will join you." I did as requested, and when he had shaken hands with some of the late arrivals we went into the Red Room. We sat on a large crimson-brocade lounge. McKinley rested his head on his hands, with elbows on knees. He was in much distress, and said: "I have been through a trying period. Mrs. McKinley has been in poorer health than usual. It seems to me I have not slept over three hours a night for over two weeks. Congress is trying to drive us into war with Spain. The Spanish fleet is in Cuban waters, and we haven't enough ammunition on the Atlantic seacoast to fire a salute."

He broke down and cried like a boy of thirteen. I put my hand on his shoulder and remained silent, as I thought the tension would be relieved by his tears. As he became calm, I tried to assure him that the country would back him in any course he should pursue. He finally said:

"Are my eyes very red? Do they look as if I had been crying?"

"Yes."

"But I must return to Mrs. McKinley at once. She is among strangers."

"When you open the door to enter the room, blow your nose very hard and loud. It will force tears into your eyes and they will think that is what makes your eyes red." He acted on this suggestion and it was no small blast.

After the musicale the President and I went into the old cabinet room and talked until very late.

A few days afterward Congress voted to put $50,000,000 in McKinley's hands— with no string on it. War was declared April 21, 1898.

Ten days later, May 1, 1898, the battle of Manila was fought. I visited the President a few days after the victory. McKinley said: "When we received the cable from Admiral Dewey telling of the taking of the Philippines I looked up their location on the globe. I could not have told where [the] islands were within 2,000 miles!" Some months later he said: "If old Dewey had just sailed away when he smashed that Spanish fleet, what a lot of trouble he would have saved us."

1. Why do you think that McKinley confided in Kohlsaat? _____

_____

_____

_____

2. Why did McKinley have Kohlsaat speak to Mrs. McKinley and then go to the Red Room?

_____

_____

_____

3. What did McKinley say to Kohlsaat that indicates that McKinley was experiencing inner turmoil over how to handle the situation in Cuba? What other situation prevented his having peace?

_____

_____

_____

4. What group did McKinley believe was behind the move toward war? _____

5. McKinley was concerned that people not know that he had been crying when he returned to the guests. What would you think of the current president if he appeared in public showing signs that he had been crying? _____

_____

_____

_____

_____

_____

_____

The Panama Canal

Refer to the feature box titled "The Panama Canal" in your textbook to answer the following questions.

1. Who led the first attempt to create a canal through Central America to connect the Atlantic and Pacific Oceans, and what country was he from? _____

2. What other great engineering wonder had that person supervised elsewhere in the world? _____
_____

3. What problems led to the unsuccessful conclusion of that first attempt to build a Central American canal?
_____
_____
_____

4. What two factors convinced the U.S. government to approve construction of a canal through Panama rather than the initially preferred Nicaragua? _____
_____
_____
_____

5. What did President Roosevelt establish as the top priority in the construction of the Panama Canal?
_____
_____

6. Whom did Roosevelt name to deal with that priority, and what steps did he take to address it?
_____
_____
_____
_____

7. Who was named to be the chief engineer for the canal construction project, and who recommended him for that position? _____
_____

8. What did President Roosevelt do to calm public fears about the Panama Canal project?

_____

_____

_____

_____

9. Why do you think the Panama Canal was so important to the United States? _____

_____

_____

_____

_____

_____

10. In 2000, the United States turned the canal over to Panama, which contracted its operation to China. Do you think that was a good or a bad decision? _____

_____

_____

_____

_____

_____

_____

Chapter Review
Five W Journalism

Good journalists try to uncover news details and file stories that answer five questions (the Five Ws): Who? What? Where? When? Why? Using the information from this chapter, provide the missing information for each of the following events or issues. (The first one has been done for you.)

Imperialism

Who? _____

What? _____

Where? _____

_____

When? _____

Why? _____

_____

_____

_____

Sinking of the U.S.S. *Maine*

Who? _____

What? _____

_____

Where? _____

When? _____

Why? _____

_____

_____

The United States Goes to War

Who? _____

What? _____

Where? _____

When? _____

Why? _____

_____

_____

Matching

Match the following people with the things for which they are noted in this chapter.

_____ 1. Secretary of state who wanted his Christianity to influence foreign policy

_____ 2. Foreign policy was "dollar diplomacy"

_____ 3. Leader of Philippine resistance to Spanish rule

_____ 4. Foreign policy was "Speak softly and carry a big stick"

_____ 5. Negotiated treaty with Panama for building of canal

_____ 6. Newspaperman; sensationalized events to sell more papers

_____ 7. In charge of U.S. Navy when it defeated Spanish navy in Manila Bay

_____ 8. Solved problems of malaria and yellow fever in Cuba

_____ 9. President during Spanish-American War

_____ 10. Evangelist; encouraged Student Volunteer Movement

A. Emilio Aguinaldo
B. William Jennings Bryan
C. Commodore Dewey
D. John Hay
E. William Randolph Hearst
F. William McKinley
G. Dwight L. Moody
H. Walter Reed
I. Theodore Roosevelt
J. William Howard Taft

Changing American Life at the Turn of the Century

For each of the following characteristics of American life, write down what you think is the best example of the changes that were occurring at the turn of the century.

People

1. population

_____

_____

2. urbanization

_____

_____

Opportunities

3. secondary schools

_____

_____

4. higher education

_____

_____

5. middle class

_____

_____

Leisure

6. working conditions

_____

_____

7. spectator sports

_____

_____

8. literature

_____

_____

Values (The answers to these items will be found in section 2.)

9. religious groups and organizations

_____

_____

10. religious liberalism

_____

_____

11. humanitarianism

_____

_____

12. Using an outside source, identify and label on the following map the states that were added to the Union between 1889 and 1912 and give the date when each was added.

Booker T. Washington
A. *Up from Slavery*

Read the following excerpt from Booker T. Washington's autobiography, *Up from Slavery* (Chapter 3, "The Struggle for an Education" and Chapter 8, "Teaching School in a Stable and a Hen-House"). As you read, try to identify Washington's central message to the young people of his day and how you can apply it to your future. Then answer the questions that follow.

As soon as possible after reaching the grounds of the Hampton Institute, I presented myself before the head teacher for an assignment to a class. Having been so long without proper food, a bath, and a change of clothing, I did not, of course, make a very favorable impression upon her, and I could see at once that there were doubts in her mind about the wisdom of admitting me as a student. I felt that I could hardly blame her if she got the idea that I was a worthless loafer or tramp. For some time she did not refuse to admit me, neither did she decide in my favor, and I continued to linger about her, and to impress her in all the ways I could with my worthiness. In the meantime, I saw her admitting other students, and that added greatly to my discomfort, for I felt, deep down in my heart, that I could do as well as they, if I could only get a chance to show what was in me.

After some hours had passed, the head teacher said to me: "The adjoining recitation-room needs sweeping. Take the broom and sweep it."

It occurred to me at once that here was my chance. Never did I receive an order with more delight. I knew that I could sweep, for Mrs. Ruffner had thoroughly taught me how to do that when I lived with her.

I swept the recitation-room three times. Then I got a dusting-cloth and dusted it four times. All the woodwork around the walls, every bench, table, and desk, I went over four times with my dusting-cloth. Besides, every piece of furniture had been moved and every closet and corner in the room had been thoroughly cleaned. I had the feeling that in a large measure my future depended upon the impression I made upon the teacher in the cleaning of that room. When I was through, I reported to the head teacher. She was a "Yankee" woman who knew just where to look for dirt. She went into the room and inspected the floor and closets; then she took her handkerchief and rubbed it on the woodwork about the walls, and over the table and benches. When she was unable to find one bit of dirt on the floor, or a particle of dust on any of the furniture, she quietly remarked, "I guess you will do to enter this institution."

I was one of the happiest souls on Earth. The sweeping of that room was my college examination, and never did any youth pass an examination for entrance into Harvard or Yale that gave him more genuine satisfaction. I have passed several examinations since then, but I have always felt that this was the best one I ever passed.

I have spoken of my own experience in entering the Hampton Institute. Perhaps few, if any, had anything like the same experience that I had, but about the same period there were hundreds who found their way to Hampton and other institutions after experiencing something of the same difficulties that I went through. The young men and women were determined to secure an education at any cost.

The sweeping of the recitation-room in the manner that I did it seems to have paved the way for me to get through Hampton. Miss Mary F. Mackie, the head teacher, offered me a position as janitor. This, of course, I gladly accepted, because it was a place where I could work out nearly all the cost of my board. The work was hard and taxing but I stuck to it. I had a large number of rooms to care for, and had to work late into the night, while at the same time I had to rise by four o' clock in the morning, in order to build the fires and have a little time in which to prepare my lessons. In all my career at Hampton, and ever since I have been out in the world, Miss Mary F. Mackie, the head teacher to whom I have referred, proved one of my strongest and most helpful friends. Her advice and encouragement were always helpful in strengthening to me in the darkest hour.

The next excerpt relates Washington's memories of his founding and opening of Tuskegee Institute.

The work to be done in order to lift [my] people up seemed almost beyond accomplishing. I was only one person, and it seemed to me that the little effort which I could put forth could go such a short distance toward bringing about results. I wondered if I could accomplish anything, and if it were worth while for me to try.

✪✪✪

After consultation with the citizens of Tuskegee, I set July 4, 1881, as the day for the opening of the school in the little shanty and church which had been secured for its accommodation. The white people, as well as the colored, were greatly interested in the starting of the new school, and the opening day was looked forward to with much earnest discussion. There were not a few white people in the vicinity of Tuskegee who looked with some disfavor upon the project. They questioned its value to the colored people, and had a fear that it might result in bringing about trouble between the races. . . .

The white people who questioned the wisdom of starting this new school had in their minds pictures of what was called an educated Negro, with a high hat, imitation gold eye-glasses, a showy walking-stick, kid gloves, fancy boots, and what not—in a word, a man who was determined to live by his wits. It was difficult for these people to see how education would produce any other kind of a colored man.

In the midst of all the difficulties that I encountered in getting the little school started, and since then through a period of nineteen years, there are two men among all the many friends of the school in Tuskegee upon whom I have depended constantly for advice and guidance; and the success of the undertaking is largely due to these men, from whom I have never sought anything in vain. I mention them simply as types. One is a white man and an ex-slaveholder, Mr. George W. Campbell; the other is a black man and an ex-slave, Mr. Lewis Adams. . . . Mr. Campbell is a merchant and banker, and had had little experience in dealing with matters pertaining to education. Mr. Adams was a mechanic, and had learned the trades of shoemaking, harness-making, and tinsmithing during the days of slavery. He had never been to school a day in his life, but in some way he had learned to read and write while a slave. From the first, these two men saw clearly what my plan of education was, sympathized with me, and supported me in every effort. . . .

✪✪✪

On the morning that the school opened, thirty students reported for admission. I was the only teacher. The students were about equally divided between the sexes. Most of them lived in Macon County, the county in which Tuskegee is situated. . . . A great many more students wanted to enter the school, but it had been decided to receive only those who were above fifteen years of age, and who had previously received some education. The greater part of the thirty were public-school teachers, and some of them were nearly forty years of age. With the teachers came some of their former pupils, and when they were examined it was amusing to note that in several cases the pupil entered a higher class than did his former teacher. . . .

✪✪✪

. . . I have never seen a more earnest and willing company of young men and women than these students were. They were all willing to learn the right thing as soon as it was shown them what was right. I was determined to start them off on a solid and thorough foundation. . . .

✪✪✪

The number of pupils increased each week, until by the end of the first month there were nearly fifty. Many of them, however, said that, as they could remain only for two or three months, they wanted to enter a high class and get a diploma the first year if possible.

✪✪✪

. . . We learned that about eighty-five per cent of the colored people in the Gulf states depended upon agriculture for their living. Since this was true, we wanted to be careful not to educate our students out of sympathy with agricultural life, so that they would be attracted from the country to the cities, and yield to the temptation of trying to live by their wits. We wanted to give them such an education as would fit a large proportion of them to be teachers, and at the same time cause them to return to the plantation districts and show the people there how to put new energy and new ideas into farming, as well as into the intellectual and moral and religious life of the people.

✪✪✪

The more we talked with the students, who were then coming to us from several parts of the state, the more we found that the chief ambition among a large proportion of them was to get an education so that they would not have to work any longer with their hands. This is illustrated by a story told of a colored man in Alabama, who, one hot day in July, while he was at work in a cotton-field, suddenly stopped, and, looking toward the skies, said: "O Lawd, de cottom am so grassy, de work am so hard, and de sun am so hot dat I b'lieve dis darky am called to preach!"

1. Why did Washington not think he made a very good first impression on the head teacher?

_____

2. What did he think she might be thinking of him? _____

3. What in Washington's account shows that he was a patient person even at that young age?

_____

_____

4. What task did the head teacher finally give him that proved to be his entrance examination?

_____

5. What about the way Washington fulfilled that assignment convinced the head teacher that she should

admit him as a student? _____

_____

_____

6. What attitude did Washington say had allowed hundreds of other young men and women like himself to

gain entrance to Hampton Institute? _____

_____

7. What did Washington say made some white people fear the education of blacks?

_____

8. From what two men did Washington say he received his greatest help in starting Tuskegee Institute?

_____

_____

_____

9. What did Washington find amusing about the first student body admitted to Tuskegee?

_____

_____

10. From this brief excerpt, what do you think was Washington's goal for Tuskegee Institute?

_____

_____

B. "Cast Down Your Bucket Where You Are"

In September 1895, Atlanta hosted the third Cotton States and International Exposition. The goals of the expo were (1) to foster trade for the South and (2) to show the latest products, technology, and facilities of the South to the rest of the nation and the world. In effect, it was all designed to promote the "New South." The expo also featured exhibits showing the accomplishments of women and blacks. Booker T. Washington was invited to be one of the opening day speakers. Read the following excerpts from his speech, and then answer the questions.

Mr. President and Gentlemen of the Board of Directors and Citizens:

One-third of the population of the South is of the Negro race. No enterprise seeking the material, civil, or moral welfare of this section can disregard this element of our population and reach the highest success. I but convey to you, Mr. President and Directors, the sentiment of the masses of my race when I say that in no way have the value and manhood of the American Negro been more fittingly and generously recognized than by the managers of this magnificent Exposition at every stage of its progress. It is a recognition that will do more to cement the friendship of the two races than any occurrence since the dawn of our freedom. Not only this, but the opportunity here afforded will awaken among us a new era of industrial progress. Ignorant and inexperienced, it is not strange that in the first years of our new life we began at the top instead of at the bottom; that a seat in Congress or the state legislature was more sought than real estate or industrial skill; that the political convention or stump speaking had more attractions than starting a dairy farm or truck garden.

A ship lost at sea for many days suddenly sighted a friendly vessel. From the mast of the unfortunate vessel was seen a signal, "Water, water; we die of thirst!" The answer from the friendly vessel at once came back, "Cast down your bucket where you are." A second time the signal, "Water, water; send us water!" ran up from the distressed vessel, and was answered, "Cast down your bucket where you are." And a third and fourth signal for water was answered, "Cast down your bucket where you are." The captain of the distressed vessel, at last heeding the injunction, cast down his bucket, and it came up full of fresh, sparkling water from the mouth of the Amazon River.

To those of my race who depend on bettering their condition in a foreign land or who underestimate the importance of cultivating friendly relations with the Southern white man, who is their next-door neighbor, I would say: "Cast down your bucket where you are"—cast it down in making friends in every manly way of the people of all races by whom we are surrounded.

Cast it down in agriculture, mechanics, in commerce, in domestic service, and in the professions. And in this connection it is well to bear in mind that whatever other sins the South may be called to bear, when it comes to business, pure and simple, it is in the South that the Negro is given a man's chance in the commercial world, and in nothing is this Exposition more eloquent than in emphasizing this chance. Our greatest danger is that in the great leap from slavery to freedom we may overlook the fact that the masses of us are to live by the productions of our hands, and fail to keep in mind that we shall prosper in proportion as we learn to dignify and glorify common labor, and put brains and skill into the common occupations of life; shall prosper in proportion as we learn to draw the line between the superficial and the substantial, the ornamental gewgaws [gyoo gaws; trinkets] of life and the useful. No race can prosper till it learns that there is as much dignity in tilling a field as in writing a poem. It is at the bottom of life we must begin, and not at the top. Nor should we permit our grievances to overshadow our opportunities.

To those of the white race who look to the incoming of those of foreign birth and strange tongue and habits for the prosperity of the South, were I permitted I would repeat what I say to my own race. "Cast down your bucket where you are." Cast it down among the eight millions of Negroes whose habits you know, whose fidelity and love you have tested in days when to have proved treacherous meant the ruin of your firesides. Cast down your bucket among these people who have, without strikes and labor wars, tilled your fields, cleared your forests, builded your railroads and cities, and brought forth treasures from the bowels of the earth, and helped make possible this magnificent representation of the progress of the South. Casting down your bucket among my people, helping and encouraging them as you are doing on these grounds, and to education of head, hand, and heart, you will find that they will buy your surplus land, make blossom the waste places in your fields, and run your factories. While doing this, you can be sure in the future, as in the past, that you and your families will be surrounded by the most patient, faithful, law-abiding, and unresentful people that the world has seen. As we have proved our loyalty to you in the past, in nursing your children, watching by the sick-bed of your mothers and fathers, and often following them with tear-dimmed eyes to their graves, so in the future, in our humble way, we shall stand by you with a devotion that no foreigner can approach, ready to lay down our lives, if need be, in defense of yours, interlacing our industrial, commercial, civil, and religious life with yours in a way that shall make the interests of both races one. In all things that are purely social, we can be as separate as the fingers, yet one as the hand in all things essential to mutual progress.

There is no defense or security for any of us except in the highest intelligence and development of all. If anywhere there are efforts tending to curtail the fullest growth of the Negro, let these efforts be turned into stimulating, encouraging, and making him the most useful and intelligent citizen. Effort or means so invested will pay a thousand percent interest. These efforts will be twice blessed—blessing him that gives and him that takes.

✪✪✪

While we take pride in what we exhibit as a result of our independent efforts, we do not for a moment forget that our part in this exhibition would fall far short of your expectations but for the constant help that has come to our educational life, not only from the southern states, but especially from northern philanthropists, who have made their gifts a constant stream of blessing and encouragement. . . .

In conclusion, may I repeat that nothing in thirty years has given us more hope and encouragement, and drawn us so near to you of the white race, as this opportunity offered by the Exposition; and here bending, as it were, over the altar that represents the results of the struggles of your race and mine, both starting practically empty-handed three decades ago, I pledge that in your effort to work out the great and intricate problem which God has laid at the doors of the South, you shall have at all times the patient, sympathetic help of my race; only let this be constantly in mind, that, while from representations in these buildings of the product of field, of forest, of mine, of factory, letters, and art, much good will come, yet far above and beyond material benefits will be that higher good, that, let us pray God, will come, in a blotting out of sectional differences and racial animosities and suspicions, in a determination to administer absolute justice, in a willing obedience among all classes to the mandates of law. This, coupled with our material prosperity, will bring into our beloved South a new heaven and a new earth.

1. What fact did Washington point out early in his speech that underscored the wisdom of the Exposition directors in inviting him to speak to them? _____

_____

2. To what situation of early Reconstruction did Booker T. Washington refer to as an unfortunate thing?

_____

_____

_____

3. Summarize the lesson Washington delivered for *whites* in the phrase "Cast down your bucket where you are" in his illustration. _____

_____

4. Summarize the lesson Washington delivered for *blacks* in that phrase. _____

_____

_____

5. What was the purpose of the Exposition, and how did that purpose fit into the theme of Washington's speech? _____

_____

_____

_____

_____

6. Based on this speech, how would you summarize Washington's philosophy of ensuring positive race relations? _____

_____

_____

_____

7. Why do you think some black leaders vehemently opposed Washington's philosophy?

_____

_____

_____

Billy Sunday Blasts Liquor

One of evangelist Billy Sunday's favorite targets in his preaching was the evils of liquor. Read the following excerpts from one of his most popular sermons (using Matthew 8:30–34 as his text), noting particularly his language and emphases. Then answer the questions that follow.

Here we have one of the strangest scenes in all the Gospels. Two men, possessed of devils, confront Jesus, and while the devils are crying out for Jesus to leave them, he commands the devils to come out, and they obey the command of Jesus. The devils ask permission to enter into a herd of swine feeding on the hillside. This is the only record we have of Jesus ever granting the petition of devils, and he did it for the salvation of men.

Then the fellows that kept the hogs went back to town and told the peanut-brained, weasel-eyed, hog-jowled, beetle-browed, bull-necked lobsters that owned the hogs, that "a long-haired fanatic from Nazareth, named Jesus, has driven the devils out of some men and the devils have gone into the hogs, and the hogs into the sea, and the sea into the hogs, and the whole bunch is dead."

And then the fat, fussy old fellows came out to see Jesus and said that he was hurting their business. A fellow says to me, "I don't think Jesus Christ did a nice thing."

You don't know what you are talking about.

Down in Nashville, Tennessee, I saw four wagons going down the street, and they were loaded with stills, and kettles, and pipes.

"What's this?" I said.

"United States revenue officers, and they have been in the moonshine district and confiscated the illicit stills, and they are taking them down to the government scrap heap."

Jesus Christ was God's revenue officer. Now the Jews were forbidden to eat pork, but Jesus [ruined their business when the devils ran the pigs off the cliff into the sea.] And they told Jesus to leave the country. They said: "You are hurting our business."

✪✪✪

I am a temperance Republican down to my toes. Who is the man that fights the whisky business in the South? It is the Democrats! They have driven the business from Kansas, they have driven it from Georgia, and Maine and Mississippi and North Carolina and North Dakota and Oklahoma and Tennessee and West Virginia. And they have driven it out of 1,756 counties. And it is the rock-ribbed Democratic South that is fighting the saloon. They started this fight that is sweeping like fire over the United States. You might as well try and dam Niagara Falls with toothpicks as to stop the reform wave sweeping our land. . . . It is simply a matter of decency and manhood, irrespective of politics. It is prosperity against poverty, sobriety against drunkenness, honesty against thieving, heaven against hell. Don't you want to see men sober? Brutal, staggering men transformed into respectable citizens? "No," said the saloonkeeper. . . . "We are interested in our business, we have no interest in humanity."

After all is said that can be said upon the liquor traffic, its influence is degrading upon the individual, the family, politics and business, and upon everything that you touch in this old world. For the time has long gone by when there is any ground for arguments as to its ill effects. All are agreed on that point. There is just one prime reason why the saloon has not been knocked [out], and that is the false statement that "the saloons are needed to help lighten the taxes." The saloon business has never paid, and it has cost fifty times more than the revenue derived from it.

I challenge you to show me where the saloon has ever helped business, education, church, morals or anything we hold dear. . . .

Listen! Seventy-five per cent of our idiots come from intemperate parents; eighty per cent of the paupers, eighty-two per cent of the crime is committed by men under the influence of liquor; ninety per cent of the adult criminals are whisky-made. The Chicago *Tribune* kept track for ten years and found that 53,556 murders were committed by men under the influence of liquor.

✪✪✪

I go to a family and it is broken up, and I say, "What caused this?" Drink! I step up to a young man on the scaffold [about to be executed] and say, "What brought you here?" Drink! Whence all the misery and sorrow and corruption? Invariably it is drink. . . .

The saloon is the sum of all villainies. It is worse than war or pestilence. It is the crime of crimes. It is the parent of crimes and the mother of sins. It is the appalling source of misery and crime in the land. And to license such an incarnate fiend of hell is the dirtiest, low-down, damnable business on top of this old earth. There is nothing to be compared to it.

✪✪✪

You say that "people will drink anyway." Not by my vote. You say, "Men will murder their wives anyway." Not by my vote. "They will steal anyway." Not by my vote. You are the sovereign people, and what are you going to do about it?

✪✪✪

In the island of Jamaica the rats increased so that they destroyed the crops, and they introduced a mongoose, which is a species of the coon. They have three breeding seasons a year and there are twelve to fifteen in each brood, and they are deadly enemies of the rats. The result was that the rats disappeared and there was nothing more for the mongoose to feed upon, so they attacked the snakes, and the frogs, and the lizards that fed upon the insects, with the result that the insects increased and they stripped the gardens, eating up the onions and the lettuce and then the mongoose attacked the sheep and the cats, and the puppies, and the calves and the geese. Now Jamaica is spending hundreds of thousands of dollars to get rid of the mongoose.

The American mongoose is the open licensed saloon. It eats the carpets off the floor and the clothes from off your back, your money out of the bank, and it eats up character, and it goes on until at last it leaves a stranded wreck in the home, a skeleton of what was once brightness and happiness.

[A man on a train turned down a drink when it was offered to him, and people laughed.] He said, "You can laugh if you want to, but I was born with an appetite for drink, and for years I have taken from five to ten glasses per day, but I was at home in Chicago not long ago and I have a friend who has a pawn shop there. I was in there when in came a young fellow with ashen cheeks and a wild look on his face. He came up trembling, threw down a little package and said, 'Give me ten cents.' And what do you think was in that package? It was a pair of baby shoes."

"My friend said, 'No, I cannot take them.' But he said, 'Give me a dime. I must have a drink.' 'No, take them back home, your baby will need them.' And the poor fellow said, 'My baby is dead, and I want a drink.'"

Boys, I don't blame you for the lump that comes up in your throat. There is no law, divine or human, that the saloon respects. Lincoln said, "If slavery is not wrong, nothing is wrong." I say, if the saloon, with its train of diseases, crime and misery, is not wrong, then nothing on earth is wrong. If the fight is to be won we need men—

men that will fight. The Church, Catholic and Protestant, must fight it or run away, and thank God she will not run away, but fight to the last ditch.

1. Give examples of Sunday's use of common, unpolished, even colloquial vocabulary to identify with his audiences. _____

_____

_____

_____

2. Of which political party did Sunday say he belonged? _____

3. Which party did he say was fighting alcoholism hardest? _____

4. List some of the problems that Sunday said are caused by alcohol.

_____

_____

5. To what animal did Sunday compare the problem of alcoholism and why?

_____

_____

6. In one illustration in Sunday's sermon, to what lengths did he show a man would go for drink?

_____

_____

7. Could Sunday's arguments be applied to the same problem today? To what other problems might they also be applied? _____

_____

_____

_____

Progressivism

Complete this summary of the Progressive Era using your textbook. Part of the introduction has been done for you. Complete that introductory paragraph and then write three short paragraphs that summarize (1) uncovering corruption, (2) revealing society's ills, and (3) attempting reforms. Be sure to include clear topic sentences. The following terms should appear somewhere in your paragraphs:

"Boss" Tweed	civil service
recall	initiative
referendum	Seventeenth Amendment

    The progressives looked to government for the answers to America's problems. Progressives had three aims:

1. _____

    _____

2. _____

    _____

3. _____

    _____

    _____

    _____

    _____

    _____

    _____

    _____

    _____

    _____

    _____

    _____

    _____

    _____

    _____

Roosevelt's Speech Following Assassination Attempt

On October 14, 1912, just before Theodore Roosevelt entered a Milwaukee auditorium to deliver a campaign speech, he was shot by John Schrank. Despite advisors' pleas that he go to a hospital to be treated, Roosevelt insisted on speaking to the crowd. Rather than his prepared speech, he delivered a shorter extemporaneous speech. Read the following excerpts from that speech. Then answer the questions.

Friends, I shall ask you to be as quiet as possible. I don't know whether you fully understand that I have just been shot; but it takes more than that to kill a Bull Moose. But fortunately I had my manuscript, so you see I was going to make a long speech, and there is a bullet [he held up the folded manuscript]—there is where the bullet went through—and it probably saved me from it going into my heart. The bullet is in me now, so that I cannot make a very long speech, but I will try my best.

And now, friends, I want to take advantage of this incident to say a word of solemn warning to my fellow countrymen. First of all, I want to say this about myself: I have altogether too important things to think of to feel any concern over my own death; and now I cannot speak to you insincerely within five minutes of being shot. I am telling you the literal truth when I say that my concern is for many other things. It is not in the least for my own life. I want you to understand that I am ahead of the game, anyway. No man has had a happier life than I have led; a happier life in every way. I have been able to do certain things that I greatly wished to do, and I am interested in doing other things. I can tell you with absolute truthfulness that I am very much uninterested in whether I am shot or not. It was just as when I was colonel of my regiment. I always felt that a private was to be excused for feeling at times some pangs of anxiety about his personal safety, but I cannot understand a man fit to be a colonel who can pay any heed to his personal safety when he is occupied as he ought to be with the absorbing desire to do his duty.

I am in this cause with my whole heart and soul. I believe that the Progressive movement is making life a little easier for all our people; a movement to try to take the burdens off the men and especially the women and children of this country. I am absorbed in the success of that movement.

Friends, I ask you now this evening to accept what I am saying as absolutely true, when I tell you I am not thinking of my own success. I am not thinking of my life or of anything connected with me personally. I am thinking of the movement. I say this by way of introduction, because I want to say something very serious to our people and especially to the newspapers. I don't know anything about who the man was who shot me tonight. He was seized at once by one of the stenographers in my party, Mr. Martin, and I suppose is now in the hands of the police. He shot to kill. He shot—the shot, the bullet went in here—I will show you [he gestures to his chest].

I am going to ask you to be as quiet as possible for I am not able to give the challenge of the bull moose quite as loudly. Now, I do not know who he was or what party he represented. He was a coward. He stood in the darkness in the crowd around the automobile and when they cheered me, and I got up to bow, he stepped forward and shot me in the darkness.

Now, friends, of course, I do not know, as I say, anything about him; but it is a very natural thing that weak and vicious minds should be inflamed to acts of violence by the kind of awful mendacity and abuse that have been heaped upon me for the last three months by the papers in the interest of not only Mr. Debs [Socialist candidate] but of Mr. Wilson [Democrat] and Mr. Taft [Republican].

Friends, I will disown and repudiate any man of my party who attacks with such foul slander and abuse any opponent of any other party; and now I wish to say seriously to all the daily newspapers, to the Republicans, the Democrat, and Socialist parties, that they cannot, month in, month out and year in and year out, make the kind of untruthful, of bitter assault that they have made and not expect that brutal, violent natures, or brutal and violent characters, especially when the brutality is accompanied by a not very strong mind; they cannot expect that such natures will be unaffected by it.

Now, friends, I am not speaking for myself at all, I give you my word, I do not care a rap about being shot; not a rap.

I have had a good many experiences in my time and this is one of them. What I care for is my country. I wish I were able to impress upon my people—our people, the duty to feel strongly but to speak the truth of their opponents. I say now, I have never said one word on the stump against any opponent that I cannot defend. I have said nothing that I could not substantiate and nothing that I ought not to have said—nothing that I—nothing that, looking back at, I would not say again.

Now, friends, it ought not to be too much to ask that our opponents—[speaking to someone on the stage]—I am not sick at all. I am all right. I cannot tell you of what infinitesimal importance I regard this incident as compared with the great issues at stake in this campaign, and I ask it not for my sake, not the least in the world, but for the sake of common country, that they make up their minds to speak only the truth, and not use that kind of slander and mendacity [untruthfulness] which if taken seriously must incite weak and violent natures to crimes of violence. Don't you make any mistake. Don't you pity me. I am all right. I am all right and you cannot escape listening to the speech either.

And now, friends, this incident that has just occurred—this effort to assassinate me—emphasizes to a peculiar degree the need of the Progressive movement. Friends, every good citizen ought to do everything in his or her power to prevent the coming of the day when we shall see in this country two recognized creeds fighting one another, when we shall see the creed of the "Havenots" arraigned against the creed of the "Haves." When that day comes then such incidents as this tonight will be commonplace in our history. When you make poor men—when you permit the conditions to grow such that the poor man as such will be swayed by his sense of injury against the men who try to hold what they improperly have won, when that day comes, the most awful passions will be let loose and it will be an ill day for our country.

[At this point, a renewed effort was made to persuade Mr. Roosevelt to conclude his speech.]

My friends are a little more nervous than I am. Don't you waste any sympathy on me. I have had an A-1 time in life and I am having it now.

I never in my life was in any movement in which I was able to serve with such wholehearted devotion as in this; in which I was able to feel as I do in this that common weal. I have fought for the good of our common country.

And now, friends, I shall have to cut short much of that speech that I meant to give you, but I want to touch on just two or three points.

[Roosevelt then proceeded to speak twice as long as he had already spoken before concluding.]

I ask you to look at our declaration and hear and read our platform about social and industrial justice and then, friends, vote for the Progressive ticket without regard to me, without regard to my personality, for only by voting for that platform can you be true to the cause of progress throughout this Union.

1. What strikes you most about Roosevelt's speech? _____

_____

_____

2. Why do you think Roosevelt twice asked his audience to be as quiet as possible?

_____

_____

_____

_____

3. Why do you think Roosevelt showed where the bullet hit him and where it went through his speech?

_____

_____

_____

_____

4. What two creeds did TR say the United States was being divided into, and what did he predict would be the consequence unless something was done? _____

_____

_____

5. What did he encourage the listeners to do before they voted? _____

_____

_____

6. What did he tell them *not* to do when they voted? _____

_____

The Progressive Presidents

Using the textbook and outside sources, complete the following chart as you study each of the Progressive presidents.

Category of information	Theodore Roosevelt	William Howard Taft	Woodrow Wilson
Years in office			
Political party			
Previous occupation			
Home			
Religion			
Foreign policy slogan	"big stick" or "gunboat diplomacy"	"dollar diplomacy"	"moral diplomacy"
Domestic policy slogan	"Square Deal"	(no slogan)	"New Freedom"
Approach toward big business			
Major laws/amendments of his term			
Progressive reforms			
Presidential "firsts"			

Find the Message

Beside each of the following phrases, write the person, term, or event that it describes. Then transfer the letters to the appropriate blanks on the next page to reveal what Theodore Roosevelt said about the "New Nationalism." Finally, answer the question that follows that message.

1. George Washington Carver's useful legume

___ ___ ___ ___
39   17   1

2. cult founded by Charles Russell

___ ___ ___ ___ ___ ___ '___
6   10   37

___ ___ ___ ___ ___ ___
   36

3. author of *Origin of Species*

___ ___ ___ ___
   27 22

4. "prohibition" amendment

___ ___ ___ ___ ___ ___
3   12   38   25

5. corrupt New York City "boss"

___ ___ ___ ___
21   7

6. journalist who exposes society's ills

___ ___ ___ ___ ___
18   32   26

7. author of *The Jungle*

___ ___ ___ ___ ___
23   31

8. voters' petition to remove an official from office

___ ___ ___ ___
16   29

9. voters' petition to stop legislation

___ ___ ___ ___ ___ ___ ___
 30   40

10. voters' petition to pass legislation

___ ___ ___ ___ ___ ___ ___
 20 9   15

11. Roosevelt's chief forester

___ ___ ___ ___ ___
42   2 13

12. subject of the Sixteenth Amendment

___ ___ ___ ___ ___
 34 33 24

13. Republican nominee in 1912

   ___ ___ ___ ___
         35

14. Roosevelt's Progressive Party

   ___ ___ ___ ___ ___ ___ ___ ___
    5   **43**   **4**   **44**

15. sponsor of the Anti-Trust Act of 1914

   ___ ___ ___ ___ ___ ___ ___
    8   **41**

16. Wilson's progressive banking system

   ___ ___ ___ ___ ___ ___ ___
   11   **19**

   ___ ___ ___ ___ ___ ___ ___
    28   **14**

17. MESSAGE:

"___ ___ ___ ___ ___ ___ ___ ___ ___ ___ ___
  1   **2**   **3**   **4**   **5**   **6**   **7**   **8**   **9**   **10** **11**

___ ___ ___ ___ ___ ___ ___ ___ ___ ___ ___ ___ ___ ___ ___
12 **13** **14** **15** **16** **17** **18** **19** **20** **21** **22** **23** **24** **25** **26**

___ ___ ___ ___ ___ ___ ___ ___ ___ ___ ___ ___
27 **28** **29** **30** **31** **32** **33** **34** **35** **36** **37** **38**

___ ___ ___ ___ ___ ___"
39 **40** **41** **42** **43** **44**

18. Do you agree with Roosevelt's philosophy of government as expressed by this statement? Why or why not?

_____

_____

_____

_____

_____

_____

_____

Experiences of World War I

Americans' experiences in the Great War differed radically from the Europeans' experiences. As you progress through this chapter, complete the following chart, showing in your answers the major differences between French and American experiences in the war. Some items have been completed for you. (At the end of the chapter, you might want to review this chart in preparation for the test.)

	France	*United States*
Background		
Reasons for war		
Prewar alliances		
Sparks of war		
Year of entry	1914	1917
Preparations		
Preparedness for war	large, powerful military	
Original size of army	4,017,000	200,000
Total forces in Army	8,410,000	400,000
Sources of money	loans from United States	

	France	*United States*
Fighting		
Commanding general		
Results of early battles		
Total years at war		
Total deaths	1,357,800	116,708
Total wounded	4,266,000	204,002
Peace		
Political leader		
Aims for peace		
Benefits from the Treaty of Versailles		
Participation in League of Nations	Major active participant	

The Sinking of the *Lusitania*, 1915

Read the account and answer the questions that follow.

It had been a very successful run. The German submarine *U-20* had entered the Irish Sea on May 5 and now, the morning of May 7, the submarine claimed its third victim. The *U-20* had only three torpedoes left in its arsenal and was low on fuel. As a result, Captain Walter Schwieger, the ship's commander, decided to steer for the open waters of the Atlantic and home. He was unaware that his greatest prize was steaming straight for him and that his actions that day would ultimately bring America into the war.

The *Lusitania* had left New York City on May 1 bound for Liverpool. On the afternoon of May 7 she was steaming off the coast of Ireland within easy sailing distance of her destination. Known as the "Greyhound of the Seas," the *Lusitania* was the fastest liner afloat and relied on her speed to defend against submarine attack. However, she was not running at full speed because of fog. Nor was the ship taking an evasive zigzag course. It was a sitting duck and was headed straight into the sights of the *U-20*.

The two ships converged at about 2 p.m. After stalking his prey for an hour, Captain Schwieger unleashed one torpedo that hit its target amidships. The initial explosion was followed quickly by a second, more powerful, detonation. Within 20 minutes the great liner had slipped under the water, taking 1,198 victims with her. Among the dead were 138 Americans. Many in the United States were outraged. A declaration of war was narrowly averted when Germany vowed to cease its policy of unrestricted submarine warfare. However, American public opinion had turned. When Germany resurrected its unrestricted submarine warfare policy in February of 1917, America decided to go to war.

Captain Schwieger kept a diary of the voyage. We join his story as he first catches sight of the *Lusitania* in the early afternoon of May 7, 1915.

2:00 pm	Straight ahead the 4 funnels and 3 masts of a steamer with a course at right angles to ours. . . . Ship is made out to be a large passenger liner.
3:05 pm	Went to 11m and ran at high speed on a course converging with that of the steamer, in hopes that it would change course to starboard along the Irish Coast. The steamer turned to starboard, headed for Queenstown and thus made it possible to approach for a shot. Ran at high speed till 3 pm in order to secure an advantageous position.

3:10 pm	Clear bow shot at 700 m . . . angle of intersection 90 [degrees] estimated speed 22 nautical miles. Shot struck starboard side close behind the bridge. An extraordinary heavy detonation followed, with a very large cloud of smoke (far above the front funnel). A second explosion must have followed that of the torpedo (boiler or coal or powder?). The superstructure above the point of impact and the bridge were torn apart; fire broke out; light smoke veiled the high bridge. The ship stopped immediately and quickly listed sharply to starboard, sinking deeper by the head at the same time.
3:10 pm	Great confusion arose on the ship; some of the boats were swung clear and lowered into the water. Many people must have lost their heads; several boats loaded with people rushed downward, struck the water bow or stern first and filled at once. On the port side, because of the sloping position, fewer boats were swung clear than on the starboard side. The ship blew off steam; at the bow the name "Lusitania" in golden letters was visible. It was running 20 nautical miles.
3:25 pm	Since it seemed as if the steamer could only remain above water for a short time, went to 24m and ran toward the Sea. Nor could I have fired a second torpedo into this swarm of people who were trying to save themselves.
4:15 pm	Went to 11m and took a look around. In the distance straight ahead a number of life-boats were moving; nothing more was to be seen of the *Lusitania*. The wreck must lie 14 nautical miles from the Old Head of Kinsale light-house, at an angle of 358 degrees to the right of it, in 90m of water (27 nautical miles from Queenstown) 51 degrees 22' 6" N and 8 degrees 31' W. The land and the lighthouse could be seen very plainly.
4:20 pm	When taking a look around, a large steamer was in sight ahead on the port side, with course laid for Fastnet Rock. Tried to get ahead at high speed, so as to get a stern shot. . . .
5:08 pm	Conditions for shot very favorable: no possibility of missing if torpedo kept its course. Torpedo did not strike. Since the telescope was cut off for some time after this shot the cause of failure could not be determined. . . . The steamer or freighter was of the Cunard Line.
6:15 pm	. . . It is remarkable that there is so much traffic on this particular day, although two large steamers were sunk the day before south of George's Channel. It is also inexplicable that the *Lusitania* was not sent through the North Channel.

1. Why was *U-20* in the "right place at the right time" to sink the *Lusitania*?

   _____

   _____

   _____

2. What feature of the *Lusitania* was considered her greatest defense against a submarine attack?

   _____

   _____

3. In relation to that supposed strength, what facts about the sinking are surprising?

_____

_____

4. How quickly did the *Lusitania* sink, and how many victims did it claim? _____

_____

_____

5. How many Americans were killed? _____

6. Why did passengers on the port side of the *Lusitania* have trouble getting into lifeboats and getting them
   lowered before the ship sank? _____

_____

_____

7. How far was the *Lusitania* from land when it sank? _____

8. At what time was the *Lusitania* first struck by the U-boat's torpedo? _____

9. From previous knowledge you might have of the sinking of the *Lusitania* or from an "educated guess," what
   might have been the reason for the "extraordinary detonation" that occurred when the ship was struck by
   the torpedo? _____

_____

_____

_____

10. Was Germany's policy of unrestricted submarine warfare justifiable? Why or why not?

_____

_____

_____

_____

_____

Objectivity and Propaganda

Propaganda is a systematic way of shaping someone's beliefs about something. Although the practice itself can be either good or bad, it is usually associated with bad. In that sense, it is an attempt to manipulate people's beliefs, attitudes, and actions toward a predetermined goal. In contrast, *objectivity* is "an honest effort to avoid appeals to emotion, conjecture, or personal prejudice." Propaganda was used widely by both sides during World War I. For each of the following statements, write whether it is an example of propaganda or objectivity.

_____ 1. The British press reports that Germany has just opened a "corpse factory" that converts human bodies into soap.

_____ 2. Both the Allies and the Central Powers violated America's neutral rights at sea.

_____ 3. The *Lusitania* was twice torpedoed off the Irish coast by a German submarine, and probably one thousand passengers are dead.

_____ 4. In an act of mass murder that would make a cannibal blush, a German sub sank the helpless *Lusitania*, killing all aboard.

_____ 5. Belgian refugees have seen with their own eyes German soldiers cutting off the hands of babies.

_____ 6. Yesterday a German firing squad shot Edith Cavell, an English nurse who had been helping Allied soldiers escape.

_____ 7. Are we neutral when we sell acid for profit and ten thousand German graves bear the legend "Made in America?"

_____ 8. Destroy this mad German brute. Enlist today!

_____ 9. Support the flag of liberty! Buy U.S. war bonds.

_____ 10. The United States has no business in this war. We're being driven into it by greedy capitalists who want to make a profit from the needless deaths of soldiers and innocent civilians.

America Declares War on Germany, 1917

Frank Cobb, editor of the *New York World* and a confidant of President Wilson, visited the president on the eve of his asking Congress for a declaration of war against Germany. Read the following account, and then answer the questions.

The night before [Wilson] asked Congress for a declaration of war against Germany, he sent for me. I was late getting the message somehow, and didn't reach the White House till one o'clock in the morning. "The old man" was waiting for me sitting in his study with the typewriter on his table, where he used to type his own messages.

I'd never seen him so worn down. He looked as if he hadn't slept, and he said he hadn't. He said he was probably going before Congress the next day to ask a declaration of war, and he'd never been so uncertain about anything in his life as about that decision. For nights, he said, he'd been lying awake going over the whole situation—over the provocation given by Germany, over the probable feeling in the United States, over the consequences to the settlement and to the world at large if we entered the melee.

He tapped some sheets before him and said that he had written a message and expected to go before Congress with it as it stood. He said he couldn't see any alternative, that he had tried every way he knew to avoid war. "I think I know what war means," he said, and he added that if there were any possibility of avoiding war he wanted to try it. "What else can I do?" he asked. "Is there anything else I can do?"

I told him his hand had been forced by Germany, that so far as I could see we couldn't keep out.

It would mean that we should lose our heads along with the rest and stop weighing right and wrong. It would mean that a majority of people in this hemisphere would go war-mad, quit thinking, and devote their energies to destruction. The President said a declaration of war would mean that Germany would be beaten and so badly that there would be a dictated peace, a victorious peace.

"It means," he said, "an attempt to reconstruct a peacetime civilization with war standards, and at the end of the war there will be no bystanders with sufficient power to influence the terms. There won't be any peace standards left to work with. There will be only war standards."

Then he began to talk about the consequences to the United States. He had no illusions about the fashion in which we were likely to fight the war.

He said when a war got going it was just war, and there weren't two kinds of it. It required illiberalism at home to reinforce the men at the front. We couldn't fight Germany and maintain the ideals of government that all thinking men shared. He said we would try it, but it would be too much for us.

"Once lead this people into war," he said, "and they'll forget there ever was such a thing as tolerance. To fight you must be brutal and ruthless, and the spirit of ruthless brutality will enter into the very fiber of our national life, infecting Congress, the courts, the policeman on the beat, the man in the street." Conformity would be the only virtue, said the President, and every man who refused to conform would have to pay the penalty.

He thought the Constitution would not survive it, that free speech and the right of assembly would go. He said a nation couldn't put its strength into a war and keep its head level; it had never been done.

"If there is any alternative, for God's sake, let's take it," he exclaimed. Well, I couldn't see any, and I told him so.

The President didn't have illusions about how he was going to come out of it, either. He'd rather have done anything else than head a military machine. All his instincts were against it. He foresaw too clearly the probable influence of a declaration of war on his own fortunes, the adulation certain to follow the certain victory, the derision and attack which would come with the deflation of excessive hopes and in the presence of world responsibility. But if he had it to do over again, he would take the same course. It was just a choice of evils.

1. Why do you think Wilson had the editor of a major national newspaper as his confidant?

_____

_____

_____

2. Cobb mentioned that Wilson used to type his own messages. How does that differ from presidential

   practice today? _____

_____

_____

3. About what two broad categories of consequences was Wilson apparently concerned as he contemplated

   his request for a declaration of war against Germany? _____

_____

4. What were some of those consequences? _____

_____

_____

_____

_____

5. What did Wilson think would be the effect of the war on Americans' liberties?

_____

_____

6. What does Cobb say that indicates that Wilson had worried long and hard over his request for a

   declaration of war? _____

_____

_____

7. Do you think that presidents today experience such soul-searching moments before they make a decision
   to thrust the nation into war, or is the situation different? (Support your answer.)

_____

_____

_____

_____

210

U.S. Preparedness: The Run-Up to War

Read the following excerpt about America's lack of preparedness for the war and the days leading up to America's entry into the conflict. Then answer the questions that follow.

The sinking of the *Lusitania* shocked an American public that, while unable to follow the President's dictum [pronouncement] on impartiality of thought, had nevertheless displayed up to this point little desire to become directly involved in Europe's bloodbath. Although most Americans had from the first resented the submarine campaign, Britain too was violating the freedom of the seas with a blockade not only of Germany but of neutral European nations as well. This had raised the question of whether the acts of both sides were not equally reprehensible; but the heavy loss of life in the sinking of the *Lusitania* invoked fresh ire against the Germans. Membership in patriotic organizations flourished, and voices advocating preparedness found new listeners.

Among the voices were those of Elihu Root, ex-President Theodore Roosevelt, and former Secretary of War Henry L. Stimson. Another was that of General Wood, whose term as the Army's Chief of Staff had expired just over a year after President Wilson and his peace-oriented administration had come to office. Following a practice he had introduced while Chief of Staff of conducting summer camps where college students paying their own way could receive military training, Wood lent his support to a similar four-week camp for business and professional men at Plattsburg Barracks, New York. Known as the "Plattsburg idea," its success justified opening other camps, assuring a relatively small but influential cadre possessing basic military skills and imbued with enthusiasm for preparedness.

Yet these were voices of a heavily industrialized and articulate East. Few like them were to be heard in the rural South, the West, or a strongly isolationist Midwest, where heavy settlements of German-Americans (called by some, derisively, "hyphenated Americans") detected in the talk of preparedness a heavy leaning toward the nation's historic Anglo-Saxon ties. There was in the country, too, a strong tide of outright pacifism, which possessed an eloquent spokesman in Wilson's Secretary of State, William Jennings Bryan.

How deep were Bryan's convictions became apparent in the government's reaction to the sinking of the *Lusitania*. Although Bryan agreed with the President's first diplomatic protest over the sinking, he dissented when the President, dissatisfied with the German reply and determined to insist on the right of neutrals to engage in commerce on the high seas, insisted on a second and stronger note. The Secretary resigned.

Although sinkings by submarine continued through the summer of 1915, Wilson's persistent protest at last produced an apparent diplomatic victory when in September the Germans promised that passenger liners would be sunk only after warning and with proper safeguards for passengers' lives. Decelerating their campaign, the Germans actually acted less in response to American protests than to a realization that they lacked enough submarines to achieve victory by that means.

American commerce with Europe meanwhile continued, particularly in munitions, but because of the British blockade almost all was with the Allied nations. The British intercepted ships carrying foodstuffs to Germany and held them until their cargoes rotted. Just after mid-1915 they put even cotton on a long list of contraband and blacklisted any U.S. firm suspected of trading with the Central Powers. These were deliberate and painful affronts, but so profitable was the munitions trade that only the Southern states, hurt by the loss of markets for cotton, raised loud protest.

In October 1915, President Wilson repealed a ban earlier imposed on loans to belligerents, thereby further stimulating trade with the Allies.

While Americans as a whole remained opposed to entering the war, their sympathy for the Allied cause grew. A combination of Allied propaganda and German ineptitude was largely responsible. The propagandists were careful to [ensure] that nobody forgot the German violation of Belgian neutrality, the ordeal of "Little Belgium." Stories of babies mutilated . . . by German soldiers were rampant. The French executed nine women as spies during the war, but it was the death of a British nurse, Edith Cavell, at the hands of the Germans that the world heard about and remembered. Clumsy German efforts at propaganda in the United States backfired when two military attaches were discovered financing espionage and sabotage. The Germans did their cause no further good when one of their submarines in October 1916 surfaced in Newport Harbor, sent an officer ashore to deliver a letter for the German ambassador, then submerged and sank nine Allied ships close off the New England coast.

Continuing to champion neutrality and seeking—however unsuccessfully—to persuade the belligerents to establish international rules of submarine warfare, President Wilson was personally becoming more aware of the necessity for military preparedness. Near the end of a nationwide speaking tour in February 1916, he not only called for creation of "the greatest navy in the world" but also urged widespread military training for civilians, lest some day the nation be faced with "putting raw levies of inexperienced men onto the modern field of battle." Still upholding the cause of freedom of the seas, he refused to go along with congressmen who sought to forbid Americans to travel on armed merchant ships.

Wilson nevertheless continued to demonstrate a fervent hope for neutrality. A submarine attack in March on the French steamer *Sussex* with Americans aboard convinced the President's advisor, Colonel House, and his new Secretary of State, Robert Lansing, that the nation should sever diplomatic relations with Germany, a course that a fiery speech of self-justification by the German chancellor in the Reichstag and a cynical reply to an American note of protest did nothing to discourage. Wilson instead went only so far as to dispatch what amounted to an ultimatum, demanding that the Germans cease the submarine war against passenger and merchant vessels or face severance of relations with the United States.

1. What fact made it hard for the United States to criticize the Germans for their unrestricted submarine warfare? _____

_____

2. Who were some of the famous people who were calling for America to prepare for the possibility of war? _____

_____

3. Which regions of the country were *least* enthusiastic in supporting preparedness?

_____

4. Who was perhaps the leading spokesman against preparing for war, and how strongly did he disagree with President Wilson? _____

_____

5. When Germany finally agreed to end unrestricted submarine warfare, the decision was based on what consideration more than American diplomatic protests? _____

_____

The Heroism of Sgt. Alvin C. York

Sergeant Alvin C. York was known as the greatest American hero of World War I. Read this account and answer the questions.

Alvin Cullum York was born on December 13, 1887, in a two-room cabin near Pall Mall in northern Fentress County, Tennessee. The third of eleven children, he was a descendant of the first settlers in the area. The Yorks eked out a bare subsistence by farming seventy-five acres of poor, rocky soil. They supplemented their produce by hunting and fishing. York became one of the area's best marksmen.

But York also gained a reputation as a drinking, gambling troublemaker. He and his brothers frequented bars and hangouts across the nearby Kentucky border. People who knew him were sure that he would "never amount to anything." But they did not allow for the power of the Holy Spirit to change a man's heart and lifestyle. In 1914, York experienced a religious conversion. One of his friends was killed in a drunken fight in a bar, and that set York to thinking about where his own life was headed. He did not want to suffer a senseless death as his friend had done. That event prompted him to attend a local prayer meeting conducted by the Church of Christ in Christian Union. That group had strict moral standards forbidding drinking, dancing, swearing, reading of popular novels, and attending movies. They were also firmly against war. He joined that church following his conversion and immediately became active in the life of the church. He also met his future wife, Gracie, there.

On June 5, 1917, just weeks after the United States declared war on Germany, he received a letter notifying him that he was being drafted into the army. He went to his pastor seeking advice on what he should do. The preacher advised him to register as a conscientious objector, meaning that he refused to serve on the grounds that his religious beliefs forbad his fighting in war. York wrote "Don't want to fight" on his draft card and returned it. Authorities denied him conscientious objector status at both the local and state levels because his church was not a recognized religious sect. After much discussion, his company commander convinced York that there are times when war is justified, moral, and ordained by God.

Following his training, York was assigned to Company G, 328th Infantry Regiment, 82nd Division, also known as the All-American Division because it included soldiers from every state of the Union. He was promoted from private to corporal and shipped out to France with his company. On October 8, 1918, they found themselves on Hill 223 in France in the midst of the Allies' Meuse-Argonne offensive, the last major engagement of the war. York and sixteen comrades, led by Sergeant Bernard Early, were ordered to advance to a portion of a railroad two miles in front of them. They moved toward the objective but because of confusion reading their map, which was in French rather than English, they ended up behind enemy lines and came under intense machine-gun fire. Nine of the Americans were cut down, and Sergeant Early was mortally wounded. York had to silence that machine gun.

York's experience in Fentress County turkey shoots now paid off. He made his way through heavy underbrush to a point where he could see the machine gun, got his rifle at the ready, and then waited patiently. A German soldier eventually poked his head up. York took careful aim and pulled the trigger. Down the German went. He waited again. Again a German raised his head. Again York squeezed the trigger on his rifle. And again a German went down. Eighteen times York did this, never missing with a shot. "Every time one of them raised his head, I jes' teched him off," York explained afterwards.

By that point, the Germans realized that only one man was causing all of the damage. Seven of them charged his position with bayonets. He shot each of them with his pistol. Then he yelled for the rest of the Germans to surrender. They did. York rounded up the surviving members of his unit and began marching the German prisoners back to the Allied lines. Along the way, they encountered other German units. York ordered the ranking German officer among his prisoners to order them to surrender, and they did. By the time he got back to American lines, he had 132 prisoners, including three officers. He had killed 25 Germans (some people said it was even more) and put 35 machine guns out of action.

In recognition of York's singular act of bravery, he was promoted to sergeant and awarded a dozen medals, including the Congressional Medal of Honor, the Distinguished Service Cross, the Legion of Honor and the Croix de Guerre by France, the Croce de Guerra by Italy, and the War Medal by Montenegro. Shy, humble, and modest, York did not like to bask in the limelight or receive the honor heaped upon him. To him, he was just doing his job, and a disgusting job at that since it involved killing fellow human beings. He never seemed proud of what he had done, and he never claimed to have acted alone. He always gave credit to the surviving members of his unit.

Nonetheless, York returned home after the war to a hero's welcome. Advertisers courted him, seeking his endorsement of their products. But York replied, "This uniform ain't for sale." He was so overwhelmed by his reception in New York and so hounded by well-wishers and hucksters hoping to capitalize on his fame that he convinced Secretary of State and fellow Tennessean Cordell Hull to take him back home quickly.

Settling back down in Pall Mall, York tried to promote the education of the youth of Fentress County. He gave speeches to raise money for a trade school that became known as York Institute. He got involved in state politics, promoting education, jobs, and improved roads in his county. Although he was a staunch Democrat, he switched parties and voted for Herbert Hoover in 1932 because the Democrat, Franklin Roosevelt, wanted to repeal Prohibition.

As tensions built in Europe before the outbreak of World War II, York adamantly opposed U.S. involvement there. He still believed that World War I had been wrong and was still opposed to war. He was pacifism and isolationism personified. Those convictions made it very difficult for Warner Brothers to convince him that he should approve the making of a movie based on his life. Eventually, however, he came to see Hitler's Nazi Germany as an evil threat to mankind and supported U.S. preparedness. He even supported the draft and was made head of the Fentress County Draft Board.

Meanwhile, Warner Brothers produced the film *Sergeant York* starring Gary Cooper. It became one of the top grossing Warner Brothers films of the World War II years and earned Cooper the Academy Award for Best Actor in 1942. York had stipulated that all profits he realized from the movie be used to found an interdenominational Bible school. The school was opened in 1942 but closed in 1943.

York's final years were spent fighting the Internal Revenue Service, which accused him of failing to report income from the movie. By 1951, York was basically destitute as a result of that fight and poor investments. In 1961, President Kennedy declared the case a national disgrace and ordered the matter closed. The York Relief Fund, started by Tennessee Congressman Joe Evins, paid the IRS $100,000 and put $30,000 in a trust for the York family. York suffered a cerebral hemorrhage and died on September 2, 1964.

1. How did Alvin York's background make him an unlikely hero? _____

_____

2. What event led to his religious conversion and change of lifestyle? _____

_____

_____

3. Describe briefly the event that won York his military honors. _____

_____

_____

_____

4. What honors did he earn by this action? _____

_____

_____

_____

5. What did he do upon returning to America that revealed his character and his attitude toward his actions

in the war? _____

_____

6. What interests and activities did York pursue after he returned from the war? _____

_____

_____

_____

7. What made York change his mind about isolationism and pacifism in connection with the increasing ten-

sions in Europe in the late 1930s? _____

_____

8. What role did he play in World War II? _____

9. Do you think York was correct in being a conscientious objector or was he right to change his mind?

(Support your answer.) _____

_____

_____

_____

_____

_____

_____

What God Says About War and Peace

In his war message to Congress, President Wilson rallied Americans behind the war by appealing to their sense of justice and their dreams of a lasting peace. Use your Bible to find what God says about man's violence, just wars, and man's hope for peace.

Mankind has suffered from violence since the beginning of time. Wilson explained his outrage at the unrestricted killing of innocent people: "The present German submarine warfare against commerce is a warfare against mankind."

1. When was the world first filled with violence (Gen. 6:10–13)? _____

2. What caused the war mentioned in Genesis 14:1–10? _____

3. What does the victor of a war normally seek (Gen. 14:11–12)? _____

4. What does Jesus warn about relying on violence (Matt. 26:52)? _____

5. What is the source of quarrels, even among Christians (James 4:1–3)? _____

Wilson believed in "just war." He said of America's entry into World War I, "We have no selfish ends to serve. We desire no conquest, no dominion. We seek no indemnities for ourselves, no material compensation for the sacrifices we shall freely make."

6. Why did Abram go to war (Gen. 14:14–16)? _____

7. What did Abram do with his spoils of war (Gen. 14:21–24)? _____

8. Why do heathen nations want rulers (1 Sam. 8:19–20)? _____

9. Why did God want all of the Canaanites to die (Deut. 20:16–18)? _____

10. Who alone has the power to stop conflicts between nations? _____

Wilson's Fourteen Points

In 1917, both Austria and the Pope presented separate peace plans. Neither succeeded. When the United States entered the war, President Wilson began working for a "just and democratic" peace, and his "Fourteen Points" became the foundation of the armistice signed on November 11, 1918. Ultimately, however, the Treaty of Versailles differed from those principles substantially. Read these excerpts from Wilson's address to Congress on January 8, 1918, and then answer the questions that follow.

. . . It will be our wish and purpose that the processes of peace, when they are begun, shall be absolutely open and that they shall involve and permit henceforth no secret understandings of any kind. The day of conquest and aggrandizement is gone by; so is also the day of secret covenants entered into in the interest of particular governments and likely at some unlooked-for moment to upset the peace of the world.

. . . We entered this war because violations of right had occurred which touched us to the quick and made the life of our own people impossible unless they were corrected and the world secure once for all against their recurrence. What we demand in this war, therefore, is nothing peculiar to ourselves. It is that the world be made fit and safe to live in; and particularly that it be made safe for every peace-loving nation which, like our own, wishes to live its own life, determine its own institutions, be assured of justice and fair dealing by the other peoples of the world as against force and selfish aggression. All the peoples of the world are in effect partners in this interest, and for our own part we see very clearly that unless justice be done to others it will not be done to us. The program of the world's peace, therefore, is our program; and that program, the only possible program, as we see it, is this:

I. Open covenants of peace, openly arrived at, after which there shall be no private international understandings of any kind, but diplomacy shall proceed always frankly and in the public view.

II. Absolute freedom of navigation upon the seas, outside territorial waters, alike in peace and in war, except as the seas may be closed in whole or in part by international action for the enforcement of international covenants.

III. The removal, so far as possible, of all economic barriers and the establishment of an equality of trade conditions among all the nations consenting to the peace and associating themselves for its maintenance.

IV. Adequate guarantees given and taken that national armaments will be reduced to the lowest point consistent with domestic safety.

V. A free, open-minded, and absolutely impartial adjustment of all colonial claims, based upon a strict observance of the principle that in determining all such questions of sovereignty the interests of the populations concerned must have equal weight with the equitable claims of the government whose title is to be determined.

VI. The evacuation of all Russian territory and such a settlement of all questions affecting Russia as will secure the best and freest cooperation of the other nations of the world in obtaining for her an unhampered and unembarrassed opportunity for the independent determination of her own political development and national policy and assure her of a sincere welcome into the society of free nations under institutions of her own choosing. . . .

VII. Belgium, the whole world will agree, must be evacuated and restored, without any attempt to limit the sovereignty which she enjoys in common with all other free nations. . . .

VIII. All French territory should be freed and the invaded portions restored, and the wrong done to France by Prussia in 1871 in the matter of Alsace-Lorraine, which has unsettled the peace of the world for nearly fifty years, should be righted, in order that peace may once more be made secure in the interest of all.

IX. A readjustment of the frontiers of Italy should be effected along clearly recognizable lines of nationality.

X. The peoples of Austria-Hungary, whose place among the nations we wish to see safeguarded and assured, should be accorded the freest opportunity of autonomous development.

XI. Rumania, Serbia, and Montenegro should be evacuated; occupied territories restored; Serbia accorded free and secure access to the sea; and the relations of the several Balkan states to one another determined by friendly counsel along historically established lines of allegiance and nationality; and international guarantees of the political and economic independence and territorial integrity of the several Balkan states should be entered into.

XII. The Turkish portions of the present Ottoman [Turkish] Empire should be assured a secure sovereignty, but the other nationalities which are now under Turkish rule [i.e., Kurds, Arabs, Armenians, and some Greeks] should be assured an undoubted security of life and an absolutely unmolested opportunity of autonomous development, and the Dardanelles [i.e., the straits leading from the Black Sea to international waters] should be permanently opened as a free passage to the ships and commerce of all nations under international guarantees.

XIII. An independent Polish state should be erected which should include the territories inhabited by indisputably Polish populations, which should be assured a free and secure access to the sea, and whose political and economic independence and territorial integrity should be guaranteed by international covenant.

XIV. A general association of nations must be formed under specific covenants for the purpose of affording mutual guarantees of political independence and territorial integrity to great and small states alike.

In regard to these essential rectifications of wrong and assertions of right we feel ourselves to be intimate partners of all the governments and peoples associated together against the Imperialists. We cannot be separated in interest or divided in purpose. We stand together until the end.

1. Why do you think that Wilson emphasized the words *no secret understandings* and *absolutely open* in his address? _____

_____

2. What part of Wilson's speech sounds a little like Jesus Christ's "Golden Rule?"

_____

3. To what issue that had divided American political parties for decades did Wilson refer in his third point?

_____

4. To what country is Wilson referring in his sixth point? _____

5. What stipulation did Wilson make concerning the Dardanelles? _____

_____

The Washington Naval Treaty

Read the following excerpts and summaries of the provision in the Washington Naval Treaty and then answer the questions that follow.

The United States of America, the British Empire, France, Italy, and Japan;

Desiring to contribute to the maintenance of the general peace, and to reduce the burdens of competition in armament;

Have resolved, with a view to accomplishing these purposes, to conclude a treaty to limit their respective naval armament, and to that end have appointed as their Plenipotentiaries; . . .

Who, having communicated to each other their respective full powers, found to be in good and due form, have agreed as follows:

CHAPTER 1

ART. I. The Contracting Powers agree to limit their respective naval armament as provided in the present Treaty.

ART. II. Disposal of ships

A. United States may complete two West Virginia-class ships currently under construction but must dispose of *North Dakota* and *Delaware*.

B. Great Britain may construct two new ships not exceeding 35,000 tons but must destroy *Thunder*, *King George V*, *Ajax*, and *Centurion*.

ART. III. No more shipbuilding will be allowed except for replacements of existing ships.

ART. IV. Replacement tonnage limits:

A. United States—525,000 tons

B. Great Britain—525,000 tons

C. France—175,000 tons

D. Italy—175,000 tons

E. Japan—315,000 tons

ART. V. No country may acquire any ships exceeding 35,000 tons.

ART. VI. No ship may carry a gun of a larger caliber than 16 inches.

ART. VII. Aircraft carrier limitations:

A. United States—135,000 tons

B. Great Britain—135,000 tons

C. France—60,000 tons

D. Italy—60,000 tons

E. Japan—81,000 tons

ART. IX. No aircraft carrier exceeding 27,000 tons can be acquired.

ART. XI. This treaty excludes nonfighting ships that might be used for fleet duties or as troop transports.

ART. XIII. No ship designated by treaty to be scrapped may be reconverted into a vessel of war.

ART. XIV. Merchant vessels may not be converted into warships or fitted or equipped with warlike armaments.

ART. XIX. The United States, Great Britain, and Japan agree to the status quo at the time this treaty is signed regarding naval bases and fortifications. No new facilities may be built or obtained.

CHAPTER 2

The following rules shall be observed for the scrapping of vessels of war which are to be disposed of in accordance with Articles II and III.

I. A vessel to be scrapped must be placed in such condition that it cannot be put to combatant use.

II. This result must be finally effected in any one of the following ways:

(a) Permanent sinking of the vessel;

(b) Breaking the vessel up.

This shall always involve the destruction or removal of all machinery, boilers and armour, and all deck, side and bottom plating;

(c) Converting the vessel to target use exclusively. . . . Not more than one capital ship may be retained for this purpose at one time by any of the Contracting Powers. . . .

1. What were the two stated purposes of this treaty? _____

_____

_____

2. Which nations were signatories to this treaty? _____

_____

3. Which branch of military was the only area affected by this treaty, and what does that say about the signatories' assumptions? _____

_____

4. Which relatively new form of naval vessel received special attention, indicating an awareness of its rising importance? _____

5. Which of the signatories seemed to get the most favorable end of the deal in this treaty?

_____

6. What aspect of the treaty made it possible for the signatories to resume a naval buildup in the future?

_____

_____

_____

7. What important feature is conspicuously missing from this treaty?

_____

_____

8. Do you think the treaty was realistic and effective? Why or why not?

_____

_____

_____

_____

_____

The Immigration Act of 1924

Read the following excerpts from the Immigration Act of 1924 and then answer the questions that follow.

. . . Under the act of 1924 the number of each nationality who may be admitted annually is limited to 2 per cent of the population of such nationality resident in the United States according to the census of 1890, and not more than 10 per cent of any annual quota may be admitted in any month except in cases where such quota is less than 300 for the entire year.

. . . Under the new act, however, immigration from the entire world, with the exception of the Dominion of Canada, Newfoundland, the Republic of Mexico, the Republic of Cuba, the Republic of Haiti, the Dominican Republic, the Canal Zone, and independent countries of Central and South America, is subject to quota limitations.

. . . Now, therefore, I, Calvin Coolidge, President of the United States of America, acting under and by virtue of the power in me vested by the aforesaid act of Congress, do hereby proclaim and make known that on and after July 1, 1924, and throughout the fiscal year 1924–1925, the quota of each nationality provided in said Act shall be as follows:

Germany	51,229	Denmark	2,789	Hungary	473
Great Britain	34,007	Russia	2,248	Lithuania	344
Italy	28,567	Switzerland	2,081	Danzig (Free City)	228
Irish Free State	28,567	Netherlands	1,648	Finland	170
Sweden	9,561	Austria	785	Latvia	142
Norway	6,453	Yugoslavia	671	Spain	131
Poland	5,982	Rumania	603	Armenia	124
France	3,954	Belgium	512	Estonia	124
Czechoslovakia	3,073	Portugal	503	Australia	121

100 each: Afghanistan, Albania, Andorra, Arabian peninsula, Bhutan, Bulgaria, Cameroon (British mandate), Cameroon (French mandate), China, Egypt, Ethiopia, Greece, Iceland, India, Iraq, Japan, Liberia, Liechtenstein, Luxemburg, Monaco, Morocco (French and Spanish zones), Muscat (Oman), Nauru, Nepal, New Zealand, New Guinea (and other Pacific islands under Australian mandate), Palestine, Persia, Ruanda and Urundi (Belgium mandate), Western Samoa, San Marino, Siam, South Africa, South West Africa, Syria and Lebanon (French mandate), Tanganyika (British mandate), Togoland (British mandate), Togoland (French mandate), Turkey, Yap (and other Pacific islands under Japanese mandate)

General Note—The immigration quotas assigned to the various countries and quota areas should not be regarded as having any political significance whatever, or as involving recognition of new governments, or of new boundaries, or of transfers of territory except as the United States Government has already made such recognition in a formal and official manner. . . .

1. Which regions of the world were given preferential treatment by this law? _____
_____

2. Which regions of the world were most restricted by this law? _____
_____

3. In relation to its size, which listed place was allowed the greatest percentage of immigrants?
_____
_____

4. Which region of the world was not affected at all by this law? _____
_____
_____

5. Why is Calvin Coolidge specified in the treaty although Congress actually passed the law?
_____
_____
_____

6. Study the first four countries listed, those with the highest quotas. Why do you think their quotas were set
so high? _____
_____
_____

7. If you know your nation(s) of ancestry, write the place(s) in the answer space along with the quota(s).
_____
_____

8. Do you think a quota system such as the one established by this law is needed in the United States today?
Why or why not? If so, what (if any) changes would you make in it? _____
_____
_____
_____
_____

9. Why are immigration laws (and their strict enforcement) important for every nation?
_____
_____
_____

★ Optional: 10. Write a three-paragraph essay addressing the benefits, problems, and needs of immigration
policy in the United States.

The Impact of Technology in the Twenties

For each invention listed in the following table, write the date of its first success in America, its creator(s), the changes it caused in daily life, famous people associated with its industry, and changes it caused in industry. As a bonus, write changes each invention caused in warfare.

	Automobile	Airplane	Radio	Motion picture
Date	1893	1903	1895	1889
Creator(s)				Thomas Edison
Changes in daily life				
Famous people				
Changes in industry				
Changes in warfare				

From Progressivism to Normalcy

After World War I, Americans wanted to "return to normalcy," but the horrors of war had destroyed their faith in progressivism. Using Chapters 20 and 22, complete this chart to reveal some of the changes that occurred in postwar America.

	Progressivism	Normalcy
Decade(s)		
Presidents		
Foreign affairs emphases		
Military power		
Immigration		
Humanitarian goals		
Rural life		
Farm economy		
Attitudes toward business		
Moral standards		

Darrow versus Bryan in the Scopes Trial

The Scopes trial has been called "the trial of the century." It pitted Bible-believing Christians against agnostics who valued so-called science above the "myth and superstition" of religion. Perhaps the most closely watched part of the testimony in the trial was the cross-examination of three-time presidential candidate and Presbyterian layman William Jennings Bryan by famed defense attorney and agnostic Clarence Darrow. Darrow admitted that he wanted to use the cross-examination to destroy Bryan and his reputation among Christians as a defender of the faith. Read the following description of part of that cross-examination, and then answer the questions that follow.

The crowd swelled as word of the encounter spread. From the 500 persons who evacuated the courtroom, the number rose to an estimated 3,000 people sprawled across the lawn—nearly twice the town's normal population. . . . The *Nashville Banner* [stated], "Then began an examination which has few, if any, parallels in court history. In reality, it was a debate between Darrow and Bryan on Biblical history, on agnosticism and belief in revealed religion." Darrow posed the well-worn questions of the village skeptic . . . : Did Jonah live inside a whale for three days? How could Joshua lengthen the day by making the sun (rather than the earth) stand still? Where did Cain get his wife? In a narrow sense, as Stewart [the chief prosecutor] persistently complained, Darrow's questions had nothing to do with the case because they never inquired about human evolution. In a broad sense, as Hays [a defense attorney from the ACLU] repeatedly countered, they had everything to do with it because they challenged biblical literalism. Best of all for Darrow, no good answers existed to them. They compelled Bryan "to choose between his crude beliefs and the common intelligence of modern times," Darrow later observed, or to admit ignorance. Bryan tried all three approaches at different times during the afternoon, without appreciable success.

Darrow questioned Bryan as a hostile witness, peppering him with queries and giving him little chance for explanation. At times it became like a firing line:

"You claim that everything in the Bible should be literally interpreted?"

"I believe everything in the Bible should be accepted as it is given there; some of the Bible is given illustratively. . . ."

"But when you read that . . . the whale swallowed Jonah . . . how do you literally interpret that?"

". . . I believe in a God who can make a whale and can make a man and make both of them do what he pleases."

"But do you believe he made them—that he made such a fish and it was big enough to swallow Jonah?"

"Yes sir. Let me add: One miracle is just as easy to believe as another."

"It is for me . . . just as hard."

"It is hard to believe for you, but easy for me. . . . When you get beyond what man can do, you get within the realm of miracles; and it is just as easy to believe the miracle of Jonah as any other miracle in the Bible."

Such affirmations undercut the appeal of fundamentalism. On the stump, Bryan effectively championed the cause of biblical faith by addressing the great questions of life: The special creation of humans in God's image gave purpose to every person and the bodily resurrection of Christ gave hope to believers for eternal life. Yet Darrow did not inquire about these grand miracles. For many Americans, laudable simple faith became laughable crude belief when applied to Jonah's whale, Noah's Flood, and Adam's rib. Yet the Commoner [Bryan] acknowledged accepting each of these biblical miracles on faith and professed that all miracles were equally easy to believe.

Bryan fared little better when he tried to rationalize two of the biblical passages raised by Darrow. In an apparent concession to modern astronomy, Bryan suggested that God extended the day for Joshua by stopping the earth rather than the sun; similarly, in line with nineteenth-century evangelical scholarship, Bryan affirmed his understanding that in Genesis, days of creation represented periods of time, which led to the following exchange:

"Have you any idea of the length of these periods?"

"No; I don't."

"Do you think the sun was made on the fourth day?"

"Yes."

"And they had evening and morning without the sun?"

"I am simply saying it is a period."

"They had evening and morning for four periods without the sun, do you think?"

"I believe in creation as there told, and if I am not able to explain it I will accept it."

Although Bryan had not ventured far beyond the bounds of biblical literalism, the defense made the most of it. "Bryan had conceded that he interpreted the Bible," Hays gloated. "He must have agreed that others have the same right." Furthermore, Scopes observed, "The Bible literalists who came to cheer Bryan were surprised, ill content, and disappointed that Bryan gave ground."

As Darrow pushed various lines of questioning, increasingly Bryan came to admit that he simply did not know the answers. He had no idea what would happen to the earth if it stopped moving, or about the antiquity of human civilization, or even about the age of the earth. "Did you ever discover where Cain got his wife?" Darrow asked. "No sir; I leave the agnostics to hunt for her," came the bittersweet reply. "Mr. Bryan's complete lack of interest in many of the things closely connected with such religious questions as he had been supporting for many years was strikingly shown again and again by Mr. Darrow," the *New York Times* reported. Stewart tried to end the two-hour interrogation at least a dozen times, but Bryan refused to step down. "I am simply trying to protect the word of God against the greatest atheist or agnostic in the United States," he shouted, pounding his fist in rage. "I want the papers to know I am not afraid to get on the stand in front of him and let him do his worst." The crowd cheered this outburst and every counterthrust attempted by the Commoner. Darrow received little applause but inflicted the most jabs. "The only purpose Mr. Darrow has is to slur the Bible, but I will answer his questions," Bryan exclaimed at the end. "I object to your statement," Darrow shouted back, both men now standing and shaking their fists at each other. "I am examining your fool ideas that no intelligent Christian on earth believes." [Judge] Raulston finally had heard enough and abruptly adjourned court for the day.

1. Although the Scopes trial was supposed to be about whether a high school teacher had violated the Tennessee law prohibiting the teaching of evolution, what did it become, as this excerpt shows?

   _____

   _____

   _____

   _____

2. On what two biblical accounts did Darrow focus his cross-examination of Bryan?

   _____

   _____

   _____

3. Although Darrow's questions never addressed the main issue of the trial (the violation of the anti-evolution law), they were important because they struck at what central issue? _____

_____

4. What legal tactic did Darrow use that probably contributed to Bryan's inability to provide the best possible answers? _____

_____

_____

_____

5. According to the author's account, what happened that revealed Bryan's growing frustration with Darrow's line of questioning? _____

_____

_____

6. How did the spectators at the trial respond to Darrow's questioning and Bryan's testimony? Why?

_____

_____

_____

_____

7. If you had been Stewart (the head prosecutor), how might you have conducted the trial differently?

_____

_____

_____

_____

_____

_____

_____

Sports in the Roaring Twenties

Select one of the following sports categories—swimming, football, boxing, baseball, golf, tennis, or auto racing—and write a brief summary of the highlights of that sport during the Roaring Twenties. Then, using outside resources, study one of the "superstars" in that sport and write a summary of his or her career and the contributions made to the sport.

Swimming: Gertrude Ederle, Johnny Weismuller
Football: "Red" Grange, Knute Rockne, the "Four Horsemen" of Notre Dame
Boxing: Jack Dempsey, Gene Tunney
Tennis: Bill Tilden, Helen Wills
Golf: Bobby Jones
Auto racing: Barney Oldfield
Baseball: Babe Ruth, Lou Gehrig, Tris Speaker

_____
_____
_____
_____
_____
_____
_____
_____
_____
_____
_____
_____
_____
_____
_____
_____
_____
_____
_____
_____
_____
_____
_____

Herbert Hoover on the Role of Government

In the 1928 election campaign, the major parties offered voters two quite different philosophies of government: a large, centralized government that promised to solve problems of all sorts or a limited, streamlined government that expected individuals to solve most of their own problems. Read Republican candidate Herbert Hoover's position as stated in his speech "The Philosophy of Rugged Individualism." Then answer the questions that follow.

. . . After the war, . . . we were faced with the problem of determination of the very nature of our national life. During one hundred fifty years we have built up a form of self-government and a social system which is peculiarly our own. It differs essentially from all others in the world. It is the American system. It is just as definite and positive a political and social system as has ever been developed on earth. It is founded upon a particular conception of self-government in which decentralized local responsibility is the very base. Further than this, it is founded upon the conception that only through ordered liberty, freedom, and equal opportunity to the individual will his initiative and enterprise spur on the march of progress. And in our insistence upon equality of opportunity has our system advanced beyond all the world.

During the war we necessarily turned to the government to solve every difficult economic problem. The government having absorbed every energy of our people for war, there was no other solution. . . . [T]he Federal Government became a centralized despotism which undertook unprecedented responsibilities, assumed autocratic powers, and took over the business of citizens. To a large degree we regimented our whole people temporarily into a socialistic state. However justified in time of war if continued in peace-time it would destroy not only our American system but with it our progress and freedom as well.

When the war closed, the most vital of all issues . . . was whether governments should continue their wartime ownership and operation of . . . production and distribution. We were challenged with a peace-time choice between the American system of rugged individualism and a European philosophy of . . . paternalism and state socialism. The acceptance of these ideas would have meant the destruction of self-government through centralization of government. It would have meant the undermining of the individual initiative and enterprise through which our people have grown to unparalleled greatness.

. . . When the Republican Party came into full power it . . . restored confidence and hope in the American people, it freed and stimulated enterprise, it restored the government to its position as an umpire instead of a player in the economic game. For these reasons the American people have gone forward in progress while the rest of the world has halted, and some countries have even gone backwards.

. . . [O]ur opponents . . . abandon the tenets of their own party and turn to state socialism as a solution for the difficulties presented by all three. It is proposed that we shall change from prohibition to the state purchase and sale of liquor. If their agricultural relief program means anything, it means that the government shall directly or indirectly buy and sell and fix prices of agricultural products. And we are to go into the hydro-electric power business. In other words, we are confronted with a huge program of government in business.

There is, therefore, . . . a question of fundamental principle . . . : shall we depart from the principles of our American political and economic system, upon which we have advanced beyond all the rest of the world, in order to adopt methods based on principles destructive of its very foundations?

I should like to state to you the effect that this projection of government in business would have upon our system of self-government and our economic system. That effect would reach to the daily life of every man and woman. It would impair the very basis of liberty and freedom not only for those left outside the fold of expanded bureaucracy but for those embraced within it.

Let us first see the effect upon self-government. When the Federal Government undertakes to go into commercial business it must at once set up the organization and administration of that business, and it immediately finds itself in a labyrinth [maze], every alley of which leads to the destruction of self-government.

Commercial business requires a concentration of responsibility. Self-government requires decentralization and many checks and balances to safeguard liberty. Our government to succeed in business would need to become in effect a despotism. There at once begins the destruction of self-government. . . .

It is a false liberalism that interprets itself into the government operation of commercial business. Every step of bureaucratizing of the business of our country poisons the very roots of liberalism—that is political equality, free speech, free assembly, free press, and equality of opportunity. It is the road not to more liberty, but to less liberty.

. . . Liberalism is a force truly of the spirit, a force proceeding from the deep realization that economic freedom cannot be sacrificed if political freedom is to be preserved. Even if Governmental conduct of business could give us more efficiency instead of less efficiency, the fundamental objection to it would remain unaltered and unabated. It would destroy political equality. It would increase rather than decrease abuse and corruption. It would stifle initiative and invention. It would undermine the development of leadership. It would cramp and cripple the mental and spiritual energies of our people. It would extinguish equality and opportunity. It would dry up the spirit of liberty and progress. For these reasons primarily it must be resisted. For a hundred and fifty years liberalism has found its true spirit in the American system, not in the European systems.

. . . By adherence to the principles of decentralized self-government, ordered liberty, equal opportunity, and freedom to the individual, our American experiment in human welfare has yielded a degree of well-being unparalleled in all the world. It has come nearer to the abolition of poverty, to the abolition of fear of want, than humanity has ever reached before. Progress of the past seven years is the proof of it. This alone furnishes the answer to our opponents, who ask us to introduce destructive elements into the system by which this has been accomplished. . . .

1. According to Hoover, why was government intrusion in business acceptable during the war?

   _____

2. Why did he think that the Republicans were responsible for the growth and prosperity after World War I?

   _____

3. Contrast the European philosophy with the American system. _____

   _____

   _____

4. Who does Hoover think is responsible for solving most of the problems of American society? _____

5. Does America follow Hoover's position or the European philosophy today? Support your answer.

   _____

6. Do you agree or disagree with Hoover's position and why?_____

   _____

Decade of Change

After World War I interrupted the Progressive Era (1901–16), Americans wanted a "return to normalcy." But the horrors of war had broken their faith in progressivism. Complete the following chart to show the changes that took place after the war and contrast the two eras.

	Progressivism	Normalcy
Foreign relations		
DECADE(S)		
PRESIDENTS		
FOREIGN AFFAIRS		
MILITARY BUILDUP (ESP. NAVY)		
PEACE TREATIES	Treaty of Portsmouth (to maintain a balance of power in Asia)	
Labor		
FARM ECONOMY		
IMMIGRATION		
Lifestyle		
HUMANITARIAN GOALS		
RURAL LIFE		
ATTITUDES TOWARD BUSINESS		
Morality		
MORAL STANDARDS		
ATTITUDES TOWARD PROHIBITION		
PRESIDENTIAL LEADERSHIP		

Following are some of the most frequently mentioned names, phrases, and events from the 1920s. Match each of them with the lesson that it *best* illustrates. (*Note: Not all choices will be used.*)

A. Sacco and Vanzetti   F. flappers   K. *The Man Nobody Knows*
B. Freud and Darwin   G. movie idols   L. Treaty of Washington
C. Al Capone   H. speculation   M. Teapot Dome scandal
D. Scopes trial   I. automobile accidents   N. Red Scare
E. Ku Klux Klan   J. "return to normalcy"   O. economic depression

_____ 1. The horrors of war often cause moral decline and following of fads and fashions.

_____ 2. When the economy is bad, prejudice and racism increase.

_____ 3. God says that Christians will be scorned if they take a stand for their faith.

_____ 4. During great prosperity, nations become materialistic and forget humanitarian goals.

_____ 5. New technology brings unexpected problems as well as benefits.

_____ 6. Media coverage often leads to worldly, rebellious practices.

_____ 7. One sign of moral decay is an excessive interest in gangsters and sensationalism.

_____ 8. After the trauma of war, society often idealizes the past.

_____ 9. Agreements to reduce arms are ineffective because nations make many exceptions.

_____ 10. The pleasures of this world last only a season.

Bonus fill-in-the-blank questions.

11. Which man showed that liberalism might force Christians to leave their jobs or churches?

_____

12. Which president illustrates the fact that one president gets blamed for problems caused by his predecessors? _____

"Crash!"

Read the following account of the 1929 stock market crash, which marks the beginning of the Great Depression. Then answer the questions that follow.

The big gong had hardly sounded in the great hall of the Exchange at ten o'clock Tuesday morning before the storm broke in full force. Huge blocks of stock were thrown upon the market for what they would bring. Five thousand shares; ten thousand shares appeared at a time on the laboring ticker at fearful recessions in price. Not only were innumerable small traders being sold out, but big ones, too, protagonists of the new economic era who a few weeks before had counted themselves millionaires. Again and again the specialist in a stock would find himself surrounded by brokers fighting to sell—and nobody at all even thinking of buying. To give one single example: during the bull market the common stock of the White Sewing Machine Company had gone as high as 48; on Monday, October 28th, it had closed at 11 1/8. On that black Tuesday, somebody—a clever messenger boy for the Exchange, it was rumored—had the bright idea of putting in an order to buy at 1—and in the temporarily complete absence of other bids he actually got his stock for a dollar a share! The scene on the floor was chaotic. Despite the jamming of the Communication system, orders to buy and sell—mostly to sell—came in faster than human beings could possibly handle them. . . . Within half an hour of the Opening the volume of trading had passed three million shares, by twelve o'clock it had passed eight million, by half-past one it had passed twelve million, and when the closing gong brought the day's madness to an end the gigantic record of 16,410,030 shares had been set. Toward the close there was a rally, but by that time the average prices of fifty leading stocks . . . had fallen nearly forty points.

So complete was the demoralization of the stock market and exhausted were the brokers and their staffs and the Stock Exchange employees, that at noon that day, when the panic was at its worst, the Governing Committee met quietly to decide, whether or not to close the Exchange. . . . After some deliberation, the governors finally decided not to close the Exchange.

The next day—Wednesday, October 30th—the outlook suddenly and providentially brightened. The directors of the Steel Corporation had declared an extra dividend; the directors of the American Can Company had not only declared an extra dividend, but had raised the regular dividend. There was another flood of reassuring statements—though by this time a cheerful statement from a financier fell upon somewhat skeptical ears. Julius Klein, Mr. Hoover's Assistant Secretary of Commerce, composed a rhapsody on continued prosperity. John J. Raskob declared that stocks were at bargain prices and that he and his friends were buying. John D. Rockefeller poured Standard Oil upon the waters: "Believing that fundamental conditions of the country are sound and that there is nothing in the business situation to warrant the destruction of values that has taken place on the exchanges during the past week, my son and I have for some days been purchasing sound common stocks." Better still, prices rose steadily and buoyantly. Now at last the time had come when the strain on the Exchange could be relieved without causing undue alarm. At 1:40 o'clock Vice-President Whitney announced from the rostrum that the Exchange would not open until noon the following day and would remain closed all day Friday and Saturday,—and to his immense relief the announcement was greeted, not with renewed panic, but with a cheer.

Throughout Thursday's short session the recovery continued. Prices gyrated wildly—for who could arrive at a reasonable idea of what a given stock was worth, now that all settled standards of value had been upset?—but the worst of the storm seemed to have blown over. The financial community breathed more easily; now they could have a chance to set their houses in order.

It was true that the worst of the panic was past. But not the worst prices. There was too much forced liquidation still to come as brokers' accounts were gradually straightened out, as banks called for more collateral, and terror was renewed. The next week, in a series of short sessions, the tide of prices receded once more—until at last on November 13th the bottom prices for the year 1929 were reached. . . .

The *New York Times* averages for fifty leading stocks had been almost cut in half, falling from a high of 311.90 in September to a low of 164.43 on November 13th; and the *Times* averages for twenty-five leading industrials had fared still worse, diving from 469.49 to 220.95.

The Big Bull Market was dead. Billions of dollars' worth of profits—and paper profits—had disappeared. The grocer, the window-cleaner, and the seamstress had lost their capital. In every town there were families which had suddenly dropped from showy affluence into debt. Investors who had dreamed of retiring to live on their fortunes now found themselves back once more at the very beginning of the long road to riches. Day by day the newspapers printed the grim reports of suicides.

Coolidge-Hoover Prosperity was not yet dead, but it was dying. Under the impact of the shock of panic, a multitude of ills which hitherto had passed unnoticed or had been offset by stock-market optimism began to beset the body economic, as poisons seep through the human system when a vital organ has ceased to function normally. Although the liquidation of nearly three billion dollars of brokers' loans contracted credit, and the Reserve Banks lowered the rediscount rate, and the way in which the larger banks and corporations of the country had survived the emergency without a single failure of large proportions offered real encouragement, nevertheless the poisons were there; overproduction of capital; overambitious expansion of business concerns; overproduction of commodities under the stimulus of installment buying and buying with stock-market profits; the maintenance of an artificial price level for many commodities, the depressed condition of European trade. No matter how many soothsayers of high finance proclaimed that all was well, no matter how earnestly the President set to work to repair the damage with soft words and White House conferences, a major depression was inevitably under way.

Nor was that all. Prosperity is more than an economic condition; it is a state of mind. The Big Bull Market had been more than the climax of a business cycle; it had been the climax of a cycle in American mass thinking and mass emotion. There was hardly a man or woman in the country whose attitude toward life had not been affected by it in some degree and was not now affected by the sudden and brutal shattering of hope. With the Big Bull Market gone and prosperity going, Americans were soon to find themselves living in an altered world which called for new adjustments, new ideas, new habits of thought, and a new order of values. The psychological climate was changing; the ever-shifting currents of American life were turning into new channels.

1. What happened at the opening bell of the stock exchange on Tuesday, October 29?

   _____

   _____

2. What one word does the author of this account use to describe the trading floor? _____

3. How many shares had sold within half an hour of the opening bell? By noon? By the closing gong?

   _____

   _____

4. What happened to the exchange on Wednesday and during the shortened session on Thursday?

_____

5. On what date did the worst prices of the stock crash occur? _____

6. What "poisons" that produced the crash did the author say were lurking in the "body economic"?

_____

_____

_____

7. According to the author, what were two ways by which Hoover tried to repair the damage?

_____

8. Rather than being merely an economic condition, prosperity, the author says, is what? _____

9. What other factors that led to the crash does your textbook reveal but the author of this selection ignore?

_____

_____

10. Who do you think was most to blame for the stock market crash and the depression that followed it?

_____

_____

_____

_____

Hoover Versus FDR

Until the election of 1932, rarely had two successive presidents been more different. Hoover was a self-made westerner; Roosevelt, a rich-born easterner. Using your textbook (and outside sources if necessary), complete the chart to show their major differences.

	Herbert Hoover	Franklin Roosevelt
Number of terms		
Political party		
Previous occupation		
Hometown		
Religious affiliation		
Domestic conditions during his presidency		
Views of federal assistance		
Major economic programs		
Public reaction to his administration		

Roosevelt's First Inaugural Address, March 4, 1933

President Hoover, Mr. Chief Justice, my friends:

This is a day of national consecration. And I am certain that on this day my fellow Americans expect that on my induction into the Presidency, I will address them with a candor and a decision which the present situation of our people impels.

This is preeminently the time to speak the truth, the whole truth, frankly and boldly. Nor need we shrink from honestly facing conditions in our country today. This great Nation will endure, as it has endured, will revive and will prosper.

So, first of all, let me assert my firm belief that the only thing we have to fear is fear itself—nameless, unreasoning, unjustified terror which paralyzes needed efforts to convert retreat into advance. In every dark hour of our national life, a leadership of frankness and of vigor has met with that understanding and support of the people themselves which is essential to victory. And I am convinced that you will again give that support to leadership in these critical days.

In such a spirit on my part and on yours we face our common difficulties. They concern, thank God, only material things. Values have shrunk to fantastic levels; taxes have risen; our ability to pay has fallen; government of all kinds is faced by serious curtailment of income; the means of exchange are frozen in the currents of trade; the withered leaves of industrial enterprise lie on every side; farmers find no markets for their produce; and the savings of many years in thousands of families are gone. More important, a host of unemployed citizens face the grim problem of existence, and an equally great number toil with little return. Only a foolish optimist can deny the dark realities of the moment.

And yet our distress comes from no failure of substance. We are stricken by no plague of locusts. Compared with the perils which our forefathers conquered, because they believed and were not afraid, we have still much to be thankful for. Nature still offers her bounty and human efforts have multiplied it. Plenty is at our doorstep, but a generous use of it languishes in the very sight of the supply.

Primarily, this is because the rulers of the exchange of mankind's goods have failed, through their own stubbornness and their own incompetence, have admitted their failure, and have abdicated. Practices of the unscrupulous money changers stand indicted in the court of public opinion, rejected by the hearts and minds of men.

True, they have tried. But their efforts have been cast in the pattern of an outworn tradition. Faced by failure of credit, they have proposed only the lending of more money. Stripped of the lure of profit by which to induce our people to follow their false leadership, they have resorted to exhortations, pleading tearfully for restored confidence. They only know the rules of a generation of self-seekers. They have no vision, and when there is no vision the people perish.

Yes, the money changers have fled from their high seats in the temple of our civilization. We may now restore that temple to the ancient truths. The measure of that restoration lies in the extent to which we apply social values more noble than mere monetary profit.

Happiness lies not in the mere possession of money; it lies in the joy of achievement, in the thrill of creative effort. The joy, the moral stimulation of work no longer must be forgotten in the mad chase of evanescent [fleeting] profits. These dark days, my friends, will be worth all they cost us if they teach us that our true destiny is not to be ministered unto but to minister to ourselves, to our fellow men.

Recognition of that falsity of material wealth as the standard of success goes hand in hand with the abandonment of the false belief that public office and high political position are to be valued only by the standards of pride of place and personal profit; and there must be an end to a conduct in banking and in business which too often has given to a sacred trust the likeness of callous and selfish wrongdoing. Small wonder that confidence languishes, for it thrives only on honesty, on honor, on the sacredness of obligations, on faithful protection, and on unselfish performance; without them it cannot live.

Restoration calls, however, not for changes in ethics alone. This Nation is asking for action, and action now.

Our greatest primary task is to put people to work. This is no unsolvable problem if we face it wisely and courageously. It can be accomplished in part by direct recruiting by the Government itself, treating the task as we would treat the emergency of a war, but at the same time, through this employment, accomplishing greatly needed projects to stimulate and reorganize the use of our great natural resources.

Hand in hand with that we must frankly recognize the overbalance of population in our industrial centers and, by engaging on a national scale in a redistribution, endeavor to provide a better use of the land for those best fitted for the land.

Yes, the task can be helped by definite efforts to raise the values of agricultural products, and with this the power to purchase the output of our cities. It can be helped by preventing realistically the tragedy of the growing loss through foreclosure of our small homes and our farms. It can be helped by insistence that the Federal, the State, and the local governments act forthwith on the demand that their cost be drastically reduced. It can be helped by the unifying of relief activities which today are often scattered, uneconomical, unequal. It can be helped by national planning for and supervision of all forms of transportation and of communications and other utilities that have a definitely public character. There are many ways in which it can be helped, but it can never be helped by merely talking about it. We must act. We must act quickly.

And finally, in our progress towards a resumption of work, we require two safeguards against a return of the evils of the old order. There must be a strict supervision of all banking and credits and investments. There must be an end to speculation with other people's money. And there must be provision for an adequate but sound currency.

These, my friends, are the lines of attack. I shall presently urge upon a new Congress in special session detailed measures for their fulfillment, and I shall seek the immediate assistance of the 48 States.

Through this program of action we address ourselves to putting our own national house in order and making income balance outgo. Our international trade relations, though vastly important, are in point of time, and necessity, secondary to the establishment of a sound national economy. I favor, as a practical policy, the putting of first things first. I shall spare no effort to restore world trade by international economic readjustment; but the emergency at home cannot wait on that accomplishment.

The basic thought that guides these specific means of national recovery is not narrowly nationalistic. It is the insistence, as a first consideration, upon the interdependence of the various elements in all parts of the United States—a recognition of the old and permanently important manifestation of the American spirit of the pioneer. It is the way to recovery. It is the immediate way. It is the strongest assurance that the recovery will endure.

In the field of world policy, I would dedicate this Nation to the policy of the good neighbor: the neighbor who resolutely respects himself and, because he does so, respects the rights of others; the neighbor who respects his obligations and respects the sanctity of his agreements in and with a world of neighbors.

If I read the temper of our people correctly, we now realize, as we have never realized before, our interdependence on each other; that we can not merely take, but we must give as well; that if we are to go forward, we must move as a trained and loyal army willing to sacrifice for the good of a common discipline, because without such discipline no progress can be made, no leadership becomes effective.

We are, I know, ready and willing to submit our lives and our property to such discipline, because it makes possible a leadership which aims at the larger good. This, I propose to offer, pledging that the larger purposes will bind upon us, bind upon us all as a sacred obligation with a unity of duty hitherto evoked only in times of armed strife.

With this pledge taken, I assume unhesitatingly the leadership of this great army of our people dedicated to a disciplined attack upon our common problems.

Action in this image, action to this end is feasible under the form of government which we have inherited from our ancestors. Our Constitution is so simple, so practical that it is possible always to meet extraordinary needs by changes in emphasis and arrangement without loss of essential form. That is why our constitutional system has proved itself the most superbly enduring political mechanism the modern world has ever seen.

It has met every stress of vast expansion of territory, of foreign wars, of bitter internal strife, of world relations. And it is to be hoped that the normal balance of executive and legislative authority may be wholly equal, wholly adequate to meet the unprecedented task before us. But it may be that an unprecedented demand and need for undelayed action may call for temporary departure from that normal balance of public procedure.

I am prepared under my constitutional duty to recommend the measures that a stricken nation in the midst of a stricken world may require. These measures, or such other measures as the Congress may build out of its experience and wisdom, I shall seek, within my constitutional authority, to bring to speedy adoption.

But, in the event that the Congress shall fail to take one of these two courses, in the event that the national emergency is still critical, I shall not evade the clear course of duty that will then confront me. I shall ask the Congress for the one remaining instrument to meet the crisis—broad Executive power to wage a war against the emergency, as great as the power that would be given to me if we were in fact invaded by a foreign foe.

For the trust reposed in me, I will return the courage and the devotion that befit the time. I can do no less.

We face the arduous days that lie before us in the warm courage of national unity; with the clear consciousness of seeking old and precious moral values; with the clean satisfaction that comes from the stern performance of duty by old and young alike. We aim at the assurance of a rounded, a permanent national life.

We do not distrust the future of essential democracy. The people of the United States have not failed. In their need they have registered a mandate that they want direct, vigorous action. They have asked for discipline and direction under leadership. They have made me the present instrument of their wishes. In the spirit of the gift I take it.

In this dedication of a Nation, we humbly ask the blessing of God.
May He protect each and every one of us. May He guide me in the days to come.

1. What words of optimism did Roosevelt speak at the beginning of his inaugural address that were designed to give the American people hope in the dark days of the Depression?

   _____

2. According to Roosevelt, what was the only thing that Americans need fear? _____

3. Whom does Roosevelt blame for the economic plight of the country? _____

   _____

4. What does Roosevelt say those people lack, and what Scripture verse does he quote in identifying it?

_____

5. By what does Roosevelt say the proposed restoration of the economy is to be measured?

_____

_____

6. Where does he say happiness lies? _____

7. What false belief does he say must be abandoned? _____

_____

_____

8. What does he say the nation is demanding of government—and demanding it now? _____

9. What does he say is the primary task in the effort to revive the economy, and how does he propose to do that? _____

10. Against what dangers does he say the government must develop "safeguards," and how does he propose to do that? _____

_____

_____

11. What term does he use to describe the foreign policy he intends to pursue as president? _____

12. To what image does Roosevelt repeatedly allude in his speech that gives listeners or readers an idea of how he will tackle the nation's problems? _____

13. If Congress fails to enact the measures that he thinks are essential to meeting the economic crisis, what does FDR say he will ask them to give him? _____

_____

_____

14. In return for the trust of the American people, what does he promise to give?

_____

15. What is your opinion of Franklin Roosevelt based on your knowledge of the Depression and this address?

_____

_____

_____

_____

_____

FDR's Fireside Chat, March 12, 1933

Read the following fireside chat, which Roosevelt delivered on Sunday, March 12, 1933. Then answer the questions that follow.

I want to talk for a few minutes with the people of the United States about banking—with the comparatively few who understand the mechanics of banking but more particularly with the overwhelming majority who use banks for the making of deposits and the drawing of checks. I want to tell you what has been done in the last few days, why it was done, and what the next steps are going to be. I recognize that the many proclamations from State Capitols and from Washington, the legislation, the Treasury regulations, etc., couched for the most part in banking and legal terms should be explained for the benefit of the average citizen. I owe this in particular because of the fortitude and good temper with which everybody has accepted the inconvenience and hardships of the banking holiday. I know that when you understand what we in Washington have been about I shall continue to have your cooperation as fully as I have had your sympathy and help during the past week.

First of all let me state the simple fact that when you deposit money in a bank the bank does not put the money into a safe deposit vault. It invests your money in many different forms of credit—bonds, commercial paper, mortgages and many other kinds of loans. In other words, the bank puts your money to work to keep the wheels of industry and of agriculture turning around. A comparatively small part of the money you put into the bank is kept in currency—an amount which in normal times is wholly sufficient to cover the cash needs of the average citizen. In other words the total amount of all the currency in the country is only a small fraction of the total deposits in all of the banks.

What, then, happened during the last few days of February and the first few days of March? Because of undermined confidence on the part of the public, there was a general rush by a large portion of our population to turn bank deposits into currency or gold. A rush so great that the soundest banks could not get enough currency to meet the demand. The reason for this was that on the spur of the moment it was, of course, impossible to sell perfectly sound assets of a bank and convert them into cash except at panic prices far below their real value.

By the afternoon of March 3 scarcely a bank in the country was open to do business. Proclamations temporarily closing them in whole or in part had been issued by the Governors in almost all the states.

It was then that I issued the proclamation providing for the nation-wide bank holiday, and this was the first step in the Government's reconstruction of our financial and economic fabric.

The second step was the legislation promptly and patriotically passed by the Congress confirming my proclamation and broadening my powers so that it became possible in view of the requirement of time to entend [sic] the holiday and lift the ban of that holiday gradually. This law also gave authority to develop a program of rehabilitation of our banking facilities. I want to tell our citizens in every part of the Nation that the national Congress—Republicans and Democrats alike—showed by this action a devotion to public welfare and a realization of the emergency and the necessity for speed that it is difficult to match in our history.

The third stage has been the series of regulations permitting the banks to continue their functions to take care of the distribution of food and household necessities and the payment of payrolls.

This bank holiday, while resulting in many cases in great inconvenience, is affording us the opportunity to supply the currency necessary to meet the situation. No sound bank is a dollar worse off than it was when it closed its doors last Monday. Neither is any bank which may turn out not to be in a position for immediate opening. The new law allows the twelve Federal Reserve banks to issue additional currency on good assets, and thus the banks which reopen will be able to meet every legitimate call. The new currency is being sent out by the Bureau of Engraving and Printing in large volume to every part of the country. It is sound currency because it is backed by actual, good assets.

As a result we start tomorrow, Monday, with the opening of banks in the twelve Federal Reserve bank cities—those banks which on first examination by the Treasury have already been found to be all right. This will be followed on Tuesday by the resumption of all their functions by banks already found to be sound in cities where there are recognized clearing houses. That means about 250 cities of the United States.

On Wednesday and succeeding days banks in smaller places all through the country will resume business, subject, of course, to the Government's physical ability to complete its survey. It is necessary that the reopening of banks be extended over a period in order to permit the banks to make applications for necessary loans, to obtain currency needed to meet their requirements and to enable the Government to make common sense checkups. Let me make it clear to you that if your bank does not open the first day you are by no means justified in believing that it will not open. A bank that opens on one of the subsequent days is in exactly the same status as the bank that opens tomorrow.

I know that many people are worrying about State banks not members of the Federal Reserve System. These banks can and will receive assistance from member banks and from the Reconstruction Finance Corporation. These state banks are following the same course as the national banks except that they get their licenses to resume business from the state authorities, and these authorities have been asked by the Secretary of the Treasury to permit their good banks to open up on the same schedule as the national banks. I am confident that the state banking departments will be as careful as the National Government in the policy relating to the opening of banks and will follow the same broad policy. It is possible that when the banks resume a very few people who have not recovered from their fear may again begin withdrawals. Let me make it clear that the banks will take care of all needs—and it is my belief that hoarding during the past week has become an exceedingly unfashionable pastime. It needs no prophet to tell you that when the people find that they can get their money—that they can get it when they want it for all legitimate purposes—the phantom of fear will soon be laid. People will again be glad to have their money where it will be safely taken care of and where they can use it conveniently at any time. I can assure you that it is safer to keep your money in a reopened bank than under the mattress.

The success of our whole great national program depends, of course, upon the cooperation of the public—on its intelligent support and use of a reliable system.

Remember that the essential accomplishment of the new legislation is that it makes it possible for banks more readily to convert their assets into cash than was the case before. More liberal provision has been made for banks to borrow on these assets at the Reserve Banks and more liberal provision has also been made for issuing currency on the security of those good assets. This currency is not fiat currency. It is issued only on adequate security—and every good bank has an abundance of such security.

One more point before I close. There will be, of course, some banks unable to reopen without being reorganized. The new law allows the Government to assist in making these reorganizations quickly and effectively and even allows the Government to subscribe to at least a part of new capital which may be required.

I hope you can see from this elemental recital of what your government is doing that there is nothing complex or radical in the process.

We had a bad banking situation. Some of our bankers had shown themselves either incompetent or dishonest in their handling of the people's funds. They had used the money entrusted to them in speculations and unwise loans. This was of course not true in the vast majority of our banks but it was true in enough of them to shock the people for a time into a sense of insecurity and to put them into a frame of mind where they did not differentiate, but seemed to assume that the acts of a comparative few had tainted them all. It was the Government's job to straighten out this situation and do it as quickly as possible—and the job is being performed.

I do not promise you that every bank will be reopened or that individual losses will not be suffered, but there will be no losses that possibly could be avoided; and there would have been more and greater losses had we continued to drift. I can even promise you salvation for some at least of the sorely pressed banks. We shall be engaged not merely in reopening sound banks but in the creation of sound banks through reorganization. It has been wonderful to me to catch the note of confidence from all over the country. I can never be sufficiently grateful to the people for the loyal support they have given me in their acceptance of the judgment that has dictated our course, even though all of our processes may not have seemed clear to them.

After all there is an element in the readjustment of our financial system more important than currency, more important than gold, and that is the confidence of the people. Confidence and courage are the essentials of success in carrying out our plan. You people must have faith; you must not be stampeded by rumors or guesses. Let us unite in banishing fear. We have provided the machinery to restore our financial system; it is up to you to support and make it work.

It is your problem no less than it is mine. Together we cannot fail.

1. On what day of the week was this radio speech delivered and why was that fact important?

2. What was the main topic of the president's "chat"? _____

3. What three-point outline does Roosevelt give at the beginning of his speech? _____

4. What misconception about bank deposits does he address first, and what is his explanation?

5. Why could banks not meet the rush that depositors made on them in the early days of the Depression?

6. What was the first step in the government's reconstruction of the banking system?

7. To reassure listeners of the strength of state banks that were not members of the Federal Reserve System, from where did Roosevelt say they would be able to get help? _____

8. What practice based on panic did he call "an exceedingly unfashionable pastime"? _____

9. What two terms does Roosevelt use to describe bankers who used depositors' money for speculation and unwise loans? _____

10. What element of the banking readjustment does he say is more important than either the currency or gold?

_____

11. Against what does he warn the people that might destroy that element? _____

_____

12. If you had money in a bank at that time and were listening to the president's fireside chat, would it give you greater confidence in the president and the government's ability to solve the problems of the economy? Why or why not? _____

_____

_____

_____

Huey Long's Plan to "Share the Wealth"

On February 5, 1934, Senator Huey Long of Louisiana delivered a speech in the U.S. Senate outlining his "Share the Wealth" program. Read the first portion of that speech, and then answer the questions that follow.

THE CONGRESSIONAL RECORD—February 5, 1934

Mr. Long: Mr. President, I send to the desk and ask to have printed in the RECORD not a speech but what is more in the nature of an appeal to the people of America.

There being no objection, the paper entitled "Carry Out the Command of the Lord" was ordered to be printed in the RECORD, as follows:

By Huey P. Long, United States Senator

People of America: In every community get together at once and organize a share-our-wealth society—Motto: Every man a king.

Principles and platform:

1. To limit poverty by providing that every deserving family shall share in the wealth of America for not less than one third of the average wealth, thereby to possess not less than $5,000 free of debt.

2. To limit fortunes to such a few million dollars as will allow the balance of the American people to share in the wealth and profits of the land.

3. Old-age pensions of $30 per month to persons over 60 years of age who do not earn as much as $1,000 per year or who possess less than $10,000 in cash or property, thereby to remove from the field of labor in times of unemployment those who have contributed their share to the public service.

4. To limit the hours of work to such an extent as to prevent overproduction and to give the workers of America some share in the recreations, conveniences, and luxuries of life.

5. To balance agricultural production with what can be sold and consumed according to the laws of God, which have never failed.

6. To care for the veterans of our wars.

7. Taxation to run the Government to be supported, first, by reducing big fortunes from the top, thereby to improve the country and provide employment in public works whenever agricultural surplus is such as to render unnecessary, in whole or in part, any particular crop.

Simple and Concrete—Not an Experiment

To share our wealth by providing for every deserving family to have one third of the average wealth would mean that, at the worst, such a family could have a fairly comfortable home, an automobile, and a radio, with other reasonable home conveniences, and a place to educate their children. Through sharing the work, that is, by limiting the hours of toil so that all would share in what is made and produced in the land, every family would have enough coming in every year to feed, clothe, and provide a fair share of the luxuries of life to its members. Such is the result to a family, at the worst.

From the worst to the best there would be no limit to opportunity. One might become a millionaire or more. There would be a chance for talent to make a man big, because enough would be floating in the land to give brains its chance to be used. As it is, no matter how smart a man may be, everything is tied up in so few hands that no amount of energy or talent has a chance to gain any of it.

Would it break up big concerns? No. It would simply mean that, instead of one man getting all the one concern made, that there might be 1,000 or 10,000 persons sharing in such excess fortune, any one of whom, or all of whom, might be millionaires and over.

I ask somebody in every city, town, village, and farm community of America to take this as my personal request to call a meeting of as many neighbors and friends as will come to it to start a share-our-wealth society. Elect a president and a secretary and charge no dues. The meeting can be held at a courthouse, in some town hall or public building, or in the home of someone.

It does not matter how many will come to the first meeting. Get a society organized, if it has only two members. Then let us get to work quick, quick, quick to put an end by law to people starving and going naked in this land of too much to eat and too much to wear. The case is all with us. It is the word and work of the Lord. The Gideons had but two men when they organized. Three tailors of Tooley Street drew the Magna Carta of England. The Lord says: "For where two or three are gathered together in My name, there am I in the midst of them."

We propose to help our people into the place where the Lord said was their rightful own and no more.

We have waited long enough for these financial masters to do these things. They have promised and promised. Now we find our country $10 billion further in debt on account of the depression, and big lenders even propose to get 90 percent of that out of the hides of the common people in the form of a sales tax.

There is nothing wrong with the United States. We have more food than we can eat. We have more clothes and things out of which to make clothes than we can wear. We have more houses and lands than the whole 120 million can use if they all had good homes. So what is the trouble? Nothing except that a handful of men have everything and the balance of the people have nothing if their debts were paid. There should be every man a king in this land flowing with milk and honey instead of the lords of finance at the top and slaves and peasants at the bottom.

Now be prepared for the slurs and snickers of some high-ups when you start your local spread-our-wealth society. Also when you call your meeting be on your guard for some smart-aleck tool of the interests to come in and ask questions. Refer such to me for an answer to any question, and I will send you a copy. Spend your time getting the people to work to save their children and to save their homes, or to get a home for those who have already lost their own.

To explain the title, motto, and principles of such a society I give the full information, viz:

Title: Share-our-wealth society is simply to mean that God's creatures on this lovely American continent have a right to share in the wealth they have created in this country. They have the right to a living, with the conveniences and some of the luxuries of this life, so long as there are too many or enough for all. They have a right to raise their children in a healthy, wholesome atmosphere and to educate them, rather than to face the dread of their under-nourishment and sadness by being denied a real life.

Motto: "Every man a king" conveys the great plan of God and of the Declaration of Independence, which said: "All men are created equal." It conveys that no one man is the lord of another, but that from the head to the foot of every man is carried his sovereignty.

1. What is the motto of Huey Long's share-our-wealth society? _____

2. What three things does his seven-point platform propose to limit? _____

3. What minimum annual debt-free income does he promise every American? _____

4. What does he propose will be the source of that guaranteed annual income?

_____

_____

5. How does he propose to pay the expenses of running the government? _____

6. What does he say every family would have as a result of adopting his plan?

_____

_____

_____

7. What are to be the dues of local share-our-wealth societies? _____

8. What Scripture does he quote to justify his plea for the forming of local share-our-wealth societies? Did he use that passage in its proper context or out of context? Why?

_____

_____

_____

_____

_____

9. According to Long, how do the "financial masters" propose to solve the problem of the national debt?

_____

_____

10. According to Long, what rights do all Americans have? _____

_____

_____

_____

_____

11. Upon what two respected things does Long claim to base the motto of his share-our-wealth societies?

_____

_____

_____

12. Is Long's "Share the Wealth" proposal biblical? Why or why not? Support your answer with Scripture.

_____

_____

_____

_____

_____

13. Is Long's program proposal constitutional? Why or why not? _____
_____
_____
_____
_____
_____

14. Do you agree or disagree with Long's philosophy and ideas? Why? _____
_____
_____
_____
_____
_____

Graphing Negative Numbers: Between the Wars (1920–1940)

Make a line graph to illustrate these data from the Census Bureau.
(Hint: Overspending is indicated by a *negative* difference.)

Year	'20	'21	'22	'23	'24	'25	'26	'27	'28	'29	'30	'31	'32	'33	'34	'35	'36	'37	'38	'39	'40
Income	6.6	5.6	4.0	3.9	3.9	3.6	3.8	4.0	3.9	3.8	4.0	3.2	2.0	2.1	3.1	3.8	4.2	5.6	7.0	6.6	6.9
Spending	6.4	5.1	3.3	3.1	2.9	2.9	2.9	2.9	3.0	2.9	3.1	4.1	4.8	4.7	6.5	6.3	7.6	8.4	7.2	9.4	9.6
Difference	0.2	0.5	0.7	0.8	1.0	0.7	0.9	1.1	0.9	0.9	0.9	-0.9	-2.8	-2.6	-3.4	-2.5	-3.4	-2.8	-0.2	-2.8	-2.7

Government Overspending (in billions)

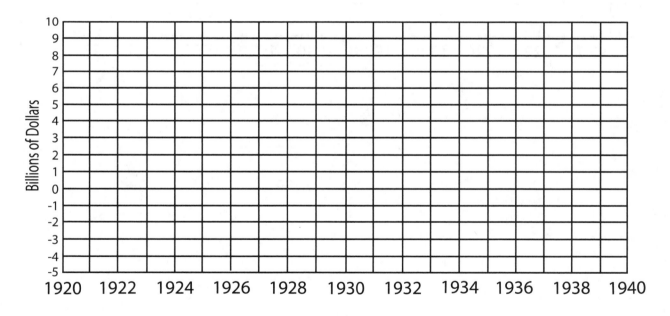

GNP means "gross national product." GNP growth shows the ups and downs of American business. Use blue bars to plot GNP increases and red bars to plot GNP declines.

Year	'20	'21	'22	'23	'24	'25	'26	'27	'28	'29	'30	'31	'32	'33	'34	'35	'36	'37	'38	'39	'40
GNP growth	-8.6	15.8	12.1	-0.2	8.4	5.9	0	0.6	6.7	-9.8	-7.6	-14.7	-1.8	9.1	9.9	13.9	5.3	-5.0	8.6	8.5	16.1

GNP Changes 1920–1940

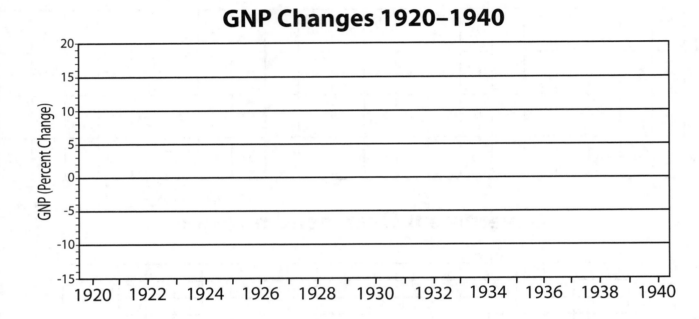

AMERICAN REPUBLIC

Name _____

Interpreting Political Cartoons of the New Deal Era

Examine carefully the following political cartoons from the New Deal era. Then, in the space provided under each one, write a brief summary of what the cartoonist is trying to say to readers. In your summary, try to answer the following questions: What is the main issue being addressed? On which side of the issue is the cartoonist? Who is caricatured in the cartoon?

The Farmer: "Sure, I'll Try Anything Once!"
By MORRIS

1. _____

_____

_____

_____

_____

_____

_____

_____

_____

Step by Step

2. _____
_____
_____
_____
_____
_____
_____
_____
_____
_____
_____

Chapter Review

Match the following people with the thing for which they are noted.

_____ 1. Opposed FDR in the presidential election of 1936

_____ 2. Challenged FDR with his "Share the Wealth" program

_____ 3. Detroit priest who challenged FDR on his national radio broadcast

_____ 4. Proposed $200/mo. pension for sixty-year-olds—if they spent it all

_____ 5. Ran on a conservative platform in the 1932 presidential campaign

_____ 6. Rightly or wrongly, received most of the blame for the Depression

A. Charles Coughlin
B. Herbert Hoover
C. Alf Landon
D. Huey Long
E. Franklin Roosevelt
F. Elmer Townsend

Identify each of the following government agencies and summarize its purpose.

7. RFC _____

_____

8. FERA _____

_____

9. WPA _____

_____

10. AAA _____

_____

11. NRA _____

_____

12. CCC _____

_____

13. TVA _____

_____

Define or state the significance of the following terms and dates.

14. speculation

_____

_____

15. buying on margin

_____

_____

16. Dust Bowl

_____

_____

17. Bonus Army

_____

_____

18. dole

_____

_____

19. New Deal

_____

_____

20. brain trust

_____

_____

21. bank holiday

_____

_____

22. recession

_____

_____

23. October 29, 1929

_____

_____

24. 1932

_____

_____

25. 1936

_____

_____

Prelude to World War II

On the following table, indicate with an *X* which country each of the statements on the left describes during the years leading up to World War II. (Some descriptions might require that you mark more than one country.)

Description	Italy	Japan	Germany
1. Not satisfied with results of the peace made after World War I			
2. Led by *Il Duce*			
3. Led by the *Führer*			
4. Established a governmental and economic system known as Fascism			
5. Established a governmental and economic system known as Nazism			
6. Invaded Manchuria in 1931			
7. Was policed by military thugs called the "Black Shirts"			
8. Set up a totalitarian government			
9. Supposedly a Third Reich			
10. Supposedly a restored Roman Empire			
11. Had to contend with the American Volunteer Group, or the "Flying Tigers"			
12. Revealed Nazi philosophy in a book titled *Mein Kampf*			
13. Defied the League of Nations by invading the Rhineland			
14. Defied the League of Nations by invading Ethiopia and Albania			
15. Became part of the Axis powers			

The War Begins: Chronological Order

Arrange the following events chronologically by numbering them from 1 to 14, with 1 being the first event to occur.

_____ 1. President Roosevelt froze all Axis assets in the United States.

_____ 2. Hitler invaded the Soviet Union.

_____ 3. The Allied army escaped from Dunkirk.

_____ 4. Hitler invaded Poland.

_____ 5. Hitler demanded and got the Sudetenland from Czechoslovakia.

_____ 6. Hitler and Stalin signed a nonaggression pact.

_____ 7. Hitler invaded France.

_____ 8. Congress passed the Lend-Lease Act.

_____ 9. Japanese diplomats arrived in Washington, D.C., to negotiate differences between Japan and the United States.

_____ 10. Hitler united Germany and Austria in the forbidden _Anschluss_.

_____ 11. The _Luftwaffe_ bombed English airfields and cities, including London.

_____ 12. Chamberlain announced that he had negotiated "peace for our time."

_____ 13. Churchill replaced Chamberlain as the British prime minister.

_____ 14. The Russians forced the Nazi armies to retreat from Moscow.

★ ★ ★ ★ ★ ★ ★ ★ ★ ★

FDR's Request for a Declaration of War Against Japan

Read President Roosevelt's address to Congress on December 8, 1941, in which he requested a declaration of war against Japan. Then answer the questions.

Mr. Vice President, and Mr. Speaker, and Members of the Senate and House of Representatives:

Yesterday, December 7, 1941—a date which will live in infamy—the United States of America was suddenly and deliberately attacked by naval and air forces of the Empire of Japan.

The United States was at peace with that Nation and, at the solicitation of Japan, was still in conversation with its Government and its Emperor looking toward the maintenance of peace in the Pacific. Indeed, one hour after Japanese air squadrons had commenced bombing in the American Island of Oahu, the Japanese Ambassador to the United States and his colleague delivered to our Secretary of State a formal reply to a recent American message. And while this reply stated that it seemed useless to continue the existing diplomatic negotiations, it contained no threat or hint of war or of armed attack.

It will be recorded that the distance of Hawaii from Japan makes it obvious that the attack was deliberately planned many days or even weeks ago. During the intervening time the Japanese Government has deliberately sought to deceive the United States by false statements and expressions of hope for continued peace.

The attack yesterday on the Hawaiian Islands has caused severe damage to American naval and military forces. I regret to tell you that very many American lives have been lost. In addition American ships have been reported torpedoed on the high seas between San Francisco and Honolulu.

Yesterday the Japanese Government also launched an attack against Malaya.

Last night Japanese forces attacked Hong Kong.

Last night Japanese forces attacked Guam.

Last night Japanese forces attacked the Philippine Islands.

Last night the Japanese attacked Wake Island. And this morning the Japanese attacked Midway Island.

Japan has, therefore, undertaken a surprise offensive extending throughout the Pacific area. The facts of yesterday and today speak for themselves. The people of the United States have already formed their opinions and well understand the implications to the very life and safety of our Nation.

As Commander in Chief of the Army and Navy I have directed that all measures be taken for our defense.

But always will our whole Nation remember the character of the onslaught against us.

No matter how long it may take us to overcome this premeditated invasion, the American people in their righteous might will win through to absolute victory. I believe that I interpret the will of the Congress and of the people when I assert that we will not only defend ourselves to the uttermost but will make it very certain that this form of treachery shall never again endanger us.

Hostilities exist. There is no blinking at the fact that our people, our territory, and our interests are in grave danger.

With confidence in our armed forces—with the unbounding determination of our people—we will gain the inevitable triumph—so help us God.

I ask that the Congress declare that since the unprovoked and dastardly attack by Japan on Sunday, December 7, 1941, a state of war has existed between the United States and the Japanese Empire.

[The resulting vote was 82–0 in the Senate and 388–1 in the House of Representatives. The lone opposing vote was cast by Jeannette Rankin, the first woman elected to Congress.]

1. How did FDR say the day of Japan's surprise attack would be remembered? _____

2. To what fact did he point as conclusive proof that the attack on Pearl Harbor was deliberate and planned?

_____

3. What did he say Japan was doing at the same time they were planning and launching the attack?

_____

4. What other places in the Pacific had the Japanese attacked in conjunction with the attack on Pearl Harbor?

_____

5. Why did he not explain the implications of this series of attacks throughout the Pacific?

_____

_____

6. Bonus: Why do you think Jeanette Rankin voted against the declaration of war when the facts for it were so

   clear? _____

_____

7. Do you think she was justified in opposing the declaration? Why or why not? _____

_____

8. FDR said that "we will not only defend ourselves to the uttermost but will make it very certain that this

   form of treachery shall never again endanger us." In light of the September 11, 2001, terrorist attacks on

   the United States, do you think that perhaps Americans have failed to live up to FDR's pledge? Why or why

   not? _____

_____

9. Compare and contrast Americans' responses (both immediate and long term) to Pearl Harbor and their

   responses to the 9/11 terrorist attacks. _____

_____

_____

_____

_____

_____

_____

_____

_____

_____

Life for a Japanese-American Internee

Read the following first-person account of a Japanese American, Estelle Ishigo, who, with her family, was interned in a relocation camp during World War II. She wrote of her experiences in a book titled *Lone Heart Mountain*. As you read, try to put yourself in the shoes of those people, many of whom had been born in the United States and knew no loyalty other than that to America. Then answer the questions that follow.

[After Pearl Harbor was bombed], the people of the United States of America united in support of the war. The great majority of Japanese Americans were a part of this unity. However, certain elements in the United States exerted effective pressure on the Government and the people, through radio and press, which succeeded in identifying Japanese Americans with Japanese militarism. Hence, at the beginning of 1942, under cover of wild rumors and suspicions, a "military necessity" was declared by the United States Command wherein all persons of Japanese ancestry living on the West Coast were placed under . . . "protective arrest." No matter how remote the ancestor, people listed as having Japanese "blood" were commanded to leave the West Coast or be placed in camps under Army supervision. Approximately 110,000 of these people from the aged to the newly born were listed. Of this number 70,000 were native born Americans and another 2,000 were university students. . . .

Nevertheless, they were forced from jobs, trades and professions. Shopkeepers had to sell at less than cost, farmers, large and small, had to lose their crops, some sold their long-established farmlands for practically nothing. There was no choice.

It was not long before many lacked even the necessities of life. In misery and despair they sold their household belongings—even down to the last cherished bowl or piece of silk—for the pittance offered by dealers.

After weeks of uncertainty and apprehension, a swift order came that those who had not been able to leave the Pacific Coast be prepared to leave for camps on a given date. Whatever belongings they might still have were to be tied, crated, and turned over to Government warehouses—in many cases never to be seen again by the owners.

No matter how staunch their loyalty to America, all were deprived of citizenship and told that evacuation and imprisonment were "for their protection."

Both my husband and I were born in California. My father was a member of Company C, 6th Regiment of Infantry, New York Volunteers, in the Civil War. My mother was from New Orleans, of French ancestry. My husband's mother and father came to this country in the 1890s from Japan.

When this crisis came, people thought above all else of keeping families together. We had no money to leave the West Coast, so my husband and I entered the camp together. . . .

The first sign of the barbed wire enclosure with armed soldiers standing guard as our bus slowly turned in through the gate stunned us with the meaning of this ordered evacuation. Here was a camp of sheds, enclosed within a high barbed wire fence, with guard towers and soldiers with machine guns. Not 25 miles from home and still in the United States of America—but suddenly like a foreign land. . . .

Warily, we stepped out of the bus and down to the ground, helping the old and carrying the very young.

A soldier pointed toward a table and ordered us to pass it single file and open our handbags to be searched for razors and flashlights, and no electric irons or radios were allowed. Then each family was registered, given an identification number and taken to a partitioned room of a shed. We were sent to a warehouse to get our mattresses and carry them back to our rooms, and when the mattresses ran out we were given sacks to fill with straw from bales stacked in the field.

These sheds were partitioned into rows of rooms by rough knotty boards with wide cracks and big knotholes through which everyone could see the families on each side. . . .

We watched in fascinated wonder as fearful and bewildered hundreds poured each day into these strange camps of "protective custody." There were some with blond, brown or red hair and eyes as blue as the sky, some were related through marriage, some were their children and some from remote ancestors of both countries who, for generations had known and loved no other country but America.

Within a few weeks 5,622 persons had been brought here. To accommodate this number there were three mess halls and the elderly, the young and even parents with small infants stood three times a day in great long lines for mess, and each one ate hastily to make room for all the others peering hungrily in through the windows out in the burning sun. . . .

A few mothers with tiny babies managed to hide an electric hot-plate and a little food in their bundles. The hotplates were forbidden and wherever they were found they were taken away.

The shed of wash tubs became a social gathering place for gossip while soiled cloths were being scrubbed.

When a letter or package was received from a friend "outside" there was great excitement and rejoicing, but all packages were first opened and searched by the Army.

And there was a visitor's day, when we went like prisoners in our camp cloths [sic] to a fenced area where we could sit and talk for a short time with those from the "outside" under the watchful eyes of armed guards. . . .

All the able were assigned jobs at keeping up the camp and wages were $12.00 and $16.00 a month. Refusal to work meant the black list with the threat of being sent to either the hottest or coldest of the future camps.

At night some tried to read despite gnats and bugs swarming around the lights. Occasionally, a thread of music floated on the air as an old one played a bamboo flute, or someone sang and plucked thin melancholy notes on a shamisen [a Japanese instrument similar to a lute]. . . .

Two small boys sat on the log, coals glowed in the tub before them.

"Are we Americans?" asked one.

"No, we are not Americans," his friend answered.

"But we were born here. If we are not Americans, what are we?"

"We are human beings."

"Who are the Americans?"

"White people are Americans."

1. What prompted the decision to relocate people of Japanese ancestry to inland areas? _____

_____

_____

2. What economic repercussions did the speed with which the Japanese Americans had to move have on them and their families? _____

_____

_____

3. What explanation were they given for their relocation and internment? _____

_____

260

4. What facts does the author point to as proof of her family's loyalty to America?

_____

_____

_____

_____

5. To what physical evidence in others in the internment camp does the author point to their Americanism?

_____

_____

_____

6. What would happen if an internee refused to work at the job they were assigned in the camp?

_____

_____

_____

7. How do you interpret the conversation between the two little Japanese American boys at the end of the selection? _____

_____

_____

_____

_____

8. What lessons do the relocation and internment of Japanese Americans hold for Americans today?

_____

_____

_____

_____

_____

_____

_____

_____

_____

_____

V-Mail from a Soldier

Hundreds of thousands of soldiers served in the United States military during World War II. Getting all of the letters they wrote home to family members and friends was a logistical nightmare. But the smooth and reliable delivery of mail to and from loved ones was critical to maintaining high morale among the troops. Colonel Bill Rose, U.S. Army Postal Director, came up with a unique and efficient way of ensuring delivery of the mail while saving valuable space on military transports. Soldiers were given small forms on which they could write a short message. A military censor read each of those one-page "V-mail" letters to ensure that no sensitive military information leaked out. Then they were photographed using 16 mm film and flown back to the States. One reel of film held 1500–1800 letters. For every 150,000 letters sent via V-mail, space was saved for one ton of war materiel. Once the film got to the States, it was developed, printed, cut apart, and mailed to the appropriate recipients. Read the following transcript of a V-mail letter from an actual soldier. Then answer the questions that follow.

PVT. DILLON C. SUMMERS
HQ BTRY 391ST F.A.BN.
APO 253.NEWYORKCITY
MON. OCT25/43
Some where in England

Dearest Mother & all.

   Will ans the letter I rec from You today. Was more than glad to hear from you again. One also from Hazel & Jean. tell them I will write later.

   Lexie was saying in her last letter that she was keeping Donald out of school that day Oct 11 because he had a cold & today I got a cablegram from Verlon saying he died the 16. It was a great shock to me. he was sick only five days wasen't he? Mama it hurt me very bad. An I know Lexie & Paul is killed nearly. we must look forward toward meeting him is all we can do. Also Very sorry about Clyde I. I have wrote Anna several times writing her again tonight. I will appreciate the paper more than a X-mas present. I meant to send Lexie a cablegram right back, but as the cablegram we can send from here don't fit in much, all I could of said is cablegram recieved. tell her for me. Many thanks. Love to all. Your Son Dillon.

1. What is one way this soldier got so much news packed into such a small space? _____
   _____

2. What do you notice is missing from this letter and why? _____
   _____
   _____

3. Why do you think the soldier said he would appreciate the paper more than a Christmas present?
   _____

4. Why was mail so important to a serviceman in the war? _____
   _____
   _____

5. Practical application: Adopt a service member and write regularly to him (or her), especially if he is serving overseas. Share with the class any responses you get.

Mapping World War II: European Theater

Locate and label the following places and/or military operations on the map.

1. London, Paris, Berlin, Moscow, Tunisia, Sicily, Rome

2. Use a brown colored pencil to indicate the beaches of Normandy.

3. Use a green colored pencil to draw arrows indicating the Allied lines of attack in Operation Torch.

4. Use a blue colored pencil to draw arrows indicating the Allied lines of attack in Operation Husky.

5. Use a red colored pencil to draw arrows indicating the Allied lines of attack in Operation Overlord.

6. Use a black colored pencil to draw arrows indicating the Russian lines of attack.

Mapping World War II: Pacific Theater

Locate and label the following places and/or military operations on the map.

1. Pearl Harbor, Tokyo, Hiroshima, Nagasaki, Midway Island, Guadalcanal, Iwo Jima, Okinawa

2. Use a brown colored pencil to draw a line indicating the greatest extent of the Japanese Empire.

3. Use a blue colored pencil to draw arrows indicating MacArthur's routes of attack.

4. Use a red colored pencil to draw arrows indicating Nimitz's routes of attack.

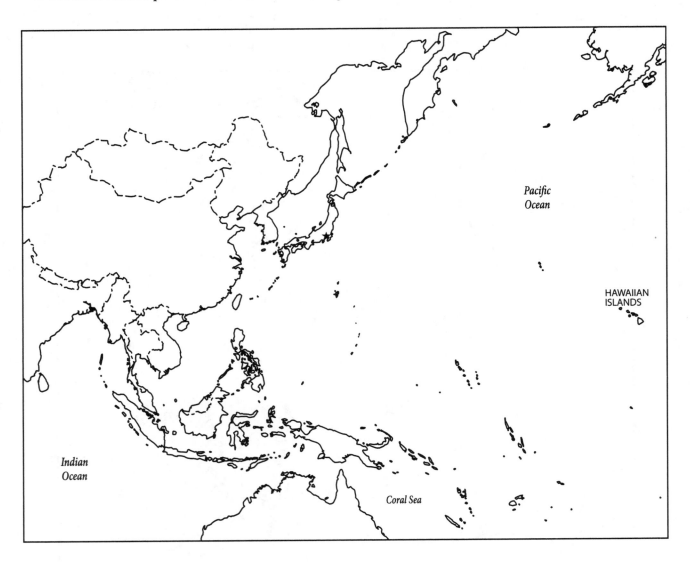

A Marine's Journal from Guadalcanal

Read these exerpts from the journal of Marine Pfc. James A. Donahue about his experiences on Guadalcanal in 1942. Then answer the questions that follow.

The jungle is thick. . . . The Fifth Regiment landed first and marched to the airport. We went straight through and then cut over to block the escape of the Japs. It took three days to go six miles. Japs took off. . . .

The second day was murder. All along the way were discarded packs, rifles, mess gear and everything imaginable. The second night it rained [hard] and the bugs were terrific. The Second Battalion (First Regiment) had reached the Lunga River. . . .

The third day we came back. The Japs had beat us in their retreat. We took up beach defense positions. We have been bombed every day by airplanes, and a submarine shells us every now and then. Our foxholes are four-foot deep. We go out on night patrols and it's plenty rugged. We lay in the foxholes for 13 to 14 hours at a clip and keep firing at the Japs in the jungle. As yet, there is no air support. The mosquitoes are very bad at night. The ants and flies bother us continually. The planes strafed the beach today. A big naval battle ensued the second day we were here, which resulted in our ship, the *Elliott*, being sunk. [The *Elliott*, a troop transport, sank when a crashing enemy bomber hit it.]

[T]he Japs landed a battalion of men on Red Beach, but we did not know about it. The next night 12 of us went on patrol and took up positions on our side of the Lunga River. About 3 A.M., . . . the Japs started to cross the stream. I want to forget all about it. My buddies being shot and blown apart. . . .

They bomb every day. Our fellows went out to the airport on working party. When air raid signal sounded, they went to a ravine. One of the personnel bombs . . . killed three, seriously wounded two. It was a horrible blow to us. Cameron was one of the best men in the Corps.

Three air raids today. They killed one and wounded three. This was our 89th bombing raid. This doesn't count the times our planes intercepted theirs. They sure had their eye on the airport and boy, did they hit it—nine direct times. . . . Toward dusk, enemy artillery opened up on us. We retaliated. At 1:30, two cruisers and one battleship shelled us for two hours. So far today we were hit by land, sea and air.

This is the first chance I had to write. For three days and nights we have been bombarded by land, sea and air. Fourteen-inch shells off a battleship kept punching our defenses. We have been hit by air three times in one hour. At night the Jap artillery gets started. Gas for the [U.S.] airplanes is very low. Situation is desperate. Our battalion pulled out of line to take up 5th position. Army relieved us on other line. Four transports of Jap troops unloaded. We sunk or damaged every one. We need reinforcements. The crisis is fast approaching. Seven Jap planes bombed us today killing six and wounding 43. I was very very close. God was with me.

If you want action, join the Marine Corps. I didn't believe it 'til I hit this island.

[During a Japanese attack], Sgt. Muth picked up a gun and started running down the line. He would stop, fire a few good bursts and then take off to a new position. J. moved up behind Murray, and I and he had a BAR [Browning automatic rifle]. He shouted if there was room for him in the foxhole. There wasn't, so we had to make room. He would be killed if he stayed on the deck [not in a foxhole]. A [Japanese] machine gun had been mounted in an abandoned alligator [an amphibious tracked landing craft] and they were throwing plenty of lead our way. J. crept as close as possible and made a dive for our hole. He landed okay and Murray and I continued our fire. About five minutes later, I said to Bottles, "Why . . . don't he fire?" Murray said slowly, "He's dead." I said, "Are you sure?" And he said, "Here is his blood; feel his pulse." But we couldn't determine whether he was alive. We couldn't move an inch either, for the Japs were really spraying our lines. So I reached over and felt his pulse. His face was sunken and there was no pulse. The blood began to fill the hole, so we fixed a poncho so that the blood would stay on the other side. The next morning I saw that he had been hit in the head and chest.

Again, I can thank God for letting me live. We were digging three alternate gun positions in case the Japs break through. . . . Suddenly, Fisher spotted 30 Jap bombers just about over us. We grabbed our helmets and ran. . . . Where we were running, I do not know, just trying to get out of reach of the bombers. It can't be done, because no one knows where they are going to bomb. Mugno and I finally spotted a small foxhole and we dove in. Just then we heard them dropping. All the time I was [praying].

There is a rumor that [Gen. Archie] Vandergrift said that the First Marine Division is through fighting in the Solomon's. . . . We will probably go back on the lines soon. Good scuttlebutt [rumors] never comes true, but the bad always comes true. I have never seen it fail.

We are now set up on the beach and what a layout! We moved into a good tent. The cots were there for us. We found a lot of food and equipment. . . . We are moving again today. We are scheduled to board ship in a few days. I hope we do before anything comes up. . . . Today is Dec. 18. We are bivouacked at Mouth of Lugna River. For the first time since we hit the island, our machine gunners have not stood gun watch. . . . What do you think happened last night? We saw a movie, and not six miles away, men were fighting for their lives. . . . We boarded ship today. . . . I now write *finis* to Guadalcanal.

1. What topics tend to recur in this Marine's journal entries and why? _____

_____

2. From various comments in the journal, in addition to the dangers of enemy attacks, what practical matters

(some explicit but others implied in the text) concerned him? _____

_____

3. What is "scuttlebutt," and why does he seem to have such a negative attitude toward it?

_____

4. What does the author say that he wants to forget, but what indicates that he will not be able to do so?

_____

_____

5. Do you believe that this Marine was a Christian? If not, how do you explain his references to God and his

gratefulness for being kept safe? If you believe he was a Christian, how would you deal with the argument

about "foxhole religion" not being genuine? _____

_____

_____

_____

_____

_____

Chapter Review

Complete the chart showing the major differences between the two theaters of World War II.

	European theater	Pacific theater
Geographic features		
Allied nations		
Axis nations		
Campaign plans	defeat Hitler first; then take back North Africa (Operation Torch); invade Sicily and Italy, driving northward toward the heart of Europe (Operation Husky); invade France at Normandy and drive eastward into Germany (Operation Overlord)	defend against Japanese advances while building up troops and supplies; then push north from the Solomons, through the Philippines, and west from the Marshalls, island-hopping toward Japan
Role of planes		
Role of ships		
Role of tanks		
Turning point(s)		
Last big battle		
Date of victory		

Identify the following terms.

_____ 1. first country attacked by Nazi "blitzkrieg"

_____ 2. where Allied armies narrowly escaped annihilation by German armies

_____ 3. Congressional act that allowed Allies to get supplies from the U.S. without paying money

_____ 4. U.S. naval base bombed by Japan on December 7, 1941

_____ 5. only person to vote against declaring war on Japan

_____ 6. general who led America's first offensive bombing raid on Tokyo

_____ 7. first Axis power to surrender to the Allies

_____ 8. French region that the Allies attacked on June 6, 1944

_____ 9. town that Germans surrounded during the Battle of the Bulge

_____ 10. conference where FDR promised the Soviets control of Eastern Europe after the war

_____ 11. where American naval aircraft stopped Japanese threatened attack on Australia

_____ 12. island in the Solomons where MacArthur began his offensive against the Japanese

_____ 13. tiny volcanic island whose name means "sulfur island," where more than 5,000 Marines died

_____ 14. last island the Allies had to capture near the Japanese mainland before Japan surrendered

_____ 15. conference where the Allies warned Japan to surrender unconditionally

_____ 16. code name of America's atomic bomb research

_____ 17. Japanese suicide pilots who tried to crash into American warships

_____ 18. first city on which an atomic bomb was dropped

_____ 19. America's "secret city" where the atomic bomb was devised

_____ 20. U.S. president who succeeded FDR upon his death

Jackie Robinson Breaks Baseball's Color Barrier, 1945

The name of Jackie Robinson made national news in 1941. That year he became the first athlete in the history of the University of California at Los Angeles to earn letters in four different sports in one year: football, basketball, track, and baseball. When he got out of the Army in 1945, he joined the Kansas City Monarchs, a team in the Negro League. Clyde Sukeforth, a scout for the Brooklyn Dodgers, saw him play and arranged a meeting for him with the Dodgers' general manager Branch Rickey on August 28, 1945. Read the following account of the conversation that occurred there, and then answer the questions.

"Are you under contract to the Kansas City Monarchs?" [Rickey asked].

"No, sir," Robinson replied quickly. "We don't have contracts."

"Do you have any agreements—written or oral—about how long you will play for them?"

"No, sir, none at all. I just work from payday to payday."

Rickey nodded and his bushy brows mashed into a scowl. He toyed with the ever-present cigar, seeking the right words. "Do you know why you were brought here?"

"Not exactly. I heard something about a colored team at Ebbets Field. That it?"

"No . . . that isn't it." Rickey studied the dark face, the half-open mouth, the widened and worried eyes. Then he said, "You were brought here, Jackie, to play for the Brooklyn organization. Perhaps on Montreal to start with—"

"Me? Play for Montreal?" the player gasped.

Rickey nodded. "If you can make it, yes. Later on—also if you can make it—you'll have a chance with the Brooklyn Dodgers." Robinson could only nod at this point.

"I want to win pennants and we need ballplayers!" Rickey whacked the desk. He sketched the efforts and the scope of his two-year search for players of promise. "Do *you think* you can do it? Make good in organized baseball?"

Robinson shifted to relieve his mounting tension.

"If . . . if I got the chance," he stammered.

"There's more here than just *playing*, *Jackie*," Rickey warned. "I wish it meant only hits, runs and errors—things you can see in a box score. . . ."

. . . "Can you do it? Can you do it?" Rickey asked over and over.

Shifting nervously, Robinson looked from Rickey to Sukeforth as they talked of his arms and legs and swing and courage. Did he have the guts to play the game no matter what happened? Rickey pointed out the enormity of the responsibility for all concerned: owners of the club, Rickey, Robinson and all baseball. The opposition would shout insults, come in spikes first, throw at his head.

"Mr. Rickey," Robinson said, "they've been throwing at my head for a long time."

Rickey's voice rose. "Suppose I'm a player . . . in the heat of an important ball game." He drew back as if to charge at Robinson. "Suppose I collide with you at second base. When I get up, I yell, 'You dirty, black—'" He finished the castigation and added calmly, "What do you do?"

Robinson blinked. He licked his lips and swallowed.

"Mr. Rickey," he murmured, "do you want a ballplayer who's afraid to fight back?"

"I want a ballplayer with guts enough *not* to fight back!" Rickey exclaimed almost savagely. He paced across the floor and returned with finger pointing. "You've got to do this job with base hits and stolen bases and fielding ground balls, Jackie. *Nothing else!*"

He moved behind his big desk again and faced the cornered Robinson. He posed as a cynical clerk in a southern hotel who not only refused him a room, but cursed him as he did so. What would Robinson do? He posed as a prejudiced sportswriter, ordered to turn in a twisted story, full of bias and racial animosity. How would Robinson answer the sportswriter? He ordered the player from imaginary dining rooms. He jostled him in imaginary hotel lobbies, railroad stations. What would Robinson do?

"Now I'm playing against you in a World Series!" Rickey stormed and removed his jacket for greater freedom. Robinson's hands clenched, trembled from the rising tension. "I'm a hotheaded player. I want to win that game, so I go into you spikes first, but you don't give ground. You stand there and you jab the ball into my ribs and the umpire yells, 'Out!' I flare up—all I see is your face—that black face right on top of me—"

Rickey's bespectacled face, glistening with sweat, was inches from Robinson's at this point. He yelled into the motionless mask, "So I haul off and punch you right in the cheek!"

An oversized fist swung through the air and barely missed Robinson's face. He blinked, but his head didn't move.

"What do you do?" Rickey roared.

"Mr. Rickey," he whispered, "I've got two cheeks. That it?"

1. For which team did Robinson play before the Dodgers signed him to a contract?

   _____

2. Who discovered Robinson? _____

3. Which member of the Dodger organization had the courage to sign Robinson to a contract, and why was

   he willing to do so? _____

   _____

   _____

4. What was the main issue about which the Dodgers were concerned with Robinson's abilities?

   _____

   _____

5. What were to be Robinson's only weapons with which he would be allowed to fight racial animosity?

   _____

   _____

6. Using the content in your textbook, show that Robinson indeed used those weapons effectively.

   _____

   _____

   _____

7. What was the significance of Robinson's becoming the first black major league baseball player?

   _____

   _____

★ ★ ★ ★ ★ ★ ★ ★ ★ ★

Understanding the United Nations

Using your textbook and perhaps some outside sources (such as world almanacs or the Internet), provide the following information about the United Nations. (Some questions will ask you to give your opinion, in which case you should support your views with facts.)

1. When and where was the United Nations formally organized? _____

2. Name the three main organizational divisions of the United Nations. _____

_____

3. What is the name of the position that heads the executive branch of the United Nations? _____

_____

4. Who was the first person to hold that position, and what country was he from? _____

5. Who is the current person holding that position, and what country is he from? _____

_____

6. How many countries are members of the United Nations? _____

7. How many members are on the Security Council (both permanent members and rotating members)?

_____

8. List the permanent members of the Security Council. _____

_____

9. List two of the most prominent agencies of the United Nations. _____

10. What are some security-related problems of the United Nations? _____

_____

_____

_____

_____

_____

11. What is your own assessment of the value or track record of the United Nations?

_____

_____

_____

_____

_____

_____

_____

12. What irony do you find in the Scripture quotation on the sculpture outside the U.N.'s New York

headquarters? _____

_____

_____

_____

_____

13. In light of the problems the United States has faced (and faces) from the United Nations, do you think the United States should continue its membership in that body? Why or why not?

_____

_____

_____

_____

_____

_____

14. Regardless of your answer to the preceding question, in light of the ease that other countries have in spying on the United States through the U.N. headquarters in New York City, do you think the United States should require the U.N. to make its headquarters in some other country? Why or why not?

_____

_____

_____

_____

_____

_____

The Berlin Candy Bomber

No group of people was more dramatically affected by the Berlin airlift than the German children who benefited from the extreme risks that the airlift pilots took to get food and other necessities to them. And no group was more affected by the children than the pilots who met them and saw the effect their dangerous work was having on those young people. Read the following account of a thirteen-year-old German girl and the man who came to mean so much to her and many other German children. Then answer the questions that follow.

There was one person who won the hearts of the Berliners—adults and children alike—and that was Lt. Gail Halvorsen who became known as the Berlin Candy Bomber.

One day during his time off duty, Lt. Halvorsen talked to a group of children who stood outside the airport fence and were watching the planes land at Tempelhof. He was impressed that they seemed to know what "freedom" meant and how important the airlift was.

The children were not begging for candy, as children everywhere else did when they encountered Americans. Wanting to give them something, Lt. Halvorsen found he had only two sticks of gum in his pocket. He split up the gum and distributed the pieces, with the promise that he would drop candy out of his airplane for them on his next flight into Berlin. Ingeniously, he made little parachutes from handerchiefs onto which he tied Hershey bars and packages of gum, then dropped those sweet treats out of the cockpit window of his airplane to the waiting children just before landing at Tempelhof.

After several days of those candy drops, Lt. Halvorsen's "secret mission" became known to his superiors because the German newspaper pictured his airplane on the front page. The Air Force found that the thoughtfulness of this kindhearted man did more to cement relations between the Allies and their former enemies than any other attempt, and encouraged Lt. Halvorsen to continue. He became known as The Berlin Candy Bomber, and his idea turned into a large scale operation. Other pilots joined Halvorsen, and pretty soon thousands of candy parachutes had been dropped.

Colonel Halvorsen became the much admired hero of the Berliners. While all airlift pilots and personnel were heroes in the eyes of the Berliners, it was Colonel Halvorsen who put the heart into the airlift. By sending gifts of candy down to the children, he told them that somebody cared about them personally. This great act of kindness gave them, as well as their parents, hope—hope for the future, hope for freedom, and hope for a better life.

"Without hope the soul dies," Colonel Halvorsen said fifty years later, when I had the splendid opportunity to meet this kindhearted man and to finally thank him personally for what he did for the children and for all the West Berliners. Throughout the intervening years, and still at this time as I am writing this, Colonel Halvorsen flies missions to war-ravaged countries and drops candy to the children.

I have often been asked if I caught any candy parachutes. The answer is that I did not go to Tempelhof Airport at that time. Peter is four years younger than I am and he did not have the responsibilities that fell to me. Besides going to Business School, I had to stand in food lines—often four to six hours at a time, several times a week—to get our rations. This took a lot of energy, and with the limited rations we were getting, there was none left for extra trips.

1. What impressed Halvorsen about the children who stood outside the fence at Tempelhof to watch the planes land and with whom he talked during his free time? _____

_____

_____

2. How did Halvorsen's superiors react when they learned about his dropping candy and gum to the German children? _____

_____

_____

3. What message did the German people get from Halvorsen's actions? _____

_____

_____

_____

4. Why did the author not catch any of Halvorsen's candy parachutes herself?

_____

_____

_____

_____

5. How has Halvorsen continued to provide hope and assistance to other children around the world?

_____

_____

6. List and briefly describe other humanitarian efforts to provide hope, encouragement, and/or material assistance to those in need. _____

_____

_____

_____

_____

7. What efforts can you individually, as a family, or as a class or school do to provide humanitarian assistance to someone in your own local area? _____

_____

_____

_____

_____

Two Views of the Firing of General MacArthur

When the Chinese Communists sent troops into North Korea to prevent the Communists in that country from being ousted and a united free Korea from coming into existence, the scope and nature of the Korean War changed. Because his military profession taught him to seek a quick victory as the means of bringing about peace, General Douglas MacArthur sought to strike at the North Koreans' ally, Communist China, to cut off supplies, end the flow of Chinese into the conflict, and win complete victory. President Harry Truman, however, was a civilian government leader who thought more about world opinion than about military victory. He wanted MacArthur to conduct a limited war. Because their views were so different and because MacArthur spoke publicly about their disagreements, bringing public criticism upon Truman, Truman felt compelled to fire MacArthur. It was not a popular decision, and it brought him even more criticism. Although he was the Commander in Chief and could fire whomever he chose, Truman thought that he must explain his decision to the American people. Even after his firing, MacArthur continued to criticize Truman's military policies, even before a joint session of Congress. Read the following two views of the firing of General Douglas MacArthur—one by Truman and the other by MacArthur. Then answer the questions that follow.

Truman's Viewpoint

[Presidential address to the nation, April 11, 1951]

I want to talk plainly to you tonight about what we are doing in Korea and about our policy in the Far East.

In the simplest terms, what we are doing in Korea is this: We are trying to prevent a third world war.

I think most people in this country recognized that fact last June. And they warmly supported the decision of the Government to help the Republic of Korea against the Communist aggressors. Now, many persons, even some who applauded our decision to defend Korea, have forgotten the basic reason for our action.

. . . . .

The question we have had to face is whether the Communist plan of conquest can be stopped without general war. Our Government and other countries associated with us in the United Nations believe that the best chance of stopping it without general war is to meet the attack in Korea and defeat it there.

. . . . .

So far, by fighting a limited war in Korea, we have prevented aggression from succeeding and bringing on a general war. And the ability of the whole free world to resist Communist aggression has been greatly improved.

. . . . .

We do not want to see the conflict in Korea extended. We are trying to prevent a world war—not to start one. The best way to do this is to make it plain that we and the other free countries will continue to resist the attack.

But you may ask: Why can't we take other steps to punish the aggressor? Why don't we bomb Manchuria and China itself? Why don't we assist Chinese Nationalist troops to land on the mainland of China?

If we were to do these things we would be running a very grave risk of starting a general war. If that were to happen, we would have brought about the exact situation we are trying to prevent.

. . . . .

A number of events have made it evident that General MacArthur did not agree with that policy. I have therefore considered it essential to relieve General

MacArthur so that there would be no doubt or confusion as to the real purpose and aim of our policy.

It was with the deepest personal regret that I found myself compelled to take this action. General MacArthur is one of our greatest military commanders. But the cause of world peace is more important than any individual.

. . . . .

The free nations have united their strength in an effort to prevent a third world war.

That war can come if the Communist rulers want it to come. But this Nation and its allies will not be responsible for its coming.

We do not want to widen the conflict. We will use every effort to prevent that disaster. And in so doing we know that we are following the great principles of peace, freedom, and justice.

MacArthur's Viewpoint

[Address to a joint session of the 82nd Congress, first session, April 19, 1951]

. . . The Communist threat is a global one. Its successful advance in one sector threatens the destruction of every other sector. You cannot appease or otherwise surrender to communism in Asia without simultaneously undermining our efforts to halt its advance in Europe. . . .

. . . While I was not consulted prior to the President's decision to intervene in support of the Republic of Korea, that decision, from a military standpoint, proved a sound one, as we hurled back the invader and decimated his forces. Our victory was complete and our objectives within reach when Red China intervened with numerically superior ground forces. This created a new war and an entirely new situation—a situation not contemplated when our forces were committed against the North Korean invaders—a situation which called for new decisions in the diplomatic sphere to permit the realistic adjustment of military strategy. Such decisions have not been forthcoming.

While no man in his right mind would advocate sending our ground forces into continental China and such was never given a thought, the new situation did urgently demand a drastic revision of strategic planning if our political aim was to defeat this new enemy as we had defeated the old.

. . . . .

For entertaining these views, all professionally designed to support our forces committed to Korea and bring hostilities to an end with the least possible delay and at a saving of countless American and Allied lives, I have been severely criticized in lay circles, principally abroad, despite my understanding that from a military standpoint the above views have been fully shared in the past by practically every military leader concerned with the Korean campaign, including our own Joint Chiefs of Staff.

I called for reinforcements, but was informed that reinforcements were not available. I made clear that if not permitted to destroy the enemy buildup bases north of the Yalu; if not permitted to utilize the friendly Chinese force of some 600,000 men on Formosa; if not permitted to blockade the China coast to prevent the Chinese Reds from getting succor from without; and if there were to be no hope of major reinforcements, the position of the command from the military standpoint forbade victory. We could hold in Korea by constant maneuver and at an approximate area where our supply line advantages were in balance with the supply line disadvantages of the enemy, but we could hope at best for only an indecisive campaign, with its terrible enemy and constant attrition upon our forces if the enemy utilized his full military potential. I have constantly called for new political decisions essential to a solution. Efforts have been made to distort my position. It has been said that I was in effect a warmonger. Nothing could be further from the truth. I know war as few other men now living know it, and nothing to me is more revolting. I have long advocated its complete abolition as its very destructiveness on both friend and foe has rendered it useless as a means of settling international disputes.

1. Why did President Truman feel compelled to address the nation about his firing of General MacArthur?

_____

_____

_____

2. Essentially, what was at the heart of the disagreement between Truman and MacArthur?

_____

_____

_____

_____

3. What, according to Truman's view, was the greatest threat of following MacArthur's advice?

_____

_____

_____

_____

4. What statement by Truman could be taken to mean that Truman thought that MacArthur's personal pride was a major factor in his disagreement with the president? _____

_____

_____

5. What statement by Truman was an admission that following his policy would not necessarily mean that a world war would *not* occur? _____

_____

_____

6. What statement in the opening lines of MacArthur's speech indicates that he understood communism to be a threat globally? _____

_____

_____

7. What situation did MacArthur say made the Korean War "a new war" or different war, necessitating a different way of waging the war? _____

_____

8. Why could MacArthur say that his proposal for bombing bases and supply lines in China was militarily realistic? _____

_____

_____

_____

9. In addition to bombing the Communists across the Yalu River in China, what other measures did MacArthur say were essential to defeating the enemy in Korea? _____

_____

_____

_____

10. What had MacArthur's opponents called him that he says was untrue, and what proof does he offer that it was indeed untrue? _____

_____

_____

11. Who do you think was correct in this dispute—Truman with his limited war of containment (or, as MacArthur termed it, appeasement) or MacArthur with his complete victory argument? Why?

_____

_____

_____

_____

12. The Korean War ended where it began—with the countries divided at the 38th parallel and communism intact in North Korea. As a result, some people have called the Korean War America's first lost war. In what other later wars was America engaged with similar limited objectives and similar (or worse) results? (This question cannot be answered from the readings but will require that you rely on what knowledge you might have of recent history and/or current events.) Support your answer.

_____

_____

_____

_____

_____

_____

_____

_____

Chapter Review

Match the person on the right with the thing for which he or she is noteworthy.

_____ 1. executed for spying, along with his wife

_____ 2. first black federal appeals court judge

_____ 3. senator whose anti-Communist investigations got out of hand

_____ 4. fired for publicly disagreeing with Truman over conduct of Korean War

_____ 5. promised a "fair deal" for the American people

_____ 6. organized relief effort for Western Europe following World War II

_____ 7. name given to laws that sought to ensure segregation of blacks and whites

_____ 8. first black major league baseball player

_____ 9. federalized Arkansas National Guard to ensure desegregation in a Little Rock school

_____ 10. refused to surrender her seat on a Montgomery bus

A. Jim Crow

B. Dwight Eisenhower

C. William Hastie

D. Douglas MacArthur

E. Joseph McCarthy

F. George Marshall

G. Rosa Parks

H. Jackie Robinson

I. Julius Rosenberg

J. Harry Truman

Complete the following statements with the correct word(s) or phrase(s).

11. World War II veterans were able to obtain educational benefits because of the _____

12. The movements of people to the South and Southwest following the war were called the

_____

13. The law that prevented unions from forcing a worker to join a union was called the

_____

14. The Supreme Court ruling that segregation of schools based on race was unconstitutional was the case of

_____

15. The executive branch of the United Nations is called the _____

16. The Truman Doctrine tried to deal with communism through _____

17. When the Soviets cut off Berlin from West Germany, the Americans responded with the

_____

18. The United States, Canada, and the free countries of Europe dealt with Soviet expansionism by forming an alliance called the _____

19. The Soviet Union in turn reacted by forming their own alliance called the _____

20. June 25, 1950, marked the beginning of the _____

21. The dividing line between North and South Korea is the _____

22. Eisenhower's opponent in the election of 1952 was _____

23. Eisenhower's accomplishments in transportation include the St. Lawrence Seaway and the

_____

_____

24. Eisenhower's policy for dealing with the Soviet threat was called _____

25. Eisenhower's Soviet counterpart was named _____

Kennedy's Inaugural Address, 1961

Read the following excerpts from John F. Kennedy's inaugural address. Then answer the questions.

Vice-President Johnson, Mr. Speaker, Mr. Chief Justice, President Eisenhower, Vice-President Nixon, President Truman, Reverend Clergy, Fellow Citizens:

We observe today not a victory of party but a celebration of freedom—symbolizing an end as well as a beginning—signifying renewal as well as change. For I have sworn before you and Almighty God the same solemn oath our forebears prescribed nearly a century and three-quarters ago.

✪✪✪

Let the word go forth from this time and place, to friend and foe alike, that the torch has been passed to a new generation of Americans—born in this century, tempered by war, disciplined by a hard and bitter peace, proud of our ancient heritage—and unwilling to witness or permit the slow undoing of those human rights to which this nation has always been committed, and to which we are committed today at home and around the world.

Let every nation know, whether it wishes us well or ill, that we shall pay any price, bear any burden, meet any hardship, support any friend, oppose any foe to assure the survival and the success of liberty.

This much we pledge—and more.

To those old allies whose cultural and spiritual origins we share, we pledge the loyalty of faithful friends. United, there is little we cannot do in a host of co-operative ventures. Divided, there is little we can do—for we dare not meet a powerful challenge at odds and split asunder.

To those new states whom we welcome to the ranks of the free, we pledge our word that one form of colonial control shall not have passed away merely to be replaced by a far more iron tyranny. . . .

To those people in the huts and villages of half the globe struggling to break the bonds of mass misery, we pledge our best efforts to help them help themselves, for whatever period is required. . . .

To our sister republics south of our border, we offer a special pledge—to convert our good words into good deeds—in a new alliance for progress—to assist free men and free governments in casting off the chains of poverty. . . .

Finally, to those nations who would make themselves our adversary, we offer not a pledge but a request: that both sides begin anew the quest for peace, before the dark powers of destruction unleashed by science engulf all humanity in planned or accidental self-destruction.

We dare not tempt them with weakness. For only when our arms are sufficient beyond doubt can we be certain beyond doubt that they will never be employed.

✪✪✪

So let us begin anew—remembering on both sides that civility is not a sign of weakness, and sincerity is always subject to proof. Let us never negotiate out of fear. But let us never fear to negotiate.

✪✪✪

All this will not be finished in the first one hundred days. Nor will it be finished in the first one thousand days, nor in the life of this administration, nor even perhaps in our lifetime on this planet. But let us begin.

In your hands, my fellow citizens, more than mine, will rest the final success or failure of our course. Since this country was founded, each generation of Americans has been summoned to give testimony to its national loyalty. The graves of young Americans who answered the call to service surround the globe.

✪✪✪

And so, my fellow Americans: ask not what your country can do for you—ask what you can do for your country.

My fellow citizens of the world: ask not what America will do for you, but what together we can do for the freedom of man.

Finally, whether you are citizens of America or citizens of the world, ask of us here the same high standards of strength and sacrifice which we ask of you. With a good conscience our only sure reward, with history the final judge of our deeds, let us go forth to lead the land we love, asking His blessing and His help, but knowing that here on earth God's work must truly be our own.

1. What did Kennedy mean when he said that his inauguration marked both an end and a beginning, renewal as well as change? _____

_____

_____

_____

_____

_____

_____

2. In saying that "the torch has been passed" from the World War II generation to the next, what did Kennedy promise had not changed or been lost? _____

_____

_____

3. According to Kennedy, to what extent was the United States willing to go to "assure the survival and the success of liberty"? _____

_____

_____

4. Do you think that a president could make the same claim about Americans today? Why or why not?

_____

_____

_____

_____

_____

5. What does Kennedy pledge to each of the following groups of nations: (a) "old allies," (b) newly formed states, (c) poverty-stricken Third World countries, (d) the countries of Central and South America, (e) countries who are potential foes? _____

_____

_____

_____

_____

_____

6. How quickly did Kennedy predict his ideas would become reality?

_____

_____

_____

7. With whom did Kennedy say the success or failure of his administration's goals lay?

_____

8. According to Kennedy, where is the proof that Americans have been dedicated to American values and answered their call to service? _____

9. What challenge did Kennedy lay before Americans of his generation as he closed his inaugural address?

_____

_____

_____

10. What principle(s) taught by Jesus Christ makes Kennedy's challenge a legitimate challenge from a biblical worldview? _____

_____

_____

_____

_____

Gulf of Tonkin Resolution, 1964

Read the full text of the Gulf of Tonkin Resolution. Then answer the questions that follow.

Joint Resolution of Congress
H.J. RES 1145 August 7, 1964

Resolved by the Senate and House of Representatives of the United States of America in Congress assembled,

That the Congress approves and supports the determination of the President, as Commander in Chief, to take all necessary measures to repel any armed attack against the forces of the United States and to prevent further aggression.

Section 2. The United States regards as vital to its national interest and to world peace the maintenance of international peace and security in southeast Asia. Consonant with the Constitution of the United States and the Charter of the United Nations and in accordance with its obligations under the Southeast Asia Collective Defense Treaty, the United States is, therefore, prepared, as the President determines, to take all necessary steps, including the use of armed force, to assist any member or protocol state of the Southeast Asia Collective Defense Treaty requesting assistance in defense of its freedom.

Section 3. This resolution shall expire when the President shall determine that the peace and security of the area is reasonably assured by international conditions created by action of the United Nations or otherwise, except that it may be terminated earlier by concurrent resolution of the Congress.

1. What phrases in this resolution were purposely vague? _____

    _____

    _____

2. How did this resolution make the Vietnam War different from other wars in American history?

    _____

    _____

    _____

3. When did the resolution state the authorization for military action would end? _____

    _____

4. Under what two circumstances could military action based on the resolution be taken? _____

    _____

    _____

5. Do you agree that this resolution was required to authorize the president to use military force, or should Congress have formally declared war? Support your answer. _____

    _____

    _____

    _____

Summary of the Vietnam War

The Vietnam War was the longest and least successful war in American history. Answer the following questions about its significance, referring as necessary to Chapter 25 and Section 3 of Chapter 26 in your textbook.

1. What country controlled Indochina before World War II? _____

2. What Communist leader fought for Vietnamese independence and later became the president of North Vietnam? _____

3. What important battle did the Communist forces win in 1954, and why was it significant?
   _____

4. Why did the United States not intervene at that time? _____
   _____

5. How did the international conference in Geneva try to settle the conflict? _____
   _____

6. Why did the Geneva settlement fail? _____
   _____

7. What two Communist countries began providing military aid to North Vietnam?
   _____

8. What alliance did the United States join in 1954 to contain communism in Asia?
   _____

9. When and why did the United States begin sending military advisors to South Vietnam?
   _____

10. Who was the U.S. president at that time? _____

11. The Gulf of Tonkin Resolution authorized the president to use "all necessary steps" to stop North Vietnamese aggression. What year did that resolution pass Congress? Who was president at the time? What incident sparked its passage? _____
    _____

12. List four disadvantages the United States faced during the conflict. _____
    _____
    _____
    _____
    _____

13. What name was given to American politicians who opposed the war? _____

14. How many troops had been sent to Vietnam by May 1965? _____

15. What term describes Communist guerrillas living and fighting in South Vietnam? _____

16. What trail did North Vietnam use to supply their troops and the guerrillas in South Vietnam?

_____

17. What was the capital of the South? of the North? _____

18. What Communist offensive caught the United States by surprise in 1968 and led to Johnson's decision not to run for reelection? _____

19. How did the American media encourage opposition to the war? _____

_____

_____

_____

_____

20. Describe Nixon's plan to pull American troops out of Vietnam "with dignity."

_____

_____

_____

21. What steps did Nixon take to force North Vietnam back to the peace table?

_____

_____

_____

22. In what year did South Vietnam fall? Who was president at the time? _____

23. List three ways the war hurt America. _____

_____

_____

_____

_____

24. After having studied the Vietnam War, what is your position on it? Should the United States have gotten involved in the war to start with? Why or why not? Given that the United States *did* get involved, if you had been president, how would you have conducted it differently?

_____

_____

_____

_____

_____

One Soldier's Experience in Vietnam

In May 1970, Ted McCormick was a nineteen-year-old infantryman, a member of B Company, 1/327ᵗʰ Infantry, 101ˢᵗ Airborne Division, in South Vietnam. His unit was on a search-and-destroy operation on Hill 882. Unknown to them at the time, they were heading into a full division of North Vietnamese Army (NVA) "sappers," Communist special forces similar to the American Green Berets. There McCormick experienced his first combat. Read the following excerpts from his account. Then answer the questions.

The helicopter's jet engines strained, with the Huey B's blades slicing through the air, making the familiar sounding "chop, chop, chop," as the bird made a sharp turn. We were sitting on our helmets to protect against rounds coming through the floor of the aircraft.

Before we knew it, we were hovering like a bee, two feet above the LZ (landing zone), on the top of Hill 882. . . . The surrounding area was devastated . . . the trees lay bent and twisted; and all the foliage had been burned away from air strikes, napalm, and artillery barrages.

✪✪✪

We were taking over from the 2/502ⁿᵈ infantry, whose primary mission had been to blow new LZs in the area. After landing, they were repeatedly ambushed by NVA regulars and had to be withdrawn because of heavy casualties. Our mission . . . was a search and destroy.

✪✪✪

We secured our equipment, got the order to move out, and quickly moved off the LZ and into the surrounding jungle to avoid a mortar attack. We descended the hill for three days, not noticing anything unusual or any sign of enemy activity.

Each day, we sent out recons [reconnaissance, scouting parties] in every direction, probing and trying to locate the supposed enemy base camp. Many times we had been sent out on search-and-destroy missions like this, and the only thing we got out of it was leeches and jungle rot, a bacterial skin infection that would eat away at the first layer of epidermis. The only known remedy was to get out of the jungle and into direct sunlight.

✪✪✪

On the third day, we were due for resupply. There were no LZs in our immediate area, so we were supposed to get it kicked out by air. The resupply helicopters would ask the ground unit to pop smoke for identification; and, when the smoke was acknowledged, they would fly in at tree-top level and kick out the resupply.

We were out of water and rations as we heard the Huey approach. A request was made for green smoke, which was popped. We waited. Nothing. Lt. Shultz raised the helo on the radio.

"What's the problem. . . ? Where are you? We are still waiting, over."

"We just kicked it out to you, over," the resupply answered.

"We never got it. You didn't kick it out to us, over," Lt. Shultz answered.

"I requested green smoke, it was popped, and I delivered, activity was observed on the ground, over."

"It wasn't my unit. Possibly you kicked it out to Delta Co. by mistake. We need a new resupply ASAP, over and out."

We stood dumbfounded. There was no other unit operating on this side of [Hill] 882. Who could it be? Delta Co.? Could the helicopter pilot's bearings have been that far off? We wondered—mixups are common in the military.

✪✪✪

What actually happened was the NVA had been monitoring our radio frequency. When the pilot asked for green smoke to be popped, having some of our smoke canisters that they had captured from the 2/502, they popped theirs at the same time. The pilot, seeing their green smoke, kicked out all our resupply to the enemy by mistake. The "activity" the pilot and his crew observed were actually NVA soldiers dressed in our fatigues that they had captured from the 2/502nd.

Now, they not only had our captured weapons; but we had supplied them with our ammunition, too. We were about to face our own weapons and ammunition in battle. It was made painfully aware to us that we were about to face a formidable adversary.

✪✪✪

Unknown to us, we had moved to within fifty meters of the NVA sapper base camp. By us moving at night, . . . they could not be sure exactly where we had set up and, by opening fire, would have given away their position from the muzzle flashes of their weapons. The enemy waited.

The next morning, I was chosen, along with five other men, to go on a recon of the surrounding area. We readied our equipment and left our position, going back up the trail ten meters, and then began cutting a trail to the left with a machete. I was walking rear security and had all five of the squad's LAWs (light, anti-tank weapons) strapped over my shoulders along with my M-16, four hand grenades, and two bandoleers of ammunition. . . . It was almost noon, and the temperature was already reaching 100 degrees.

The NVA were battlefield opportunists—they were always ready to exploit any battlefield situation. They would wait for their enemy to make a mistake, then take advantage of it. In combat, they were a formidable opponent. They were masters at camouflage, mortars, and flanking tactics.

They dressed one of their soldiers in our fatigues and sent him out to meet us. He led the team into an infantry-classic "L"-shaped ambush. He made noises, shook the bushes, gave the pointman fleeting glimpses of his silhouette, and led us unsuspecting to our fate. The pointman, leery and confused, held his fire, not sure of his target. We had stopped again, and I sat down and leaned back against a tree, daydreaming, lost in pleasant thoughts of family and home. Then they sprung the ambush.

We were hit simultaneously with three RPG-7 rockets [rocket-propelled grenades], two from the front and one from the right flank. Boom, Boom, Boom! We were showered with dirt and rocks from the explosions. Machine-gun and small-arms fire started to strafe from the front and right. We were in the center of the kill zone, frozen in shock and fear, unable to move, and pinned down. The acrid smell of gunpowder from the explosions filled the air.

The small-arms fire picked up, sounding like popcorn, with rounds whizzing all around us. We had to react or be cut to pieces in the crossfire. Lt. Shultz screamed for the LAWs to be brought to the front. Frozen with shock and fear, I somehow managed enough courage to move. Under fire, I ran to the front of the column.

When I got to the front, I found Lt. Shultz dazed and crouched over the pointman behind a fallen tree. He was barking orders into the radio receiver but was unable to hear; his right ear was bleeding, indicating a blown ear drum from the concussions. He was in shock and had a possible head concussion. The pointman, covered in blood, lay in a fetal position and was unconscious; he had suffered multiple wounds and was losing a lot of blood. He looked ashen and close to death.

"Keep your heads down," I hollered and quickly fired all five LAWs and then began to fire my M-16, switching back and forth with three-round burst from full-auto to semi-automatic to conserve ammunition. At this point, I was the only one returning fire; everyone else in the squad was frozen in place, unable to mount any kind of defensive counter fire.

Lt. Shultz handed me the handset of the radio; he wanted me to . . . direct artillery fire. . . . "Drop five, left five, fire for effect!" I hollered into the receiver, then waited for the explosions, only to hear the rounds landing harmlessly, hundreds of meters away.

I tried to readjust again, with the same result. It was very difficult to hear with all the small-arms fire and explosions. After throwing several hand grenades and expending the rest of my M-16 ammunition, I informed Lt. Shultz that our position was futile; we needed reinforcements.

I told him I was going for help; and I ran, under fire, through the jungle, back to our staging area. When I arrived, I found them under attack, too. . . . We returned to the ambush site to find the situation the same. The squad was still pinned down, caught in the crossfire.

At this point, we began to return fire defensively to extract our wounded. The pointman was still alive but very close to death as we withdrew. And the NVA were flanking to the right and left, probing with small-arms fire.

After regrouping at our staging area, we set up a defensive perimeter and called in a Medivac for the wounded lieutenant and pointman. As the Medivac came in at tree-top level and lowered a basket, we all opened fire with everything we had to keep the NVA's heads down while the wounded were extracted.

✪✪✪

We regrouped and were resupplied at the top of 882 the next morning. Our orders were to assault the NVA base camp after resupply. No one talked about the battle that lay ahead. . . .

Slowly, we moved ahead. We were ten feet apart from one another, close enough to see a man on either side. The enemy waited until the last second, then had to open fire or be overrun. We hit the dirt in a hail of small-arms fire from both sides.

After a brief but very intense small-arms exchange, we pulled back as planned, about one-hundred-and-fifty meters, over a small finger of the hill. It was 11:00 in the morning. We were very close to their position but fairly safe on the other side of a small finger of the mountain. Strike after strike of Cobra gunship attacks pulverized the enemy base camp with 2.75 rockets and mini-gun fire; then we used artillery from surrounding fire bases—105 mm and 155 mm howitzers completed fire missions.

In the early afternoon, we called in TAC (tactical air command) jets flying out of the Air Force base at Da Nang. They began the strike by dropping 500-lb. bombs. At the distance we were from the target, I felt it was too close. It began by a tremendous "Boom!" as the jet passed directly over us at tree-top level, breaking the sound barrier. . . . The NVA had the jets timed, too, and at the last possible second would open up with everything they had, hoping to place a round in one of the jet engines.

✪✪✪

After the jets had exhausted their supply of 500-lb. bombs, they began using napalm. Napalm is a mixture of gasoline and a jelly-like substance, which is designed to stick to anything it comes in contact with. The first pass went well, directly hitting the enemy positions; but on the next run, the pilot miscalculated; and the canister exploded, splashing over onto our position. We were engulfed by flames. Triple-canopy jungle instantly was burned away. Horrible screams could be heard throughout our position, as men were being burned. I was covering rear security.

The second we were hit, I looked to my left and saw . . . a fellow soldier who was the assistant gunner on the M-60. He ran towards me. His fatigues had been burned away, and he held his arms outstretched. He ran towards my position, in shock and fear, stumbling up the hill.

I stuck out my foot and tripped him, trying to avoid touching his burning skin. I held [him] down to prevent him from getting up and running off into the jungle and certain death. I called for the Medic, who was busy attending other burn victims.

The jungle was gone, completely burned away. A gooey, white-plastic material dripped down the tops of the trees, still on fire. There was a sick, sweet smell of cordite and burning plastic. We suffered five casualties, three from napalm and two from small-arms fire.

Then we received orders to assault the enemy camp, and I was ordered to take over the machine gun. Slowly, we approached the enemy positions.

After the napalm hit, the firefight had ended. We were within their bunker complex before we knew it. Two dead NVA soldiers lay half buried in their exposed bunker which had taken a direct hit from a 500-lb. bomb. Their faces looked serene, despite the violent way in which they had died. There were 20–25 bunkers—15 were destroyed, all were hit with napalm.

Burned fatigues and equipment lay everywhere. They had a "highway" as wide as a city street cut through the triple-canopy jungle, leaving the very top of the canopy intact to conceal it from the air. This clearly was a major sapper base. Barbed wire lay in rows, which they used as a practice area for the sappers.

✪✪✪

The next morning, we received word that 2nd platoon had been ambushed and had suffered casualties. The enemy had also shot down a LOH [light observation helicopter]—the welfare of the pilot and crew was unknown. We were to move immediately to 2nd platoon's location and mount a search and rescue for the downed airmen. We marched all morning until we reached their area. . . . [W]e had to retrieve the mini-gun that was on the aircraft so it wouldn't fall into enemy hands.

I was carrying the M-60, and Captain Mills told me to walk his point. He would walk my slack (second man back). We started out towards the downed helicopter. I was tense and nervous as I walked down the trail; and, with each step, I had to look for the wire of a booby trap while at the same time look ahead, scanning the surrounding jungle for an ambush. . . . It took us all day; but, by late in the afternoon, I began to notice AK-47 shell casings strewn on the trail. . . . Suddenly, we were on top of the crash site. . . .

That night, as I pulled guard . . . , I was very reflective of my life, this war, and what part I was playing in it. . . . I thought of these dead pilots' families as their bodies lay in pieces, burned beyond recognition. I was prepared to give my life but not for country and cause. I was ready to die for "esprit de corps" and my fellow soldiers. I had become adept at fighting guerrilla warfare. I was nineteen.

1. How old was McCormick when he experienced this combat? _____

2. What was the mission of McCormick's unit that brought them into the combat situation? _____

_____

3. On similar missions, what had the unit gotten for their troubles? _____

4. What happened in the unit's efforts to obtain additional supplies and water?

_____

_____

_____

5. In the process of carrying out their mission, what did the unit unexpectedly do?

_____

_____

6. What assessment did McCormick make of the North Vietnamese soldiers?

_____

_____

_____

_____

_____

_____

7. What happened when McCormick's unit called for air support to bomb the NVA base camp?

_____

_____

_____

8. How did McCormick describe napalm and its effect in combat? _____

_____

_____

_____

_____

9. In moving through the jungle, what did American troops have to be vigilant to avoid?

_____

_____

_____

10. What were two important reasons for McCormick's unit to quickly find the helicopter that had been shot

down? _____

_____

_____

_____

_____

11. What thoughts engaged McCormick's mind as he performed guard duty the night after they found the

downed helicopter? _____

_____

_____

12. Why would a soldier like McCormick be unwilling to die for cause and country yet ready to die for "esprit de corps" and his fellow soldiers? _____

_____

_____

_____

_____

The Resignation of Richard Nixon

Read the resignation speech of President Richard Nixon, which he delivered on live television on August 8, 1974. Then answer the questions.

Good evening:

This is the 37th time I have spoken to you from this office, where so many decisions have been made that shape the history of this nation. Each time I have done so to discuss with you some matter that I believe affected the national interest. In all the decisions I have made in my public life I have always tried to do what was best for the nation.

Throughout the long and difficult period of Watergate, I have felt it was my duty to persevere—to make every possible effort to complete the term of office to which you elected me. In the past few days, however, it has become evident to me that I no longer have a strong enough political base in the Congress to justify continuing that effort. As long as there was such a base, I felt strongly that it was necessary to see the constitutional process through to its conclusion; that to do otherwise would be unfaithful to the spirit of that deliberately difficult process, and a dangerously destabilizing precedent for the future. But with the disappearance of that base, I now believe that the constitutional purpose has been served. And there is no longer a need for the process to be prolonged.

I would have preferred to carry through to the finish whatever the personal agony it would have involved, and my family unanimously urged me to do so. But the interests of the nation must always come before any personal considerations. From the discussions I have had with Congressional and other leaders I have concluded that because of the Watergate matter I might not have the support of the Congress that I would consider necessary to back the very difficult decisions and carry out the duties of this office in the way the interests of the nation will require.

I have never been a quitter.

To leave office before my term is completed is abhorrent to every instinct in my body. But as President, I must put the interests of America first.

America needs a full-time president and a full-time Congress, particularly at this time with problems we face at home and abroad. To continue to fight through the months ahead for my personal vindication would almost totally absorb the time and attention of both the President and the Congress in a period when our entire focus should be on the great issues of peace abroad and prosperity without inflation at home.

Therefore, I shall resign the Presidency effective at noon tomorrow.

Vice President Ford will be sworn in as President at that hour in this office.

As I recall the high hopes for America with which we began this second term, I feel a great sadness that I will not be here in this office working on your behalf to achieve those hopes in the next two and a half years. But in turning over direction of the Government to Vice President Ford, I know, as I told the nation when I nominated him for that office ten months ago, that the leadership of America would be in good hands.

In passing this office to the Vice President, I also do so with the profound sense of the weight of responsibility that will fall on his shoulders tomorrow, and therefore of the understanding, the patience, the cooperation he will need from all Americans. As he assumes that responsibility he will deserve the help and the support of all of us. As we look to the future, the first essential is to begin healing the wounds of this nation. To put the bitterness and divisions of the recent past behind us and to rediscover those shared ideals that lie at the heart of our strength and unity as a great and as a free people.

By taking this action, I hope that I will have hastened the start of that process of healing which is so desperately needed in America. I regret deeply any injuries that may have been done in the course of the events that led to this decision. I would say only that if some of my judgments were wrong—and some were wrong—they were made in what I believed at the time to be the best interests of the nation.

To those who have stood with me during these past difficult months, to my family, my friends, the many others who joined in supporting my cause because they believed it was right, I will be eternally grateful for your support. And to those who have not felt able to give me your support, let me say I leave with no bitterness toward those who have opposed me, because all of us in the final analysis have been concerned with the good of the country, however our judgments might differ.

So let us all now join together in affirming that common commitment and in helping our new President succeed for the benefit of all Americans. I shall leave this office with regret at not completing my term but with gratitude for the privilege of serving as your President for the past five and a half years. These years have been a momentous time in the history of our nation and the world. They have been a time of achievement in which we can all be proud, achievements that represent the shared efforts of the administration, the Congress and the people. But the challenges ahead are equally great. And they, too, will require the support and the efforts of the Congress and the people, working in cooperation with the new Administration.

We have ended America's longest war. But in the work of securing a lasting peace in the world, the goals ahead are even more far-reaching and more difficult. We must complete a structure of peace, so that it will be said of this generation—our generation of Americans—by the people of all nations, not only that we ended one war but that we prevented future wars.

We have unlocked the doors that for a quarter of a century stood between the United States and the People's Republic of China. We must now ensure that the one-quarter of the world's people who live in the People's Republic of China will be and remain, not our enemies, but our friends.

In the Middle East, 100 million people in the Arab countries, many of whom have considered us their enemy for nearly 20 years, now look on us as their friends. We must continue to build on that friendship so that peace can settle at last over the Middle East and so that the cradle of civilization will not become its grave.

Around the world—in Asia, in Africa, in Latin America, in the Middle East—there are millions of people who live in terrible poverty, even starvation. We must keep as our goal turning away from production for war and expanding production for peace so that people everywhere on this earth can at last look forward, in their children's time, if not in our own time, to having the necessities for a decent life. Here, in America, we are fortunate that most of our people have not only the blessings of liberty but also the means to live full and good, and by the world's standards even abundant lives.

We must press on, however, toward a goal not only of more and better jobs but of full opportunity for every American, and of what we are striving so hard right now to achieve—prosperity without inflation.

For more than a quarter of a century in public life, I have shared in the turbulent history of this evening. I have fought for what I believe in. I have tried, to the best of my ability, to discharge those duties and meet those responsibilities that were entrusted to me. Sometimes I have succeeded. And sometimes I have failed. But always I have taken heart from what Theodore Roosevelt once said about the man in the arena, whose face is marred by dust and sweat and blood, who strives valiantly, who errs and comes short again and again because there is not effort without error and shortcoming, but who does actually strive to do the deed, who knows the great enthusiasms, the great devotions, who spends himself in a worthy cause, who at the

294

best knows in the end the triumphs of high achievements and with the worst if he fails, at least fails while daring greatly.

I pledge to you tonight that as long as I have a breath of life in my body, I shall continue in that spirit. I shall continue to work for the great causes to which I have been dedicated throughout my years as a Congressman, a Senator, Vice President and President, the cause of peace—not just for America but among all nations—prosperity, justice and opportunity for all of our people.

There is one cause above all to which I have been devoted and to which I shall always be devoted for as long as I live.

When I first took the oath of office as President five and a half years ago, I made this sacred commitment: to consecrate my office, my energies, and all the wisdom I can summon to the cause of peace among nations. I've done my very best in all the days since to be true to that pledge. As a result of these efforts, I am confident that the world is a safer place today, not only for the people of America but for the people of all nations, and that all of our children have a better chance than before of living in peace rather than dying in war.

This, more than anything, is what I hoped to achieve when I sought the Presidency.

This, more than anything, is what I hope will be my legacy to you, to our country, as I leave the Presidency.

To have served in this office is to have felt a very personal sense of kinship with each and every American.

In leaving it, I do so with this prayer: May God's grace be with you in all the days ahead.

1. As Nixon opened his address to the nation and repeatedly throughout, what did he declare had always been the basis for all of the decisions he had made in his public life, including his decision to resign the presidency? _____

2. What did he say he had thought was his responsibility throughout the long ordeal of Watergate?
_____

3. What made him change his mind about remaining in office? _____
_____

4. What did he fear his resignation would do to the future of politics in the nation? _____
_____

5. What did he allege that his family unanimously urged him to do? _____
_____

6. In spite of the fact that he was announcing his resignation, what did he deny being? _____

7. What were his twin goals for the United States both while he was in office and after his resignation?
_____

8. Approximately how much of his term remained after he resigned? _____

9. How long had Ford been vice president when Nixon resigned? _____

10. How did Nixon deflect attention from his resignation and toward the incoming president?
_____
_____
_____

11. What did Nixon state was the first priority of the nation for the future?

_____

_____

12. Although Nixon expressed deep regret for "any injuries that may have been done" before he decided to

resign, how did he attempt to deflect criticism from himself? _____

_____

_____

_____

13. What did he have to say to those who opposed him as president? _____

_____

14. Much of the latter part of his speech is a tally sheet of his accomplishments. What were the main

achievements to which he pointed? _____

_____

_____

_____

15. The words of which other president gave Nixon encouragement and hope whenever he had failed?

_____

16. What is your own assessment of the presidency and character of Richard Nixon? Support your answer.

_____

_____

_____

_____

_____

_____

_____

Chapter Review

Mark and label the following events in their appropriate places on the timeline.

A. Assassination of John Kennedy
B. Assassination of Martin Luther King Jr.
C. Assassination of Robert Kennedy
D. Berlin Wall erected
E. Election of Lyndon Johnson as president
F. Election of Richard Nixon as president
G. Election of John Kennedy as president

H. Paris Peace Agreement signed
I. March on Washington
J. Tet Offensive
K. Gulf of Tonkin Resolution
L. Resignation of Nixon
M. Voting Rights Act signed

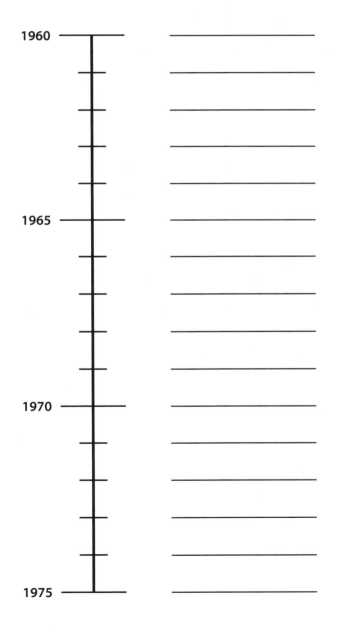

Indicate the primary significance in this chapter of the following people.

1. Lee Harvey Oswald _____

2. Jack Ruby _____

3. Barry Goldwater _____

4. Malcolm X _____

5. James Earl Ray _____

6. William Westmoreland _____

7. Robert Kennedy _____

8. Sirhan Sirhan _____

9. Spiro Agnew _____

10. Henry Kissinger _____

11. Warren Burger _____

12. César Chavez _____

13. Russell Means _____

14. Betty Friedan _____

15. Gerald Ford _____

Indicate the primary significance in this chapter of the following terms.

16. New Frontier

_____

_____

17. Twenty-third Amendment

_____

_____

18. Peace Corps

_____

_____

19. Alliance for Progress

_____

_____

20. Bay of Pigs

_____

_____

21. Great Society

_____

_____

22. Twenty-fourth Amendment

_____

_____

23. Viet Cong

_____

_____

24. Ho Chi Minh Trail

_____

_____

25. counterculture

_____

_____

26. Vietnamization

_____

_____

27. Twenty-sixth Amendment

_____

_____

28. Kent State

_____

_____

29. Tet Offensive

_____

_____

30. War Powers Act

_____

_____

31. détente

_____

_____

32. SALT

_____

_____

33. shuttle diplomacy

_____

_____

34. recession

_____

_____

35. oil embargo

_____

_____

36. _Roe v. Wade_

_____

_____

37. AIM

_____

_____

38. ERA

_____

_____

39. Watergate

_____

_____

Ford's Dilemma: The Nixon Pardon

Read the public statement of President Gerald R. Ford, made on national television on September 8, 1974. Then answer the questions that follow.

Ladies and gentlemen:

I have come to a decision which I felt I should tell you and all of my fellow American citizens, as soon as I was certain in my own mind and in my own conscience that it is the right thing to do.

I have learned already in this office that the difficult decisions always come to this desk. I must admit that many of them do not look at all the same as the hypothetical questions that I have answered freely and perhaps too fast on previous occasions.

My customary policy is to try and get all the facts and to consider the opinions of my countrymen and to take counsel with my most valued friends. But these seldom agree, and in the end, the decision is mine. To procrastinate, to agonize, and to wait for a more favorable turn of events that may never come or more compelling external pressures that may as well be wrong as right, is itself a decision of sorts and a weak and potentially dangerous course for a president to follow.

I have promised to uphold the Constitution, to do what is right as God gives me to see the right, and to do the very best that I can for America.

I have asked your help and your prayers, not only when I became President but many times since. The Constitution is the supreme law of our land and it governs our actions as citizens. Only the laws of God, which govern our consciences, are superior to it.

As we are a nation under God, so I am sworn to uphold our laws with the help of God. And I have sought such guidance and searched my own conscience with special diligence to determine the right thing for me to do with respect to my predecessor in this place, Richard Nixon, and his loyal wife and family.

Theirs is an American tragedy in which we all have played a part. It could go on and on and on, or someone must write the end to it. I have concluded that only I can do that, and if I can, I must.

There are no historic or legal precedents to which I can turn in this matter, none that precisely fit the circumstances of a private citizen who has resigned the Presidency of the United States. But it is common knowledge that serious allegations and accusations hang like a sword over our former President's head, threatening his health as he tries to reshape his life, a great part of which was spent in the service of this country and by the mandate of its people.

After years of bitter controversy and divisive national debate, I have been advised, and I am compelled to conclude that many months and perhaps more years will have to pass before Richard Nixon could obtain a fair trial by jury in any jurisdiction of the United States under governing decisions of the Supreme Court.

I deeply believe in equal justice for all Americans, whatever their station or former station. The law, whether human or divine, is no respecter of persons; but the law is a respecter of reality.

The facts, as I see them, are that a former President of the United States, instead of enjoying equal treatment with any other citizen accused of violating the law, would be cruelly and excessively penalized either in preserving the presumption of his innocence or in obtaining a speedy determination of his guilt in order to repay a legal debt to society.

During this long period of delay and potential litigation, ugly passions would again be aroused. And our people would again be polarized in their opinions. And the credibility of our free institutions of government would again be challenged at home and abroad.

In the end, the courts might well hold that Richard Nixon had been denied due process, and the verdict of history would even more be inconclusive with respect to those charges arising out of the period of his Presidency, of which I am presently aware.

But it is not the ultimate fate of Richard Nixon that most concerns me, though surely it deeply troubles every decent and every compassionate person. My concern is the immediate future of this great country.

In this, I dare not depend upon my personal sympathy as a long-time friend of the former President, nor my professional judgment as a lawyer, and I do not.

As President, my primary concern must always be the greatest good of all the people of the United States whose servant I am. As a man, my first consideration is to be true to my own convictions and my own conscience.

My conscience tells me clearly and certainly that I cannot prolong the bad dreams that continue to reopen a chapter that is closed. My conscience tells me that only I, as President, have the constitutional power to firmly shut and seal this book. My conscience tells me it is my duty, not merely to proclaim domestic tranquility but to use every means that I have to insure it.

I do believe that the buck stops here, that I cannot rely upon public opinion polls to tell me what is right.

I do believe that right makes might and that if I am wrong, 10 angels swearing I was right would make no difference.

I do believe, with all my heart and mind and spirit, that I, not as President but as a humble servant of God, will receive justice without mercy if I fail to show mercy.

Finally, I feel that Richard Nixon and his loved ones have suffered enough and will continue to suffer, no matter what I do, no matter what we, as a great and good nation, can do together to make his goal of peace come true.

[At his point, the President began reading from the proclamation granting the pardon.]

"Now, therefore, I, Gerald R. Ford, President of the United States, pursuant to the pardon power conferred upon me by Article II, Section 2, of the Constitution, have granted and by these presents do grant a full, free, and absolute pardon unto Richard Nixon for all offenses against the United States which he, Richard Nixon, has committed or may have committed or taken part in during the period from January 20, 1969, through August 9, 1974."

[The President signed the proclamation and then resumed reading.]

"In witness whereof, I have hereunto set my hand this eighth day of September, in the year of our Lord nineteen hundred and seventy-four, and of the Independence of the United States of America the one hundred and ninety-ninth."

[NOTE: The President spoke at 11:05 a.m. in the Oval Office at the White House, where he signed Proclamation 4311 granting the pardon.]

1. What did Ford say that indicates that he made his decision to pardon Nixon regardless of public opinion?

_____

_____

_____

2. To what document and what person did Ford repeatedly appeal in making the case for his decision to pardon Nixon? _____

3. To what precedent(s) did Ford turn for help in making his decision? _____

4. What legal argument did Ford use in making his case for pardoning Nixon?

_____

_____

_____

5. What did he say always had to be the primary concern of every president?

_____

6. What messages did he say his conscience told him as he contemplated his decision?

_____

_____

_____

7. To whom did he say he was ultimately responsible for the decision he made? _____

8. What was Ford's final consideration in making his decision?

_____

9. Why do you think Ford signed the official document pardoning Nixon on national television?

_____

_____

_____

10. Do you think Ford did the right thing in pardoning Nixon? Why?

_____

_____

_____

_____

The Story Behind the Camp David Accords

Read the following excerpts of President Jimmy Carter's account of how the Camp David Accords between the leaders of Israel and Egypt—Menachem Begin and Anwar Sadat—came about during September 1978. Then answer the questions.

I directed our negotiating group to assume as our immediate ambition a written agreement for peace between Egypt and Israel, with an agenda for implementation of its terms during the succeeding months. I was convinced that if we three leaders could not resolve the very difficult issues, some of which had never before been addressed forthrightly, then no group of foreign ministers or diplomats could succeed. Both President Sadat and Prime Minister Begin were courageous men, well-liked and trusted in their own countries, who could make tough decisions with relative political impunity. If the *overall* settlement proved to be popular, then some of the unpopular details would be acceptable.

I had no idea whether we would succeed. I only knew that we were at a turning point and that the stakes were very high. We were prepared to stay as long as necessary to explore all the potential agreements. Our plans called for three days, but we were willing to stay as long as a week if we were making good progress and success seemed attainable. We never dreamed we would be there through thirteen intense and discouraging days, with success in prospect only during the final hours.

✪✪✪

All the physical arrangements had been made, and they taxed the capacity of the small mountain camp. It had not been designed to accommodate so many people, especially when they came from three different nations and represented three distinct cultures. Each of us had his own secretarial staff, communication facilities for managing the affairs of his respective government, personal physicians, cooks trained in the preparation of American, Egyptian, or kosher food, and major advisers who were expert in the subjects we were to discuss. Sadat, Begin, and I had private cabins within a stone's throw of each other. None of the other cottages was more than a few hundred yards from us, and all of them were packed to the limit with people. These constraints were a blessing in disguise, because hundreds of other bureaucrats and would-be advisers from all three countries were struggling to find an excuse to join the historic deliberations. We were remarkably successful in keeping them out and in minimizing visits to and from our private place.

✪✪✪

Sadat was strong and bold, very much aware of world public opinion and of his role as the most important leader among the Arabs. I always had the impression that he looked on himself as inheriting the mantle of authority from the great pharaohs and was convinced that he was a man of destiny. Deeply religious, he had asked that a special place be found for him to worship. We set aside the room in Hickory cottage where we always had church services when our family was at Camp David.

Sadat was, perhaps, excessively impatient with the weakness of others and frequently derided some of his fellow leaders in the Middle East, but at least he respected Begin's strength and courage. With Sadat, that was a good place to start.

Nevertheless, Sadat also seemed somewhat impatient with Begin, distrustful of him. Determined to succeed, he was therefore inclined to form a partnership with me in opposition to Begin. His first preference was obviously a settlement; his second, an agreement with me which would be so good for Israel that Begin would be condemned if he rejected it.

✪✪✪

When he and I sat behind my cabin—Aspen—on the terrace, he did not waste any time expressing his thoughts and plans. He emphasized that he was eager to conclude a total settlement of the issues, and not merely establish procedures for future negotiations. He was convinced that Begin did not want an agreement and would try to delay progress as much as possible. Sadat stated that he would back me in all things, and that he had a comprehensive settlement plan "here in my pocket." He let me know that he was prepared to be flexible on all issues except two: land and sovereignty.

✪✪✪

About two hours later, Prime Minister Begin landed on the mountaintop, and we went down to Aspen for a brief conversation. I was pleased that his wife, Aliza, was scheduled to arrive in a few hours. The Begins always seemed very close, and I was sure Aliza would be as helpful to him during the coming days as Rosalynn [Carter] would be to me.

Our greetings were friendly, but we were both somewhat ill at ease. I had wanted to generate an atmosphere of informality from the beginning, but in his attitude and words, Begin approached the initiation of talks in a very thorough and methodical way. His questions were not about substance; he was concerned about the daily schedule, the procedures to be followed, the time and place of meetings, how a record of the proceedings would be kept, how many aides would be permitted on each side, and so forth. This approach was one of his characteristics with which we were familiar, and I was not surprised. He and I were both very methodical about such matters, and I would have wanted answers to the same questions. I responded that my preference was to meet privately and separately with him and Sadat first, and then the three of us could decide how best to proceed. He seemed reluctant about this kind of session with principals only, and was eager to have us meet with at least two advisers each, referring to this as a "three-three-three" meeting.

Begin, too, seemed to look on himself as a man of destiny, cast in a biblical role as one charged with the future of God's chosen people. A student of the Bible, he preferred to use biblical names for places, and referred frequently to God's messages to Moses and to other leaders of the Jews. A man of deep beliefs, he had during his entire adult life demonstrated his dedication to the establishment and preservation of his country, and I knew that he deserved the respect he received from his associates. However, I also knew that his preoccupation with language, names, and terms could severely impede free-flowing talk.

✪✪✪

He pointed out to me that there had not been an agreement between a Jewish nation and Egypt for more than two thousand years, and that our meeting was historically unprecedented. However, unlike Sadat, Begin was clearly planning for an agreement at Camp David only on general principles, which might then serve as a basis for future meetings, when the specifics and remaining differences could be resolved by the Ministers of Foreign Affairs and Defense. I objected strongly to this plan, and told the Prime Minister that we three principals could not expect others to settle major issues later if we could not do so now, and that all the controversial questions should be addressed among us directly.

As he was preparing to leave after our stilted and somewhat superficial discussion, I told him that Sadat had expressed a concern about Begin's preoccupation with details at the expense of the major issues. Begin looked up quickly and said, "I can handle both." I believed him, and hoped he would be inclined to prove it.

✪✪✪

From the beginning, our differences were obvious, even in personal habits. Prime Minister Begin was the soul of propriety. He preferred to wear a tie and coat and strictly observed protocol, always reminding President Sadat and me that he was not a head of state and therefore did not rank as an equal with us. When I wanted to see him, he insisted that he come to my cottage and not the other way around. He stayed up late hours, worked very hard, kept close to his aides and advisers, and walked to the dining area at Laurel Lodge to eat with all the other Israelis and with most of the Egyptians and Americans.

President Sadat wore immaculate sports clothes—usually without a tie. He stayed in his cabin more than the rest of us, observed the greatest possible self-discipline on exercise, rest, and diet, and took a four-kilometer walk at the same time early each morning. He never ate at Laurel with the others, but preferred to dine in privacy. When I wanted to talk to him on the spur of the moment, I would call first and then go to his cottage.

We Americans looked upon ourselves as a bridge between the other two camps, and tried to ease tensions and make everyone feel at home.

✪✪✪

[Talks proceeded for ten days, looking sometimes promising and sometimes sour. Carter then reports what happened on Day Eleven.]

After [Secretary of Defense] Harold [Brown] and I had been at work for about twenty minutes, [Secretary of State Cyrus] Vance burst into the room. His face was white, and he announced, "Sadat is leaving. He and his aides are already packed. He asked me to order him a helicopter!"

It was a terrible moment. Now, even my hopes for a harmonious departure were gone. I sat quietly and assessed the significance of this development—a rupture between Sadat and me, and its consequences for my country and for the Middle East power balance. . . . I told Vance that the best thing for us to do now, to salvage what we could, would be to refuse to sign any document with either country—just to terminate the talks and announce that we had all done our best and failed.

Then I asked Brown and Vance to leave me. When they were gone, I remained alone in the little study where most of the negotiations had taken place. I moved over to the window and looked out to the Catoctin Mountains and prayed fervently for a few minutes that somehow we could find peace.

Then, for some reason, I changed into more formal clothes before going to see Sadat. He was on his porch with five or six of his ministers, and Vance and Brown were there to tell them all good-bye.

I nodded to them, and walked into the cabin. Sadat followed me. I explained to him the extremely serious consequences of his unilaterally breaking off the negotiations: that his action would harm the relationship between Egypt and the United States, he would be violating his personal promise to me, and the onus [responsibility] for failure would be on him. I described the possible future progress of Egypt's friendships and alliances—from us to the moderate and then radical Arabs, thence to the Soviet Union. I told him it would damage one of my most precious possessions—his friendship and our mutual trust.

He was adamant, but I was dead serious, and he knew it. I had never been more serious in my life. I repeated some of the more telling arguments I had previously used at our meeting by the swimming pool. He would be publicly repudiating some of his own commitments, damaging his reputation as the world's foremost peacemaker, and admitting the fruitlessness of his celebrated visit to Jerusalem. His worst enemies in the Arab world would be proven right in their claims that he had made a foolish mistake.

I told Sadat that he simply had to stick with me for another day or two—after which, if circumstances did not improve, all of us simultaneously would take the action he was now planning.

He explained the reason for his decision to leave. . . . I thought very rapidly and told him that we would have a complete understanding that if any nation rejected *any* part of the agreements, *none* of the proposals would stay in effect.

Sadat stood silently for a long time. Then he looked at me and said, "If you give me this statement, I will stick with you to the end." (He kept his promise, but it never proved necessary to give him any such statement.)

✪✪✪

[The talks continued into Day Twelve.]

In the meantime, a serious problem had erupted with the Israelis. Vance had just shown them a copy of our draft letter that would go to Sadat, restating the United States position on Jerusalem, which had been spelled out officially in United Nations debates over the years. There was an absolute furor, and Begin announced that Israel would not sign *any* document if we wrote *any* letter to Egypt about Jerusalem.

[Begin determined that he would leave the talks.]

✪✪✪

Earlier, my secretary, Susan Clough, had brought me some photographs of Begin, Sadat, and me. They had already been signed by President Sadat, and Prime Minister Begin had requested that I autograph them for his grandchildren. Knowing the trouble we were in with the Israelis, Susan suggested that she go and get the actual names of the grandchildren, so that I could personalize each picture. I did this, and walked over to Begin's cabin with them. He was sitting on the front porch, very distraught and nervous because the talks had finally broken down at the last minute.

I handed him the photographs. He took them and thanked me. Then he happened to look down and saw that his granddaughter's name was on the top one. He spoke it aloud, and then looked at each photograph individually, repeating the name of the grandchild I had written on it. His lips trembled, and tears welled up in his eyes. He told me a little about each child, and especially about the one who seemed to be his favorite. We were both emotional as we talked quietly for a few minutes about grandchildren and about war.

Then he asked me to step into his cabin, requesting that everyone else in the room leave. He was quiet, sober, surprisingly friendly. There were no histrionics. He said that the Jerusalem matter was fatal, that he was very sorry but he could not accept our letter to Egypt. I told him I had drafted a new version and submitted it to [his aides Moshe] Dayan and [Aharon] Barak. He had not yet seen it. I suggested he read it over and let me know his decision, but that there was no way that I could go back on my commitment to Sadat to exchange letters. The success of any future peace talks might depend on his and Sadat's assessment of my integrity, and I could not violate a promise once it was made.

I walked back to Aspen, very dejected. Sadat was there . . . dressed to go back to Washington. I asked everyone else to leave and told Sadat what was happening. We realized that all of us had done our best, but that prospects were dim indeed.

Then Begin called. He said, "I will accept the letter you have drafted on Jerusalem." I breathed a sigh of relief, because it now seemed that the last obstacle had been removed.

We frantically worked on a final draft of the agreements, clearing the texts with [each side's aides] as we went along. We were making plans to return to Washington. . . . I prepared a schedule and gave it to [Vice President] Fritz [Mondale] to carry to both leaders for their approval.

I looked up to see Hamilton [Jordan] and Jody [Powell, Carter's aides] anxiously peering into my window. When I gave them a thumbs-up sign, they beamed with relief.

✪✪✪

In a few minutes I went into my front room and was surprised to see Fritz there. He said that the two leaders were together in Sadat's cottage, and he had been reluctant to interrupt them. I decided to go myself, because I thought it was crucial for me to intercede if they were arguing.

I ran toward Sadat's cabin, and saw that Begin was just leaving in a golf cart with Barak. He was quite happy as he told me that they had had a love feast and that Sadat had agreed to Begin's language on the Knesset vote. I knew this could not be true, and I asked Barak to tell me exactly what Sadat had said. Each time he tried to answer, Begin would have something else to say. I finally asked the Prime Minister point-blank to let Barak answer my question.

Barak described the conversation to me. What Begin had asked was, "Do you think the Knesset [Israeli parliament] should be under pressure when it votes?" Predictably, Sadat had replied, "No, the Knesset should not be under pressure." That was all. Begin had interpreted this to mean that he could draft any language he preferred to insure that the Knesset would be free of any implied adverse consequences if its decision should be negative.

I asked Barak to come with me. Begin excused him, and we went to my cabin just a few steps away. I checked the Israeli language most carefully. It was a *very* confusing point, and all of us were dead tired. Momentarily, my mind seemed to clear and I thought of a way to phrase all three final letters that would be satisfactory to both Begin and Sadat. Susan typed them, and I sent a copy to each leader and to all our own delegation with the instructions, "This is the exact language to be used. Do not use any other language on or off the record."

Only then did I fully realize we had succeeded.

1. Why did Carter choose to hold the peace talks with Begin and Sadat at Camp David rather than in Washington, D.C.? _____

_____

_____

2. Compare and contrast the personal characteristics of Begin and Sadat. _____

_____

_____

_____

_____

_____

_____

3. How did Sadat and Begin view themselves in relation to their national histories?

_____

_____

_____

4. With which of the leaders—Begin, Sadat, or Carter—did you most relate as you read Carter's account? Why? _____

_____

_____

5. What did Carter do to ensure that the negotiations would not be undercut or misrepresented by the media during the summit? _____

_____

_____

6. What arrangements did Carter make for the two leaders' different cultural needs and expectations?

_____

_____

_____

7. How did Begin's official position differ from that of Sadat and Carter?

_____

_____

8. Which leader threatened to break off negotiations first, and how did Carter persuade him to stay?

_____

_____

_____

9. What bit of advice did Carter's secretary give the president that softened Begin's heart and enabled him to see the wisdom of agreeing to the wording of the letters? _____

_____

_____

_____

10. In light of this reading, what is your assessment of the Camp David Accords? Were Carter's efforts worth it in the long run? _____

_____

_____

_____

_____

Interpreting Editorial Cartoons

Study the following cartoon. Then explain what it is saying about Carter's response to the Iran hostage crisis. What does the cartoon say about Carter's character and leadership? About his ideas concerning the Iranians in power at the time? What does the final frame say about Carter's political future?

_____

_____

_____

_____

_____

_____

_____

_____

_____

The Attempted Assassination of Reagan—In His Own Words

Read President Reagan's account of how he was nearly assassinated. Then answer the questions that follow.

I put on a brand-new blue suit for my speech to the Construction Trades Council. But for reasons I'll never know, I took off my best wristwatch before leaving the White House and put on an old one Nancy had given me that I usually wore only when I was doing chores outside at the ranch.

My speech at the Hilton Hotel was not riotously received—I think most of the audience were Democrats—but at least they gave me polite applause.

After the speech, I left the hotel through a side entrance and passed a line of press photographers and TV cameras. I was almost to the car when I heard what sounded like two or three firecrackers over to my left—just a small fluttering sound, *pop, pop, pop.*

I turned and said, "What . . . [was] that?"

Just then, Jerry Parr, the head of our Secret Service unit, grabbed me by the waist and literally hurled me into the back of the limousine. I landed on my face atop the arm rest across the backseat and Jerry jumped on top of me. When he landed, I felt a pain in my upper back that was unbelievable. It was the most excruciating pain I had ever felt.

"Jerry," I said, "get off, I think you've broken one of my ribs."

"The White House," Jerry told the driver, then scrambled off me and got on the jump seat and the car took off.

I tried to sit up on the edge of the seat and was almost paralyzed by pain. As I was straightening up, I had to cough hard and saw that the palm of my hand was brimming with extremely red, frothy blood.

"You not only broke a rib, I think the rib punctured my lung," I said.

Jerry looked at the bubbles in the frothy blood and told the driver to head for George Washington University Hospital instead of the White House.

By then my handkerchief was sopped with blood and he handed me his. Suddenly, I realized I could barely breathe. No matter how hard I tried, I couldn't get enough air. I was frightened and started to panic a little. I just was not able to inhale enough air.

We pulled up in front of the hospital emergency entrance and I was first out of the limo and into the emergency room. A nurse was coming to meet me and I told her I was having trouble breathing. Then all of a sudden my knees turned rubbery. The next thing I knew I was lying face up on a gurney and my brand-new pin-striped suit was being cut off me, never to be worn again.

❁❁❁

I was . . . only half-conscious when I realized that someone was holding my hand. It was a soft, feminine hand. I felt it come up and touch mine and then hold on tight to it. It gave me a wonderful feeling. Even now I find it difficult to explain how reassuring, how wonderful, it felt.

It must have been the hand of a nurse kneeling very close to the gurney, but I couldn't see her. I started asking, "Who's holding my hand? . . . Who's holding my hand?" When I didn't hear any response, I said, "Does Nancy know about us?"

Although I tried afterward to learn who the nurse was, I was never able to find her. I had wanted to tell her how much the touch of her hand had meant to me, but I never was able to do that.

Once I opened my eyes and saw Nancy looking down at me.

"Honey," I said, "I forgot to duck, ..."

Seeing Nancy in the hospital gave me an enormous lift. As long as I live I will never forget the thought that rushed into my head as I looked up into her face. Later I wrote it down in my diary: *"I pray I'll never face a day when she isn't there. . . . Of all the ways God had blessed me, giving her to me was the greatest—beyond anything I can ever hope to deserve."*

❂❂❂

Within a few minutes after I arrived, the room was full of specialists in virtually every medical field. When one of the doctors said they were going to operate on me, I said, "I hope you're a Republican."

He looked at me and said, "Today, Mr. President, we're all Republicans."

I also remember saying, after one of the nurses asked me how I felt, "All in all, I'd rather be in Philadelphia"—the old W. C. Fields line.

For quite a while when I was in the emergency room, I still thought I was there because Jerry Parr had broken my rib and it had punctured my lung. Little by little, though, I learned what had happened and what the situation was: I had a bullet in my lung; Jim Brady, my press secretary, had been shot in the head; Secret Service agent Tim McCarthy had been shot in the chest; policeman Tom Delehanty had been shot in the neck. All of us had been hit by the gun of a young lone assailant who was in police custody.

When Jim Brady . . . was wheeled by me unconscious on his way to the operating room, someone told me he was hit so badly he probably wouldn't make it, and I quickly said a prayer for him. I didn't feel I could ask God's help to heal Jim, the others, and myself, and at the same time feel hatred for the man who had shot us, so I silently asked God to help him deal with whatever demons had led him to shoot us.

As people began to tell me more about what had happened, I began to realize that when Jerry Parr had thrown his body on me, he was gallantly putting his own life on the line to save mine, and I felt guilty that I'd chewed him out right after it happened. Like Jerry, Tim McCarthy had also bravely put his life on the line for me. Some weeks later I was shown the TV shots of what happened that day. As I was being thrown into the limo, there, facing the camera between me and the gunman, spread-eagling himself to make as big a target as possible, was Tim McCarthy. He was shot right in the chest. Thank heaven he lived.

I thanked God for what He and they had done for me, and while I was waiting to be taken into the operating room, I remembered the trip I had made just the week before to Ford's Theater and the thoughts I'd had while looking up at the flag-draped box where Lincoln had died. Even with all the protection in the world, I'd thought, it was probably impossible to guarantee completely the safety of the president. Now I'd not only benefited from the selflessness of these two men; God, for some reason, had seen fit to give me His blessing and allow me to live a while longer.

John Hinckley, Jr.'s bullet probably caught me in midair at the same moment I was being thrown into the back of the car by Jerry Parr. After they took it out of me, I saw the bullet. It looked like a nickel that was black on one side; it had been flattened into a small disc and darkened by the paint on the limousine. First the bullet had struck the limousine, then it had ricocheted through the small gap between the body of the car and the door hinges. It hit me under my left arm, where it made a small slit like a knife wound.

I'd always been told that no pain is as excruciating as a broken bone; that's why I thought Jerry had broken my rib when he landed so hard on me. But it wasn't Jerry's weight I felt; according to the doctors, the flattened bullet had hit my rib edgewise, then turned over like a coin, tumbling down through my lung and stopping less than an inch from my heart.

❂❂❂

After I left the hospital and was back in the White House, I wrote a few words about the shooting in my diary that concluded: "Whatever happens now I owe my life to God and will try to serve him in every way I can."

1. Reagan made his wearing of an old watch on the day of the attempt on his life just a coincidence, but what in his narrative might be taken to indicate that he did it intentionally?

   _____

   _____

   _____

2. Where did Jerry Parr first tell the driver to take the President? _____

3. What prompted Parr to change his instructions to the driver moments later?

   _____

   _____

4. What did Reagan think had happened to him? _____

   _____

   _____

5. Give one example that proved that Reagan's sense of humor remained with him even at that grave moment.

   _____

   _____

   _____

   _____

6. What was Reagan's first reaction when he learned of the condition of James Brady, Tim McCarthy, and Tom Delehanty? What was his second reaction? _____

   _____

   _____

7. Give two instances of Reagan's concern for the feelings of others that he exhibited in this incident.

   _____

   _____

   _____

   _____

   _____

   _____

8. Where had Reagan visited the week before the assassination attempt, and what were his thoughts at that place? _____

   _____

   _____

   _____

9. How do we see the providence of God at work in this seeming tragedy? _____

_____

_____

_____

_____

_____

_____

10. What indication did Reagan give in his account that shows that he, too, recognized God's protective providence? _____

_____

_____

_____

_____

11. How do you think you would be affected by such a "close call"? _____

_____

_____

_____

_____

Federal Spending Under Recent Presidents

Government spending that is not for defense (including homeland security) is for either entitlements or discretionary purposes. Entitlements are programs that have become "rights" to those who benefit from them. They include such programs as welfare and Social Security. Discretionary spending is any spending that is not mandated by law (such as an entitlement) or necessary for defense. Examples of such spending are federal buildings, research grants, or disaster relief. With these definitions in mind, study the following two graphs. Then answer the questions about each.

Growth of Federal Non-defense Spending by President

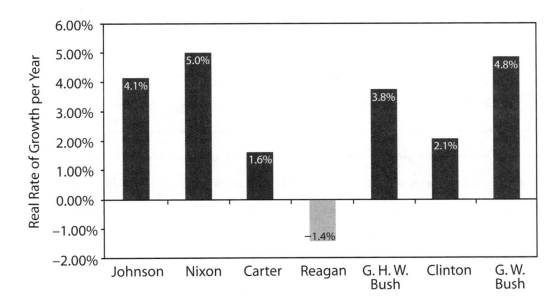

Growth of Total Federal Spending by President

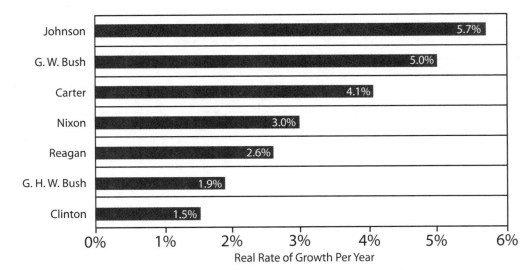

[Source: Stephen Slivinski, "The Grand Old Spending Party, How Republicans Became Big Spenders," *Policy Analysis*, May 3, 2005.]

1. Under which president did total government spending increase the most? Based on your knowledge of that president's administration, why did he spend more than other presidents? _____

_____

2. Although presidents generally get blamed for spending money, who actually is more to blame and why?

_____

_____

_____

3. Who was the only president on the charts who actually cut discretionary spending? _____

4. If that president cut discretionary spending, how is it that spending under his administration actually increased? _____

_____

_____

5. Under which Republican president did total spending increase the most? What do you think are the major reasons for that increase? _____

_____

_____

6. Overall, presidents of which party tended to hold the line on discretionary and entitlement spending better—Democrats or Republicans? _____

_____

7. Which president of that party allowed the least discretionary and entitlement spending? _____

8. What are some ways in which Congress and the presidents could spend less?

_____

_____

_____

_____

_____

_____

Chapter Review: The Presidents after Nixon

Match the following presidents with the phrases that are *best* associated with each of them.

A. Gerald Ford   C. Ronald Reagan
B. Jimmy Carter   D. George Bush

_____ 1. peanut farmer

_____ 2. former actor

_____ 3. governor of Georgia

_____ 4. reelected by a landslide

_____ 5. never elected to an executive office

_____ 6. pardoned Nixon

_____ 7. offered amnesty to draft dodgers

_____ 8. Rehnquist court

_____ 9. Bicentennial

_____ 10. Iran-Contra affair

_____ 11. collapse of the Soviet Union

_____ 12. 1979 energy crisis

_____ 13. first vice president elected president since 1836

_____ 14. bombing of Libya

_____ 15. invasion of Grenada

_____ 16. Persian Gulf War

_____ 17. Panama Canal Treaty

_____ 18. Camp David Accords

_____ 19. largest income-tax cut in U.S. history

_____ 20. 1990 budget deal

_____ 21. "Star Wars" program (SDI)

_____ 22. WIN anti-inflation program

_____ 23. supply-side economics

_____ 24. Americans with Disabilities Act

_____ 25. governor of California

To which political party did each of the following presidents belong?

26. George Bush _____

27. Jimmy Carter _____

28. Gerald Ford _____

29. Ronald Reagan _____

Hillary Clinton and the Health-Care Debate

Americans already enjoy the best health care in the world, so they fear changes to the health-care system. The secrecy that surrounded the preparation of Hillary Clinton's health-care plan only intensified their fears. Democrats tried to present the plan in the best light, but Americans did not agree. Read each statement and the truth behind it. Match the best label to each example of faulty reasoning.

A. hasty generalization from too little evidence

B. appeal to emotions, such as fear, pity, shame, or national pride

C. suppressed (or withheld) evidence

D. false dichotomy (limiting choices to "either . . . or")

_____ 1. Clinton said that 15 percent of Americans (thirty-eight million) did not have health insurance. But she did not mention that most of those people were temporary cases involving healthy young people. Only 3 percent (six million) of them were unwillingly uninsured for a long time.

_____ 2. Clinton chided America because foreign health care is "cheaper." She wanted Americans to be ashamed of their system, even though health care in the United States is the envy of the world.

_____ 3. Clinton said that her reforms were the only way to keep health care from becoming 28 percent of the federal budget by the year 2002. But without her plan, costs began to drop.

_____ 4. Clinton said that this rich nation had a moral obligation to give all citizens "security of mind" about health care. But her wording made Clinton's opponents seem to be heartless, cruel, and uncaring.

_____ 5. Clinton said that her system was "streamlined and simpler." But she did not show the details. Opponents of Clinton's system said that the plan would "create fifty-nine new federal programs or bureaucracies, expand twenty others, impose seventy-nine new federal mandates, and make major changes in the tax code."

_____ 6. Clinton said that she would "pay" for health-care reforms through savings generated by less paperwork and increased efficiency. But she had little basis for that claim. Her system had never been tested.

_____ 7. Clinton said that she would not propose raising taxes, except on cigarettes. But she did not acknowledge that forcing businesses to pay insurance premiums is a "tax" that, according to the Congressional Budget Office, would cost businesses hundreds of billions of dollars.

At the heart of the debate over Clinton's plan was the question of whether providing health-care coverage was a constitutional function of government. Obtain a copy of the U.S. Constitution (or use the one in your textbook), and answer the following questions.

8. According to the Constitution, what is the proper role of the national government in American society? (You do not need to list the specific responsibilities of each branch of the government, only general principles that apply to all branches.)

_____

_____

_____

_____

_____

9. What two vague items in the Constitution might some people use to justify government involvement in other areas such as health care? (Hints: see the preamble and Article I, Section 8.)

_____

_____

_____

_____

10. What do *you* think? Do you agree with Hillary Clinton that government is responsible for providing cradle-to-grave health care for the people of the United States, or do you think government's role is limited by the Constitution to specifically stated powers? Support your opinion.

_____

_____

_____

_____

_____

_____

_____

_____

_____

_____

_____

Contract with America

In 1994, Newt Gingrich masterminded a plan for reforming how Congress conducted business and for reforming key aspects of American life. By signing the Contract with America, the Republican majority pledged themselves to pass certain reforms on the first day of the new Congress and bring to a vote certain key pieces of legislation in the first one hundred days. Read the following excerpts from that contract and the brief summary of its results and then answer the questions.

As Republican Members of the House of Representatives and as citizens seeking to join that body we propose not just to change its policies, but even more important, to restore the bonds of trust between the people and their elected representatives.

That is why, in this era of official evasion and posturing, we offer instead a detailed agenda for national renewal, a written commitment with no fine print.

✪✪✪

On the first day of the 104th Congress, the new Republican majority will immediately pass the following major reforms, aimed at restoring the faith and trust of the American people in their government:

FIRST, require all laws that apply to the rest of the country also apply equally to the Congress;

SECOND, select a major, independent auditing firm to conduct a comprehensive audit of Congress for waste, fraud or abuse;

THIRD, cut the number of House committees, and cut committee staff by one-third;

FOURTH, limit the terms of all committee chairs;

FIFTH, ban the casting of proxy votes in committee;

SIXTH, require committee meetings to be open to the public;

SEVENTH, require a three-fifths majority vote to pass a tax increase;

EIGHTH, guarantee an honest accounting of our Federal Budget by implementing zero base-line budgeting.

Thereafter, within the first 100 days of the 104th Congress, we shall bring to the House Floor the following bills, each to be given full and open debate, each to be given a clear and fair vote and each to be immediately available this day for public inspection and scrutiny.

1. THE FISCAL RESPONSIBILITY ACT: A balanced budget/tax limitation amendment . . . line-item veto . . . requiring [Congress] to live under the same budget constraints as families and businesses.

2. THE TAKING BACK OUR STREETS ACT: . . . stronger truth-in-sentencing, "good faith" exclusionary rule exemptions, effective death penalty provisions, and cuts in social spending. . . .

3. THE PERSONAL RESPONSIBILITY ACT: Discourage illegitimacy and teen pregnancy by prohibiting welfare to minor mothers and denying increased AFDC [Aid to Families with Dependent Children] for additional children while on welfare, cut spending for welfare . . . enact a tough two-years-and-out provision with work requirements. . . .

4. THE FAMILY REINFORCEMENT ACT: Child support enforcement, tax incentives for adoption, strengthening rights of parents . . . stronger child pornography laws. . . .

5. THE AMERICAN DREAM RESTORATION ACT: A $500 per child tax credit, . . . repeal of the marriage tax penalty . . . middle class tax relief.

6. THE NATIONAL SECURITY RESTORATION ACT: No U.S. troops under U.N. command . . . funding [increases] to strengthen our national defense. . . .

7. THE SENIOR CITIZENS FAIRNESS ACT: Raise the Social Security earnings limit . . . repeal the 1993 tax hikes on Social Security benefits . . . provide tax incentives for private long-term care insurance. . . .

8. THE JOB CREATION AND WAGE ENHANCEMENT ACT: Small business incentives, capital gains [tax] cut . . . unfunded mandate reform to create jobs and raise worker wages.

9. THE COMMON SENSE LEGAL REFORM ACT: "Loser pays" laws, reasonable limits on punitive damages and reform of product liability laws. . . .

10. THE CITIZEN LEGISLATURE ACT: . . . term limits to replace career politicians with citizen legislators.

✪✪✪

Respecting the judgment of our fellow citizens as we seek their mandate for reform, we hereby pledge our names to this Contract with America.

Action Summary: All ten of these pledged actions were brought to the House floor for a vote. Nine of them passed the House. (The only one that did not pass the House was term limits.) On 302 roll-call votes associated with their passage, conservatives (supporters of the Contract with America) won 299. Three of the nine bills that passed the House also passed the Senate. Those bills (under new names) were the Congressional Accountability Act of 1995 (required Congress to follow eleven workplace laws), the Unfunded Mandates Reform Act of 1995 (prevented Congress from imposing inadequately funded mandates on the states), and the Paperwork Reduction Act of 1995 (reduced government paperwork). The balanced budget amendment failed by only one vote to get the two-thirds required in the Senate.

1. Who was the "mastermind" behind the Contract with America? _____

2. According to the Contract, what was to be the first order of business on the first day of the new Congress?

_____

3. What did that first order of business signal about the signers of the Contract? _____

_____

_____

4. How many issues did the Contract promise to bring to a vote, and what was the reason for numbering them in the Contract? _____

_____

5. On what percentage of the issues did the House vote? What percentage of those bills passed the House? What percentage also passed the Senate and became law? _____

6. What is your assessment of the Contract? Was it a useful tool or merely a political ploy? Support your answers. _____

_____

_____

7. If you were a Congressman assigned to draft a Contract for today, what issues would you include and why?

_____

_____

_____

What the Bible Says About Modern Issues

The Scriptures tell us all we need to know about "modern" issues. One modern belief is that mankind can solve his own problems. Look up each Scripture passage and place its letter in the blank beside the truth that Scripture teaches.

A. Genesis 3:16–19   E. John 14:27   I. 1 Timothy 6:6–8

B. Ecclesiastes 1:15   F. Ephesians 2:1–3   J. 2 Timothy 3:1, 7

C. Ecclesiastes 3:19–20   G. Ephesians 2:8

D. Luke 12:15   H. Ephesians 2:11–12

_____ 1. God has placed a curse on this world so that man must always live in sorrow and earn his living by hard work.

_____ 2. People in the end times will be constantly learning but never able to find the truth.

_____ 3. The world does not give lasting peace.

_____ 4. Mankind cannot straighten all that is crooked or supply all that is lacking.

_____ 5. Without Christ we have no hope.

_____ 6. All men, like beasts, will one day return to dust.

_____ 7. All people are dead and ruled by Satan until Christ gives them life.

_____ 8. No one can save himself; salvation is a gift of God.

_____ 9. A man's life consists not in the abundance of his possessions.

_____ 10. True wealth comes from godliness and contentment.

Modern Americans tend to reject absolute moral standards, yet they advocate various "human rights." Look up the following verses and write out what they teach about human rights and responsibilities.

11. Jeremiah 22:3 _____

_____

12. Matthew 12:36–37 _____

_____

13. Mark 7:20–23 _____

_____

14. John 8:31–36 _____

_____

15. John 12:48 _____

_____

16. 1 Timothy 5:8 _____

_____

17. 1 Timothy 5:9–11 _____

_____

_____

18. James 1:27 _____

_____

Ending the Welfare State Through the Power of Private Action

By Richard M. Ebeling

Read the following essay and answer the questions at the end.

Despair about the current direction of American public policy is easily understood. In whichever direction we look, government seems to be growing larger and more intrusive. For example, in February [2007] the Associated Press (AP) reported that in spite of the 1996 welfare reform, which has reduced the number of people on the welfare rolls, "Nearly one in six people rely on some form of public assistance, a larger share [of the population] than at any time since the government started measuring two decades ago."

Those receiving welfare payments from the federal or state governments may have decreased from 14.2 million people in 1994 to 5.1 million in 2005. But 45 million people are on Medicaid, the AP said, and almost 26 million people receive food stamps every month.

Government continues to be out of control, and too many of our fellow Americans appear not to care enough to do anything about it, especially when so many of them are beneficiaries of government largess in one form or another. A disregard of the harmful effects from any and all forms of dependency on the welfare state is reinforced by the media, which almost always implies there "ought to be a law" to solve every supposed social problem, and a public-education establishment that indoctrinates young people in our schools and colleges with "politically correct" propaganda for political paternalism.

But appearances do not always tell the real story of everything that is going on. People often act more wisely in taking personal initiative and reclaiming self-responsibility than their stated or unstated political views would suggest. I believe that while many Americans find it difficult to think politically "outside the box" of Big Government, they have in fact lost confidence in much of what government has promised or tried to deliver. As this confidence has been eroded, people have begun once more to take care of themselves and their families.

Social Security is one area where this is happening. While most Americans cannot imagine a world without a government-guaranteed pension, a growing number of Americans have been turning their backs on this government promise of a secure and comfortable retirement. Over the last 20 years private retirement planning has exploded. In 1985 there were 1,528 mutual funds offering investment opportunities to private investors. By 2004, however, 8,044 mutual funds existed. Total mutual-fund assets increased from $495 billion to 8.1 trillion. The number of shareholder accounts went from 296,000 to over 267.4 million.

This tells us the extent to which the American people have implicitly declared that they have no confidence in Social Security. Whether they are setting aside before or after-tax income, tens of millions of Americans have decided that they cannot and will not depend on Washington when they retire and are planning for their own future.

Another example is education. For well over a century compulsory public education has been one of the most sacred cows of public policy. The few private schools have often been viewed as only for the children of the elite. And 20 years ago, home-schooling was considered eccentric or for the shut-in child.

Yet between 1990 and 2004 attendance at private schools (K–12) increased from 4.8 million to over 6.2 million, a 29 percent increase. About 11.5 percent of all students in the United States are now enrolled in more than 29,000 private schools; these schools represent around 23 percent of all schools in the country. A national survey in 2000 found that 48.6 percent of the schools were Catholic, 15.7 percent nonsectarian, 15 percent conservative Christian, 6.1 percent Baptist, 4.3 percent Lutheran, and 3.3 percent Jewish. Many of the remaining private schools also were affiliated with religious denominations.

The parents of these privately schooled children choose to pay tuition on top of their school taxes. According to many studies, the growth in private schooling would be greater if not for the tax burden on the average family, including those taxes for the government schools many parents wish to shun.

In a 1985 public-opinion poll, only 16 percent of respondents thought home-schooling was a good thing, but by 2001 41 percent gave that response. In the early 1990s an estimated 400,000–600,000 children were being homeschooled. Today, well over one million children may be homeschooled.

Homeschooling parents are willing to bear another heavy burden to assure their children's education. They not only pay taxes for a government school their children do not attend, but one parent gives up the opportunity to earn income in the work-place by staying home, mastering many academic subjects, and teaching.

As a percentage of all students enrolled throughout the United States, the numbers for both private- and home-schooled children are still relatively low, totaling no more than around 12 percent of the student population.

But the parents of these young people no longer trust government education. Some parents oppose what is taught in government schools, believing that wrong values and beliefs are fostered there. Others are angered and frustrated that their children do not learn to read. They understand that their children only get one chance to be educated while they are young and will not leave that one chance to the government—regardless of the cost to the family.

The enthusiasm of many parents for the voucher system is also a strong indication of how much they want to reduce government control over their children's education. Even if the friend of freedom has doubts about the workability of the voucher system, and whether it would really free education from the state monopoly, its growing popularity demonstrates that many parents want to take greater responsibility for their children's schooling.

Health-Care Revolt

Even while the Medicare and Medicaid rolls are growing, a "counterrevolution" against government-provided health care is starting. A handful of physicians have begun to opt out of the system and all the paperwork and regulations socialized medicine entails. They only accept patients who are willing to pay out of their own pockets, rather than with government dollars taken from the taxpayers. Some of their patients gladly follow their doctors out of the labyrinth of government medical care as they learn that by doing so the long-run cost of their medical services could fall. In addition, these patients rediscover the benefits of more directly choosing the type and quality of care they desire. And it helps restore the personal relationship between doctor and patient that government health care has severely undermined.

In these three areas individuals are taking back personal responsibility from the government. They are not waiting for a political movement to "free" them. Instead their actions preceded and sparked the political debate over whether government should monopolize these services.

These individual private choices rarely capture the headlines. But like many real social shifts they are occurring all around us, slowly and incrementally through the separate actions of millions of people. Their cumulative effect has the potential to transform society.

This is also the reason for long-run optimism about the prospects for liberty. The American heritage of freedom still is the fertile soil in which individuals can challenge the idea of political paternalism. By taking care of their own affairs, they are delegitimizing the welfare state. Their actions then influence the arena of ideas.

The paternalistic state was not created in a day. It has grown in size and legitimacy over a century, and it will not be gone in the blink of an eye. But it is being undermined by a real "people's" movement, the spontaneous choices and actions of millions of Americans wanting greater self-responsibility and less dependency on the powers that be. They are moving the world away from the welfare state one person at a time. That is the strength and the power of liberty.

1. According to the AP, what part of the U.S. population receives some form of public assistance?

   _____

2. What example does Ebeling give to support his thesis that the people are losing confidence in the government and its promises to care for them? _____

   _____

   _____

   _____

3. To what does Ebeling say parents are turning as their expression of lack of confidence in public education? What about those alternatives proves the parents' commitment to them?

   _____

   _____

   _____

   _____

   _____

4. What proof does Ebeling offer that people distrust government in health care?

   _____

   _____

   _____

   _____

5. In what ways—other than education and health care—can the people of the United States reduce their dependence on government? _____

   _____

   _____

   _____

   _____

   _____

   _____

6. In what ways could you individually (or your family) increase your own self-dependence and reduce your dependence on government? _____

_____

_____

_____

_____

7. What applications of Ebeling's essay could be made to the first months of the Obama presidency?

_____

_____

_____

_____

_____

Impeachment

Using outside sources, find the answers to the following questions about the process and history of impeachment.

Background

1. What does the word *impeach* mean? _____

2. Which part of government has the sole power of impeachment of federal officials?

   _____

3. Which part of government sits as the jury in an impeachment trial? _____

4. Who presides over any impeachment trial? _____

5. Using outside resources, determine how many federal officials have been impeached. Of that number, how many have actually been convicted and removed from office? _____

6. Of those who have been impeached, what position did most of them hold? _____

7. How many U.S. presidents have been impeached? _____

   _____

How Did Your Congressman Vote in the Clinton Impeachment?

Using the Internet or print resources, find out how *your* state's representatives voted on each article of impeachment against President Clinton. Then answer the questions that follow the chart.

Article of impeachment	How my congressman voted
Article I: Did Clinton commit perjury before the grand jury?	
Article II: Did Clinton commit perjury in the Paula Jones case?	
Article III: Did Clinton obstruct justice?	
Article IV: Did Clinton abuse his power?	

8. How did your congressman vote on each article of impeachment in relation to other congressmen from your state? _____

   _____

9. What reasons (if any) did he or she offer for voting in that way? _____

   _____

10. If your congressman voted "yes" on any of the four articles of impeachment, did he win reelection in the next congressional race? _____

11. If your congressman voted "yes" on one or more of the articles of impeachment and did *not* win reelection, do you think his vote(s) on impeachment influenced the results of his campaign? Why or why not?

_____

_____

_____

12. How would *you* have voted on each article if you had been a congressman at that time? Explain why.

_____

_____

13. The only guidelines in the Constitution as grounds for impeachment are "high crimes and misdemeanors." What do you think those broad categories of offenses include? Did any of Clinton's actions fit this description? Why or why not? _____

_____

_____

_____

_____

Comparing Impeachment Trials

Compare and contrast the impeachment trials of Andrew Johnson (see Chapter 15) and Bill Clinton using the following chart.

Similarities	Differences

Chapter Review

Match the following people in the chapter with their descriptions.

_____ 1. Defeated George H.W. Bush to become president

_____ 2. Third-party candidate in 1992

_____ 3. Controversial attorney general nominated by Clinton

_____ 4. Leader of cult whose compound and followers were destroyed in botched raid

_____ 5. Blew up the Murrah Federal Building in Oklahoma City

_____ 6. Wrote *It Takes a Village*

_____ 7. Mastermind of the Contract with America and the Republican Revolution of 1994

_____ 8. Preacher who was the leader of the Moral Majority

_____ 9. Preacher who was a TV host and in the Christian Coalition

_____ 10. Conservative talk radio host who energized Republican voters

_____ 11. Republican opponent of Clinton in 1996 election

_____ 12. Woman who refused to testify against the Clintons in Whitewater scandal

_____ 13. Witness who testified about Clinton's moral indiscretions

_____ 14. Independent Counsel who investigated Clinton's indiscretions and filed report that led to his impeachment

_____ 15. First female secretary of state

_____ 16. Haitian leader whom Clinton returned to power but was later forced into exile

A. Madeleine Albright
B. Jean-Bertrand Aristide
C. Bill Clinton
D. Hillary Clinton
E. Bob Dole
F. Jerry Falwell
G. Newt Gingrich
H. Paula Jones
I. David Koresh
J. Rush Limbaugh
K. Susan McDougal
L. Timothy McVeigh
M. Ross Perot
N. Janet Reno
O. Pat Robertson
P. Kenneth Starr

Identify each of the organizations, terms, or items described in the following statements.

19. Clinton's community service organization for the nation's young people _____

20. Clinton program that established "voluntary" educational standards that states had to meet to receive federal funds _____

21. Government grants that parents could use to send their children to the schools of their choice

_____

22. The practice of listening to many countries' opinions before making policy decisions or taking action in world affairs _____

23. Clinton-brokered peace agreement between the warring factions on the Balkan Peninsula

_____

24. Trade agreement between Canada, Mexico, and the United States that reduced barriers to international

trade _____

"Let's Roll!" The Story of the Passengers of United Flight 93

Authorities think that the brave action of the passengers of United Flight 93 on September 11, 2001, might have prevented a terrorist attack on either the White House or the U.S. Capitol and saved countless lives. One thing that is certain is that Todd Beamer led those passengers in overpowering the terrorists who hijacked that plane. Read the following account of his brave self-sacrifice as told by his wife in her book _Let's Roll!_. Then answer the questions.

The plane was scheduled to take off at 8:00 a.m., and in fact the Boeing 757 did push back from Gate A-17 at 8:01. But, as is often the case at Newark International, runway traffic delayed the takeoff. For the next 40 minutes the plane remained on the ground.

. . . The four Middle Eastern-looking young men, all deeply religious, were led by Ziad Samir Jarrah, who sat in first-class seat 1B, the seat closest to the cockpit door. The 27-year-old Lebanese man was a licensed pilot who had taken flying lessons as well as self-defense classes in Florida less than a year earlier. Jarrah's cohorts were in seats 3C, 3D, and 6B.

At least one of the young religious zealots carried a copy of specific handwritten instructions from Mohamed Atta, the Egyptian ringleader of the four groups of Islamic terrorists assigned to U.S. planes that day. Atta's five pages of instructions (later found at the crash site) included spiritual readings the terrorists were to meditate on the night before the attacks, as well as practical matters such as "bathe carefully, shave excess body hair," and "make sure you are clean, your clothes are clean, including your shoes." Possibly these instructions were for spiritual purification or possibly to avoid notice. Most telling were Atta's pointed reminders to bring "knives, your will, your IDs, your passport, all your papers."

The terrorists were told to clench their teeth when the moment to strike came. They were to "shout, _Allahu akbar_ [Arabic for "God is great"] because this strikes fear in the hearts of the unbelievers. . . . When the confrontation begins, strike like champions who do not want to go back to this world."

. . . United Flight 93 took off from Newark International Airport, across the river from New York City, at 8:42 a.m. The plane was still climbing over the New York–New Jersey coastline when, just six minutes later, American Airlines Flight 11 blasted into the north tower of the World Trade Center. The skies were clear . . . , and one of the men in the cockpit of Todd's plane noticed the smoke rising from below. "Is everything okay on the ground?" he asked air-traffic control.

"Everything is fine," he was told.

Flight 93 continued climbing to its cruising altitude and headed west, across New Jersey into Pennsylvania. At 9:03 a.m., United Flight 175 smashed into the south tower of the World Trade Center. With both buildings burning in New York, United Airlines flashed an alert to all its cockpit computer screens: "Beware cockpit intrusion."

. . . By now the pilots had learned that something was awry in New York, and they calmly asked Cleveland for more information.

About that time Cleveland controllers were receiving bomb threats on the ground, as were controllers in Boston—possibly in an attempt to create further fear and chaos and to distract controllers from tracking the hijacked planes. A minute later, at 9:28, the Cleveland controllers clearly heard screams over the open mike aboard Flight 93.

. . . The controllers radioed the plane, but there was no answer. After about 40 seconds, the Cleveland controllers heard more muffled cries. "Get out of here!" an

English-speaking voice implored. "Get out of here!" . . . [T]he pilot and copilot were yanked out of the cockpit. Passengers, including Todd, later reported seeing two people lying motionless on the floor near the cockpit, possibly with their throats cut.

. . . As soon as the hijackers took over the plane's controls, they disengaged the autopilot. The plane bounced up and down, and Arabic voices could be heard reassuring each other, "Everything is fine." Apparently the hijackers didn't realize that the microphone was still open and their words were audible to other aircraft as well as to controllers on the ground.

✪✪✪

Lisa Jefferson was at work at the GTE Airfone Customer Care Center in Oakbrook, Illinois, a Chicago suburb, when she first heard news of the terrorist attacks in New York and Washington, D.C. A supervisor with more than 18 years of experience at her job, she came out of her office to get more information. Just then, at about 8:45 a.m. CDT (9:45 EDT), the operator at Station 15 received an urgent call. The operator signaled for Lisa's assistance.

. . . "When I took over the call, there was a gentleman on the phone. He was very calm and soft-spoken. I introduced myself to him as Mrs. Jefferson and told him, 'I understand this plane is being hijacked. Can you please give me detailed information as to what is going on?'" Then Lisa began going through her GTE Distress-Call Manual, asking questions such as, "How many people are on board? How many hijackers? Are they armed? Are there any children on board?"

The man answered Lisa Jefferson in an equally calm manner. He was sitting next to a flight attendant who helped him relay the information: 27 passengers in coach, 10 in first class, five flight attendants, and no children that he could see. "He told me that three people had taken over the plane," said Lisa, "two with knives and one with a bomb strapped around his waist with a red belt. The two with knives had locked themselves in the cockpit. They ordered everyone to sit down, as the flight attendants were still standing. One of the flight attendants just happened to sit next to Todd in the back of the plane. The hijacker with the bomb pulled the curtain that divided first class from coach so the passengers in the back couldn't see what was going on."

But Todd did see two people on the floor. "He couldn't tell if they were dead or alive," said Lisa. "The flight attendant told him she was pretty sure it was the pilot and the copilot.

"I asked the caller's name and he told me, 'Todd Beamer.' He told me he was from Cranbury, New Jersey.

. . . "Suddenly Todd's voice inflection went up a little bit and he said, 'We are going down! We're going down. No, wait. We are coming back up. No, we are turning around, we are going north. . . . I really don't know where we are going. Oh, Jesus, please help us!'"

. . . What actually happened in the next several minutes is unclear. Apparently the plane's autopilot and transponder—the device that emits a signal by which radar can track a plane—were switched off, and the hijackers were flying erratically. The plane began plunging, lurching, and bobbing from the altitude it had maintained previously. Perhaps the hijackers were simply trying to keep the passengers off guard by jolting them around. . . . Flight 93 maintained its new course, heading southeast . . . straight toward Washington, D.C.

✪✪✪

It's not known whether the passengers aboard Flight 93 truly knew what a formidable force they represented that morning. . . . Besides the assortment of athletic colleagues such as Jeremy Glick [an NCAA judo champion], Tom Burnett [a former football quarterback], and Mark Bingham [a former player on a national championship rugby team], several other passengers were well able to take care of themselves.

CeeCee Ross-Lyles, one of the flight attendants, was a former police officer. Lou Nacke was a human fireplug at five feet, three inches, and 200 pounds . . . and a weight lifter. . . . Rich Guadagno was an enforcement officer with California Fish and Wildlife and had been trained in hand-to-hand combat. Linda Gronlund, a lawyer, had a brown belt in karate. Although he was 60 years of age, William Cashman was a former paratrooper with 101ˢᵗ Airborne, and he was still in good shape. Alan Beaven, over six feet tall, was a former Scotland Yard prosecutor who enjoyed rock climbing as a pastime. He had a sign on his desk: "Fear—who cares?" And then there was Todd—strong, athletic, a gamer, the go-to guy.

✪✪✪

[Lisa Jefferson continued relating her phone conversation with Todd.] "'We're going to do something. . . . I don't think we're going to get out of this thing,' Todd said. 'I'm going to have to go out on faith.' He told me they were talking about jumping the guy with the bomb."

"Are you sure that's what you want to do, Todd?" Lisa asked.

"It's what we have to do," Todd told her.

"He asked me to recite the Lord's Prayer with him," Lisa said, "and I did. We recited it together from the start to the finish. . . ."

At the conclusion of the prayer aboard Flight 93, Todd said, "Jesus, help me."

"I knew that if Todd didn't make it, . . . he was definitely going to the right place."

. . . Following the prayer, Todd recited the 23ʳᵈ Psalm, *Yea though I walk through the valley of the shadow of death, I will fear no evil.* . . . Other men apparently joined in with him or recited the psalm themselves. . . .

Lisa Jefferson recalls, "After that, he had a sigh in his voice, and he took a deep breath. He was still holding the phone, but I could tell he had turned away from the phone and was talking to someone else. He said, 'Are you ready? Okay. Let's roll!'"

It was nearly 10:00 a.m. EDT. The plane was 15 to 20 minutes away from Washington, D.C.

. . . *Big men move quickly up a narrow aisle, accompanied perhaps by a flight attendant or two carrying coffeepots, spilling boiling water on themselves as they run. Some jump over seats to get as much manpower to the front of the plane as possible. A food cart is used to ram the enemy. All around the airplane is filled with screams and commotion. . . .*

Just what they were doing or how they were doing it may never be completely known. The cockpit voice recorder contains sounds of dishes shattering and other objects being hurled. The hijackers are heard screaming at each other to hold the cockpit door.

Someone cries out in English, "Let's get them!"

One of the hijackers frantically attempts to cut off the oxygen in order to quell the passengers' fight. Another of the terrorists tells his cohorts, "Take it easy."

Pounding sounds on the cockpit door . . . a male passenger shouts. . . .

More screaming!

The plane begins to dive.

The hijackers shout, "Allahu akbar!" God is great!

Papers rustle within the cockpit as the hijackers begin fighting among themselves for the plane's controls. "Give it to me!" one of them commands. Too late.

The plane rocks from side to side and then flips over before streaking straight down, blasting a hole in the earth 50 feet deep. Thousands of gallons of burning jet fuel spray the trees, instantly scorching the tree line as though a raging forest fire has recently been put out.

The airplane is obliterated. . . .

Yet United Flight 93 had not crashed into the Capitol; nor had it smashed into the White House, Camp David, or any other national landmark. Instead, it crashed at 10:03 a.m. on September 11 in an open field with only a stone cabin nearby and the closest home more than a quarter of a mile away.

1. Who apparently was the ringleader of the terrorists who hijacked the planes on September 11?

   _____

2. In addition to the actions of the passengers, what else might have played a role in the terrorists' inability to crash the plane into an American symbol in Washington, D.C.? _____

   _____

3. Why were the hijackers instructed to shout, "*Allahu akbar!*" when it came time to crash the jet into a structure? _____

   _____

4. What happened to the pilot and copilot? _____

   _____

5. What equipped many of the passengers aboard Flight 93 to act as they did?

   _____

   _____

   _____

6. Why do you think God allowed the hijackers to overlook the facts that their voices were being recorded on the flight recorder and that passengers were calling family members on their cell phones?

   _____

   _____

   _____

7. What lessons were or can be learned from this seeming tragedy?

   _____

   _____

   _____

   _____

The Faith of George W. Bush

George W. Bush was more overtly Christian in his presidency than many other presidents. He professed Christianity. He campaigned on Bible values. He sought to involve faith-based organizations in the affairs of government. What made his religious faith so different from that of other public officials? Why did it characterize his administration? Read the following excerpts from Stephen Mansfield's book *The Faith of George W. Bush*. Then answer the questions that follow.

George W. Bush entered the presidency sounding an unapologetically religious tone. On his very first day in office, he called for a day of prayer. . . . He speaks of being called to the presidency, of a God who rules in the affairs of men, and of the United States owing her origin to Providence. . . . In no previous administration has the White House hosted so many weekly Bible studies and prayer meetings, and never have religious leaders been more gratefully welcomed.

[Bush] attended Episcopal and Presbyterian churches until he married and through his wife's influence became a Methodist. The seeds of faith were planted, and he experienced what he calls "stirrings," but there was no single moment of spiritual awakening. Then came business failures, seasons of excessive drinking, and a marriage that began showing signs of strain. [H]e took the now-famous walk on a Maine beach with Billy Graham, who asked him if he was "right with God." He was not, and he knew it, but his time with Graham made him aware of his need. Bush joined a businessmen's Bible study in Midland, and before long his friends noted something different about him. Asked who his favorite philosopher was during his presidential campaign, he quickly answered . . . : "Christ, because He changed my heart."

What distinguishes . . . George W. Bush . . . is not just the openness with which he . . . discussed his personal conversion and spiritual life [or] . . . the intensity of his public statements about faith. Rather, he . . . seems to genuinely believe privately what he says publicly about religion . . . and . . . seeks to integrate faith with public policy at the most practical level.

It is not without significance that George W. Bush chose one of the hymns for [his] inaugural prayer service. . . . The hymn was a Methodist standard, one of Charles Wesley's best-known and one that George W. had come to love and make his own. It was called "A Charge to Keep I Have." . . . The words come almost without change from *Matthew Henry's Commentary on the Bible*. . . . They are drawn from Henry's reflections on Leviticus 8:35 where the temple priesthood is told to "keep the charge of the Lord."

[O]nce he came to faith, once he came to believe that his life was about a Jesus who died for him, he found both the purpose and the discipline to do something that nothing else in his life could induce him to do: sacrifice pleasure on the altar of a greater cause.

Bush continues to let faith frame his presidency. Indeed, it seems . . . that politics takes a back seat to the religious imprint he hopes to make on the nation. As he told a gathering of ministers in the Oval Office, "I'm not after the votes. . . . I am here . . . sharing concerns because someday I am going to stand before God, and I want to hear Him say, 'Well done!' I hope that's why we're all here."

1. What action did Bush take on his very first day as president that signaled the major role that religious values would play in his administration? _____

2. In what other ways was the welcome of religion into the nation's highest office evident?

_____

_____

_____

3. What was Bush's religious background? _____

4. What problems in Bush's life prepared him to make a personal commitment of faith?

_____

5. Which hymn did Bush choose for his inaugural prayer service that reflected his outlook toward his responsibilities as both a Christian and the president? _____

6. What realization did Bush claim motivated his overt emphasis on Christianity in his administration?

_____

_____

7. Do you agree or disagree with Bush's emphasis on Christianity in his administration and public life? Why?

_____

_____

_____

_____

_____

_____

_____

_____

Katrina: A True Story of Grace
by Dr. Carl Abrams

Read the following true story. Then answer the questions that follow.

Grace called home on Friday night.

"Mom, what should I do?" she asked urgently.

Katrina, a monster storm, was headed straight for New Orleans. Should Grace stay and head for one of the shelters—maybe the Superdome, which was only a block from her apartment in downtown New Orleans? Some officials were advising people to go to Jackson, Mississippi, to avoid the storm. Others were telling them to go to Houston.

"Fill your car with gas tonight, so you won't have to wait in longer lines tomorrow. Dad and I will talk and pray about it, and then we'll decide what you should do," Mom reassured her.

Grace had been at Tulane University, in the heart of New Orleans, for only six days. She was about to begin work on a graduate degree in international public health. For several summers, she had gone to Kenya on missions trips with her parents, who took students from the Christian university where they taught. She had worked at a medical clinic in rural Kenya. A master's degree in tropical medicine had attracted her to Tulane's highly respected program. She had settled into her apartment and met a friend from Colorado. She had already found a church they could attend the next Sunday.

By Saturday morning, Katrina was getting stronger and closer. Tulane's president wisely ordered all students to leave town. After talking to her parents on the phone, Grace decided to drive home to Vertevilla, about the same distance as other places students were headed. Her friend went to Jackson. Both expected to return to New Orleans in a few days. By early evening, Grace had arrived home. There, in the safety of the den, she and her family watched the horror unfold in the city she had known for only six days.

Katrina bore down on New Orleans and the Gulf Coast on Monday. The eye of the storm had missed New Orleans and the city had little wind damage. But beginning early Tuesday morning the levees broke. Soon, about 80 percent of the city was severely flooded. After several days, Tulane officials concluded that school would not reopen in a couple of weeks as planned but would resume classes in January.

In January? What would Grace do during the intervening time? The Lord's mercy that had brought her safely home continued to work. Tulane quickly worked out an arrangement with other universities that allowed its displaced students to attend those schools for the fall semester. After a few days of praying and planning, Grace applied online to Boston University. Like Tulane, it was one of only a few American colleges that offered an international public health program. Boston University accepted her immediately. Ironically, months earlier, Boston University had been her first choice, but they had not accepted her. Tulane, with a better reputation in public health, had accepted her.

Living in Boston? But where? She feared that with the semester under way few places would be available and those that were would be out of her price range. She called the university's housing office. The lady there told her about an offer from a family to house three public health student "refugees" from Tulane.

Grace called the home, talked to the wife, and discovered that the Lord had granted more mercy. The lady said that she could stay with the family as long as she needed, rent-free. She would be sharing an entire floor of a five-story townhouse in Boston's Back Bay with another displaced Tulane girl. Who were these generous people? The husband taught at Harvard Medical School and currently served on the jury for Nobel prizes in science.

Soon Grace found a good church to attend, fell in love with Boston, and decided to remain there to finish her degree. Boston had been her first choice, and God's mercy during a storm made it a reality.

1. Which university was Grace's first choice and why? _____

_____

2. Where did she end up enrolling instead, where is it located, and in what did she plan to major?

_____

3. What in her life experience seemed to point her in the direction of a major in that field?

_____

_____

4. What event changed all of her plans in that regard? _____

_____

_____

5. What provisions did Tulane University make for its students? _____

_____

_____

6. What kind of housing arrangement did Grace work out? _____

_____

_____

7. What "extra benefits" did that arrangement provide? _____

_____

_____

_____

8. How does this account reveal the providence of God in His children's lives?

_____

_____

_____

_____

_____

Chapter Review

Match the people on the right with that for which they are most noted.

_____ 1. Ran against Bush in the disputed election of 2000

_____ 2. Put together a "coalition of the willing" to fight world terrorism

_____ 3. Mastermind behind the 9/11 terrorist attacks on America

_____ 4. First secretary of the Department of Homeland Security

_____ 5. Secretary of state who tried to convince the U.N. that Iraq should be dealt with

_____ 6. Ran against Bush in the election of 2004

_____ 7. First Hispanic attorney general of the United States

_____ 8. Christian who was Bush's first attorney general

_____ 9. Christian who was Bush's second secretary of state

_____ 10. Head of Enron who was imprisoned for corporate corruption

_____ 11. Bush's nominee for chief justice of the U.S. Supreme Court

_____ 12. Bush's nominee for justice on the U.S. Supreme Court

A. Samuel Alito

B. John Ashcroft

C. Osama bin Laden

D. George W. Bush

E. Al Gore

F. Alberto Gonzales

G. John Kerry

H. Ken Lay

I. Colin Powell

J. Condoleeza Rice

K. Tom Ridge

L. John Roberts

Answer each of the following questions, putting your answers in the blanks.

13. Which federal agency did some people accuse of purposely responding too slowly in helping victims of Hurricane Katrina? _____

14. What term is used to refer to huge churches with large attendance that appeal to the felt needs of "seekers" by using nontraditional styles of worship? _____

15. What international agreement reached during the Clinton administration was designed to bring about Palestinian self-rule? _____

16. Which federal entity was formed following the terrorist attacks of September 11, 2001?

_____

17. What Bush policy approved of hitting a potential enemy before it attacked the United States?

_____

18. What was responsible for widespread destruction in New Orleans and coastal areas of Mississippi in 2005?

_____

19. What Bush policy promised kindness while adhering to traditional values?

_____

20. What piece of legislation was designed to make it easier for the federal government to apprehend, convict, and punish suspected terrorists and those who aided them? _____

21. What was responsible for widespread destruction in Southwest Florida in 2004? _____

22. Which international network was responsible for the attacks on the World Trade Center and other U.S. interests? _____

23. Who seemed to be the presumptive nominee for the Democratic Party in the 2008 presidential race?

_____

24. Which candidate won the nomination for president by the Republican Party in the 2008 presidential race?

_____

25. What was President Obama's first priority following his election as president of the United States in 2008?

_____

Photograph Credits

The following agencies and individuals have furnished materials to meet the photographic needs of this textbook. We wish to express our gratitude to them for their important contribution.

Gerald R. Ford Library
Hobokam Observer
Library of Congress
Ray Osrin Collection. Special Collections,
 Cleveland State University Library
Volck, Adalbert
Warren, Bill

Chapter 11
Library of Congress 80

Chapter 15
Adalbert Volck 127; public domain 128
(top); Library of Congress 128 (bottom)

Chapter 16
Library of Congress 145

Chapter 23
Hobokam Observer 251; Bill Warren
252

Chapter 27
Courtesy Gerald R. Ford Library 301;
Ray Osrin Collection. Special Collections,
Cleveland State University Library 310

Acknowledgments

Careful effort has been made to trace the copyright ownership of selections included in this textbook. Errors or omissions are inadvertent and will be corrected in subsequent editions, provided written notification is made. The publisher gratefully acknowledges the following individuals and publishers for copyright material:

Chapter 2

Excerpts from OF PLYMOUTH PLANTATION: SIXTEEN TWENTY TO SIXTEEN FORTY-SEVEN by William Bradford and edited by Samuel Eliot Morison, copyright © 1952 by Samuel Eliot Morison and renewed 1980 by Emily M. Beck. Used by permission of Alfred A. Knopf, an imprint of the Knopf Doubleday Publishing Group, a division of Random House LLC. All rights reserved. Any third party use of this material, outside of this publication, is prohibited. Interested parties must apply directly to Random House LLC for permission.

Chapter 3

Excerpts from *A True History of the Captivity and Restoration of Mrs. Mary Rowlandson*. Public Domain. 13–14

Chapter 4

Scattered excerpts from *The Journal of Esther Edwards Burr, 1754–1757*, edited by Carol F. Karlsen and Laurie Crumpacker. Copyright 1984 by Yale University Press. Reprinted by permission of Yale University Press. 19–20

Chapter 5

George Washington. Public Domain. 29

Excerpt taken from *The Spirit of Seventy-Six: The Story of the American Revolution as Told by Participants*, edited by Henry Steele Commager and Richard B. Morris. Reprinted by permission of Mary E. P. Commager. 31–32

Chapter 6

Excerpt taken from *Debating the Issues in Colonial Newspapers: Primary Documents on Events of the Period* by David A. Copeland. Copyright ©2000 by David A. Copeland. Published by Greenwood Press. Reproduced with permission by ABC-CLIO, LLC. 39

Excerpts taken from *The Spirit of Seventy-Six: The Story of the American Revolution as Told by Participants*, edited by Henry Steele Commager and Richard B. Morris. Reprinted by permission of Mary E. P. Commager. 41–44

Chapter 8

"The Inauguration of George Washington, 1789." Reprinted by permission of EyeWitnesstoHistory.com 53–54

Abigail Adams. Public Domain. 57

Chapter 9

The Journals of Lewis and Clark. May 14, 1804–September 24, 1806. Public Domain. 63–66

Tyrone G. Martin. *A Most Fortunate Ship*. Public Domain. 68

Chapter 11

"The Inauguration of President Andrew Jackson, 1829." Reprinted by permission of EyeWitnesstoHistory.com 77–78

"Jackson Vetoes the Bank Recharter (1832)." Public Domain. 81

Chapter 12

Nathanial Hawthorne. "The Canal Boat." *New-England Magazine*, No. 9, December, 1835, pp. 398–409. Public Domain. 87–89
Rev. Henry A. Miles. *As It Was and As It Is*. Public Domain. 93–94

Chapter 13

Diaries and Journals of Narcissa Whitman 1836. Public Domain. 103–7

Chapter 14

"Escape from Slavery, 1838." Reprinted by permission of EyeWitnesstoHistory.com 115–17

Mary Chestnut. *A Diary from Dixie*. Edited by Isabella D. Martin and Myrta Lockett Avary. Public Domain. 123

Chapter 15

Excerpt taken from Bitner Collection: Cressler, Alex. "Letter to Henry A. Bitner," Special Collections, University of Virginia Library. 129

Excerpt from Milton Asbury Ryan's memoirs. Reprinted by permission from Michael Gay. 129–30

Chapter 16

Excerpt taken from "President Johnson on the Restoration of the Southern States to the Union, Second Annual Message to Congress, December 3, 1866" by Henry Steele Commager, comp. Reprinted by permission of Mary E. P. Commager 139–40

"The Trial of Andrew Johnson, 1868" by William H. Crook. Reprinted by permission of EyeWitnesstoHistory.com 143–44

"Sandhog: Building the Brooklyn Bridge, 1871." Reprinted by permission of EyeWitnesstoHistory.com 147–48

"Ku Klux Klan, 1868" by Ben Johnson. Reprinted by permission of EyeWitnesstoHistory.com 149–50

Chapter 17

Central Pacific Railroad. Public Domain. 155–57

Andrew Carnegie. *The Autobiography of Andrew Carnegie*; and *The Gospel of Wealth*. Public Domain. 159–60

Chapter 18

"A Cowboy in Dodge City, 1882" by Andy Adams. Reprinted by permission of EyeWitnesstoHistory.com 165–66

"Ranchers and Farmers Collide in Nebraska, 1884" by Solomon Butcher. Reprinted by permission of EyeWitnesstoHistory.com 167–68

"The Death of Billy the Kid, 1881" by Pat Garrett. Reprinted by permission of EyeWitnesstoHistory.com 169

"Massacre at Wounded Knee, 1890" by Philip Wells. Reprinted by permission of EyeWitnesstoHistory.com 171–72

Chapter 19

"The United States Declares War on Spain, 1898" by H. H. Kohlsaat. Reprinted by permission of EyeWitnesstoHistory .com 179

Chapter 20

Booker T. Washington. *Up from Slavery.* Public Domain. 187–89

Booker T. Washington. Speech at the Atlanta Cotton States and International Exposition, September 18, 1895. Public Domain. 190–92

Billy Sunday. Public Domain. 193–95

Theodore Roosevelt. "It Takes More Than That to Kill a Bull Moose: The Leader and the Cause." October 14, 1912. Public Domain. 197–98

Chapter 21

"The Sinking of the *Lusitania*, 1915" by Captain Schwieger. Reprinted by permission of EyeWitnesstoHistory.com 205–6

"America Declares War on Germany, 1917" by Frank Cobb. Reprinted by permission of EyeWitnesstoHistory.com 209–10

Excerpt from Chapter 17 of *World War I: The First Three Years*, extracted from the American Military History Army Historical Series, Office of the Chief of Military History, U.S. Army. 211–12

Chapter 22

Excerpts from *Summer for the Gods*, by Edward J. Larson. Copyright ©1997 by Edward J. Larson. Reprinted by permission of Basic Books, a subsidiary of Perseus Books, LLC. All Rights Reserved. 225–26

Chapter 23

Excerpt from *Only Yesterday: An Informed History of the Nineteen-Twenties* by Frederick Lewis Allen. 233–34

Chapter 24

Excerpt from *Lone Heart Mountain*, by Estelle Ishigo. 259–60

V-mail from a Soldier. © Dennis Peterson 262

Excerpt from *To Hell and Back: A Guadalcanal Journal* by Nance Croce. 265–66

Chapter 25

"Jackie Robinson Breaks Baseball's Color Barrier, 1945." Reprinted by permission of EyeWitnesstoHistory.com 269–70

Reprinted with permission from *Memories of World War II and Its Aftermath: By a Little Girl Growing Up in Berlin* by Inge E. Gross. Published by Island in the Sky Publishing Co., 2005. 273

Chapter 26

Excerpt from "Hill 882" by Ted McCormick. Used by permission from Ted McCormick. 287–90

Chapter 27

Jimmy Carter, excerpts from *Keeping Faith: Memoirs of a President.* Copyright ©1982, 1983, 1995 by Jimmy Carter. Used by permission of the University of Arkansas Press, www.uapress.com 304–8

Reprinted with the permission of Simon & Schuster Adult Publishing Group from AN AMERICAN LIFE by Ronald Reagan. Copyright ©1990 by Ronald W. Reagan. 311–13

Chapter 28

Used with permission from the Foundation for Economic Education. 325–27

Chapter 29

Taken from *Let's Roll!* by Lisa Beamer and Ken Abraham. Copyright ©2002 by Lisa Beamer and Ken Abraham. Used by permission of Tyndale House Publishers, Inc. All Rights Reserved. 333–35

Stephen Mansfield, *The Faith of George W. Bush* (Lake Mary, FL: Charisma House, 2003). Used by permission. 337

"Katrina: A True Story of Grace" by Dr. Carl Abrams. © Dr. Carl Abrams 339–40